WANDERINGS IN SOUTH AMERICA

Charles Waterton was born in 1782—the eldest son of Thomas Waterton and his wife Anne—at Walton Hall in Yorkshire. His family were one of the oldest in the North of England and well respected. He succeeded to the estate in 1806 and made his home there. His brief marriage in 1829 ended little more than a year later in the death of his wife, leaving him with an infant son. His overriding interest was natural history and it is obvious from *Wanderings in South America* that he was happier living with Indians and monkeys in the forests of Guiana than living the life of a gentleman in Yorkshire. The story of his wanderings starts with his first wandering in April 1812 and covers four journeys. However, it is the genuine zeal and inexhaustible delight with which he describes all the barbarous countries he visited that makes this remarkable book such a joyous record. He seemed to love the forests, the tigers and the apes and to rejoice in being the only Englishman there. His interest extends to the Indians and his strange fascination with the wourali poison the Indians use on their arrows gives another dimension to this marvellous chronicle of adventure and natural history.

WANDERINGS IN SOUTH AMERICA

THE NORTH-WEST OF THE
UNITED STATES AND
THE ANTILLES,
IN THE YEARS 1812, 1816,
1820 & 1824

With Original Instructions for the perfect preservation
of Birds, Etc. for Cabinets of Natural History

CHARLES WATERTON

Edited with Biographical Introduction and
Explanatory Index by The Rev. J. G. Wood

Introduction by David Bellamy

CENTURY PUBLISHING
LONDON
HIPPOCRENE BOOKS INC.
NEW YORK

Introduction copyright © David Bellamy 1983

First published in Great Britain in 1825
First published in this edition in 1878 by
Macmillan and Co., London

This edition published in 1984 by Century
Publishing Co. Ltd,
Portland House, 12–13 Greek Street, London W1V 5LE

Published in the United States of America by
Hippocrene Books Inc.
171 Madison Avenue
New York, NY 10016

ISBN 0 7126 0340 9

Front and back covers show Blue and Yellow Macaw
and Blue and Red Macaw by Edward Lear

Reprinted in Great Britain by
Richard Clay (The Chaucer Press) Ltd,
Bungay, Suffolk

PREFACE.

MANY years ago, while barely in my "teens," I had the
good fortune to fall in with Waterton's *Wanderings*, then
newly placed in the school library. The book fascinated
me. Week after week I took it out of the library, and
really think that I could have repeated it verbatim from
beginning to end. It was a glimpse into an unknown
world, where I longed to follow the Wanderer, little
thinking that I should ever have the privilege of visiting
him in his wonderful Yorkshire home. I looked upon
Waterton much as the pagans of old regarded their
demi-gods, and not even Sinbad the Sailor was so interesting a personage to me as Waterton the Wanderer.

But there was one drawback to the full enjoyment
and comprehension of the book. It mentioned all kinds
of animals, birds, and trees, and I did not know what
they were, nor was there any one who could tell me. I
did not know what a Salempenta was, except that it

was good to eat. It might be a monkey, a fish, or a fruit. Neither could I identify the Couanacouchi, Labarri, Camoudi, Duraquara, Houtou, or Karabimiti, except that the three first were snakes and the three last were birds.

It was certainly pleasant to learn that the traveller in Guiana would be awakened by the crowing of the Hannaquoi, but there was no one who could tell me what kind of a bird the Hannaquoi might be. Then, as to trees, I did not know the Siloabali, or the Wallaba, or even the Purple-heart, nor how the last mentioned tree could be made into a Woodskin. I wanted a guide to the *Wanderings*, and such a guide I have attempted to supply in the "Explanatory Index." I believe that there is not a single living creature or tree mentioned by Waterton concerning which more or less information cannot be found in this Index.

The *Wanderings* I have left untouched as Waterton wrote them, not adding or altering or cancelling a syllable. They constitute, so to speak, the central brilliant of a ring, round which are arranged jewels of inferior value, so as to set off the beauty of the principal gem.

The plan of arrangement is as follows: First comes a short biography of Waterton as the Wanderer, and then a memoir of Waterton at home. Next come the *Wanderings*, exactly as he wrote them. Then there is an Explanatory Index, and lastly a few remarks on the system of Taxidermy which he created, and in which he gave me personal instruction.

I have much pleasure in recording my obligations to Edmund Waterton, Esq., who kindly permitted access to the old famiiy records, which he is now arranging for publication. Also to A. R. Wallace, Esq., and Dr. P. L. Sclater, Secretary of the Zoological Society, for the assistance which they rendered in identifying several of the birds; and to J. Britten, Esq., of the British Museum, for the great pains which he took in ascertaining the names of some of the Guianan trees, without which names the work would have been imperfect.

PREFACE TO THE FIRST EDITION

I OFFER this book of *Wanderings* with a hesitating
hand. It has little merit, and must make its way through
the world as well as it can. It will receive many a jostle
as it goes along, and perhaps is destined to add one more
to the number of slain, in the field of modern criticism.
But if it fall, it may still, in death, be useful to me; for,
should some accidental rover take it up, and, in turning
over its pages, imbibe the idea of going out to explore
Guiana, in order to give the world an enlarged description of that noble country, I shall say, " fortem ad fortia
misi," and demand the armour; that is, I shall lay claim
to a certain portion of the honours he will receive, upon
the plea, that I was the first mover of his discoveries;
for, as Ulysses sent Achilles to Troy, so I sent him to
Guiana. I intended to have written much more' at
length; but days, and months, and years, have passed
away, and nothing has been done. Thinking it very
probable that I shall never have patience enough to sit
down and write a full account of all I saw and examined

in those remote wilds, I give up the intention of doing
so, and send forth this account of my *Wanderings*, just
as it was written at the time.

If critics are displeased with it in its present form, I
beg to observe, that it is not totally devoid of interest,
and that it contains something useful. Several of the
unfortunate gentlemen who went out to explore the
Congo, were thankful for the instructions they found in
it; and Sir Joseph Banks, on sending back the journal,
said in his letter, " I return your journal, with abundant
thanks for the very instructive lesson you have favoured
us with this morning, which far excelled, in real utility,
everything I have hitherto seen."   And in another letter
he says, " I hear with particular pleasure your intention
of resuming your interesting travels, to which natural
history has already been so much indebted."   And again
" I am sorry you did not deposit some part of your last
harvest of birds in the British Museum, that your name
might become familiar to naturalists, and your unrivalled
skill in preserving birds be made known to the public.'
And again, " You certainly have talents to set forth a
book, which will improve and extend materially the
bounds of natural science."

Sir Joseph never read the third adventure.   Whilst
I was engaged in it, death robbed England of one of her
most valuable subjects, and deprived the Royal Society
of its brightest ornament.

CONTENTS.

CHAPTER III.

CHAPTER IV.

CHAPTER V.

FIRST JOURNEY.

CHAPTER I.

CHAPTER II.

CHAPTER III.

SECOND JOURNEY.

CHAPTER I.

CHAPTER II.

CHAPTER III.

THIRD JOURNEY.

CHAPTER I.

CHAPTER II.

CHAPTER III.

CHAPTER IV.

FOURTH JOURNEY.

CHAPTER I.

CHAPTER II.

ON PRESERVING BIRDS FOR CABINETS OF NATURAL HISTORY.

INTRODUCTION.

THINK of the tropical rain forests of the River Amazon and South America and beyond those scenes of Twentieth Century destruction which at last are beginning to prick the conscience of the thinking world; remember those heydays of exploration. Then men like Henry Walter Bates, Richard Spruce and Charles Darwin discovered so much within those boundless forests that they changed not only the course of natural science, but also of human thinking.

Yet thirteen years before Bates and five years before Spruce were born, and when Darwin was a mere three years old, Charles Waterton, author of this book, was, to use his own words, " wandering in those forests " and setting down this vibrant account of what he saw and experienced.

1812 was the year of Waterton's first trip which took him into what is now known as Guiana, and this account is a fitting overture to that Century of exploration when there were exciting discoveries to be made on every continent and at every turn of the river.

Oh to have lived in those not too far off days, to have had the privilege and excitement of being the first to see and to record so many things.

Then there were no package deals, no immunisation, no cures for tropical diseases, no chains of hotels to see you on your way. So why was it that a Yorkshire Gentleman of considerable wealth set out on such hazardous missions? Well, partly it was because of his aversion to English society as it was then " spoke ". Here was a man who revelled in things natural and took enormous delight in recording the wonders which nature has afforded in that lush place. His experiences will become yours as you are led wide-eyed through the forest, you will smell the dark, dank aftermath of tropical rain distilling through cathedral trees and see all the seasons of the year compressed into one day by their myriad presence. You will listen apprehensively to the noises of the night, feel the light of insects and be cooled by the flapping of the wings of vampire bats. Compassion for the slaves will be thrust upon you as will admiration for the skills of the local Indians. Above all you will strain with every sense to discover and to delight in that next surprise which waits around the corner.

All you need do is turn the pages. Charles Waterton walked, climbed, perspired, swam, canoed and endured— no enjoyed—all the discomforts and dangers in his quest for knowledge.

These pages overflow with a wealth of stories and accounts and though I don't want to spoil it for you in any way, there are two I will recount.

The first may seem quaint to us today but when written it contained much more than a grain of truth. In telling of the local tribes, Waterton writes,

" their women never die in childbed, owing, no doubt to their never wearing stays."

The second is as true today as when he wrote it, for in entreating others to follow in his footsteps and discover the riches of the forest he writes,

" No doubt there is many a balsam and many a root yet to be discovered, and many a resin, gum and oil yet unnoticed."

Today as I write these words the forests of South America and the rest of the world are being destroyed at the rate of a hundred and fifty acres every minute. What is more, despite the fact that a hundred and seventy years have passed since Waterton wandered and wondered through Guiana, most of these forests have not been systematically studied and a mere one per cent of the world's plants have been investigated for their medicinal and other economic properties.

As there were back in 1812, even today there are many fascinating things still waiting to be discovered in those tropical forests but if the present rate of destruction continues, by the bicentenary of Waterton's Wanderings all will have been swept away and the world will have lost its most precious resource, the genetic diversity of the tropics. What is more, by that time any person craving to shun the company of human society and the monopoly of managed landscapes will find it impossible.

We may yet learn from natural history and mend our ways. Here is a piece of that natural history which everyone should read.

DAVID BELLAMY
Bedburn 1983

BIOGRAPHY.

CHAPTER I.

Autobiography of Waterton.—Descent from Sir Thomas More.—Twenty-seventh Lord of Walton, and sixteenth in descent from John Waterton. —Religious faith of the family.—Persecutions of Roman Catholics and confiscation of the estates.—Double taxes and fines.—Birth and early life.—Escapades at Tudhoe.—The cow and the washing-tub.—Removal to Stonyhurst.—Birds'-nesting, a chase and a pigstye.—Good advice from one of the fathers.—Parting with Stonyhurst.—First voyage to Cadiz.—The apes at Gibraltar.—Habits of the animals.—Stay in Malaga.—Acquirement of Spanish.—Projected visit to Malta.—Advent of the plague.—Seized with the disease and recovery.—Closing of the ports.—A hazardous and carefully-planned escape.—Preparations on board ship.—The opportunity seized.—Escape successful.—Death of an uncle.—Discovery of an old friend.—Failing health.—Voyage to Demerara.—Death of his father and succession to the family estates.

In the introductory prefaces to *Waterton's Wanderings*, the author has afforded but little account of himself, but in the volumes of his *Essays*, and some of his Letters, he has fortunately given a sufficiency of information to furnish a tolerably unbroken biography from his birth to his death. His was a very long life, and as he considered that life as a sacred trust, he never wasted an hour of it.

WATERTON was the representative of one of the most ancient English families, and was justly proud of his descent from Sir Thomas More. A clock which had belonged to that great ancestor is still in existence, and occupied a place of honour on the upper landing of the central staircase of Walton Hall. It is but a little clock, and has only a single hand, but it keeps time as well as ever, and the sound of its bell is so clear, that it can be heard at a considerable distance from the house. He mentions in his own quaint way, that if his ancestors had been as careful of their family records as Arabs are of the pedigrees of their horses, he might have been able to trace his descent up to Adam and Eve.

The following account of the Waterton family is taken from the *Illustrated London News* of June 17, 1865, and has been revised by a member of the house.

" The good and amiable old Lord of Walton, Charles Waterton, better known for miles around his ancestral domain as " *the* squire," was the representative of one of our most ancient untitled aristocratic families, and, what is more deserving of record in these days, in the male line.

" His ancestor, Reiner, the son of Norman of Normandy, who became Lord of Waterton in 1159, was of Saxon origin. The Watertons of Waterton became extinct in the male line in the fifteenth century, when their vast possessions passed away, through Cecilia, wife of Lord Welles and heiress of her brother, Sir Robert Waterton, to her four daughters and co-heiresses, who married, respectively, Robert, Lord Willoughby de Eresby, Sir Thomas Dymoke, Thomas Laurence, Esq., and Sir Thomas Delaware.

" Sir John Waterton was high sheriff of Lincoln in 1401, and master of the horse to Henry V. at Agincourt. Sir Robert, his brother, whose wife was a lady of the garter, was governor of Pontefract Castle while Richard II. was confined there: he had been master of the horse to Henry IV. Sir Hugh, another brother, held high offices of state. Charles Waterton, in whom the representation of his ancient house was vested, was descended from Richard, second son of William Waterton, Lord of Waterton, who died in 1255. In 1435 John Waterton married the heiress of Sir William Ashenhull, and became Lord of Walton and Cawthorne, *jure uxoris*.

"Walton formed part of the Honour of Pontefract, of which Ashenhold, a Saxon thane, was the Lord, and which was held by his son Ailric, in the reign of S. Edward the Confessor. At the Conquest it was given by William the Norman to one of his followers, Ilbert de Lacy, who granted it back again to Ailric, father of Suein. Adam, the son of Suein, Lord of Brierley, Cawthorne, and Walton, was the founder of the priory of Monk Bretton, and left two daughters and co-heiresses, Amabil and Matilda. The former had Walton and Cawthorne, and became the wife of William de Nevile. They had one daughter and heiress, who married Thomas, the son of Philip de Burgh. Walton and Cawthorne remained in the possession of the De Burghs for seven generations, and then passed with the co-heiress of Sir John de Burgh to Sir William Ashenhull, whose heiress conveyed it to John Waterton in 1435.

"Thus Mr. Waterton was twenty-seventh Lord of Walton, and sixteenth from John Waterton, who acquired that lordship. There was a grant of free warren at Walton in the reign of Edward I., and a license to crenellate in 1333. Without reference to the numerous distinguished alliances of his ancestors, it may be interesting to state that Mr. Waterton, through distinct sources, traced his descent several times over from S. Matilda, Queen of Germany; S. Margaret of Scotland, S. Humbert of Savoy, S. Louis of France, S. Ferdinand of Castile, and Wladimir

the Great, called S. Wladimir of Russia, and Anne, called
S. Anne of Russia. Through his grandmother he was
ninth in descent from Sir Thomas More."

The Watertons fared but badly in the stormy times of
the Reformation, and, preferring conscience to property,
they retained their ancient faith, but lost heavily in this
world's goods. The many coercive acts against the Roman
Catholics naturally had their effect, not only on those
who actually lived in the time of the Reformation, but
upon their successors. A Roman Catholic could not sit in
parliament, he could not hold a commission in the army,
he could not be a justice of the peace, he had to pay
double land-tax, and to think himself fortunate if he had
any land left on which taxes could be demanded. He was
not allowed to keep a horse worth more than five pounds,
and, more irritating than all, he had either to attend the
parish church or to pay twenty pounds for every month of
absence. In fact, a Roman Catholic was looked upon and
treated as a wholly inferior being, and held much the same
relative position to his persecutors as Jews held towards
the Normans and Saxons in the times of the Crusades.

Within the memory of many now living, the worst of
the oppressive acts have been repealed, and Roman Catholics
are now as free to follow their own form of worship as
before the days of Henry VIII. They have seats in
parliament and on the bench, they hold commissions both
in the army and navy, and all the petty but galling inter-
ferences with the details of their private life have been
abolished.

Still, Waterton was, during some of his best years, a
personal sufferer from these acts, and they rankled too
deeply in his mind to be forgotten. Hence, the repeated
and mostly irrelevant allusions in his writings to Martin
Luther, Henry VIII., Queen Bess, Archbishop Cranmer,

Oliver Cromwell, Charles Stuart, " Dutch William " (mostly associated with the " Hanoverian " rat and the national debt), and other personages celebrated in history.

Deeply as he felt the indignities to which he and his family and co-religionists had been subjected, and frequently as he referred to them, both in writing and conversation, he never used a worse weapon than irony, and even that was tempered by an underlying current of humour. He had felt the wounds, but he could jest at the scars.

On principle he refused to qualify as Deputy-Lieutenant and magistrate, because he had been debarred from doing so previously to the Emancipation Act. His son, however, serves both offices.

Born in 1782, he spent his childish years in the old mansion and grounds of the family, and at a very early age displayed those powers of observation, love of nature and enterprise, which enabled him to earn a place among the first order of practical naturalists both at home and abroad.

At ten years of age he was placed under the Rev. A. Strong's care, in a school just founded at Tudhoe, a village near Durham. From Waterton's reminiscences, his instructor seems to have inclined to the severe order of discipline, and to have been rather liberal of the birch, of which instrument Waterton had his full share. His account of storming the larder for the support of hungry inmates; of the anxious glances which he cast in the morning to judge by the master's wig of the state of his temper; and of being captured in the very act of getting through a barred window, is exceedingly humorous.

He also relates two anecdotes, both telling against himself, and both prospective, as it were, of the celebrated fact of riding on the back of a cayman and of his shipwreck. He was " dared" by his comrades to get on the back of a cow, which he did, but less fortunate than in his cayman adventure, was ignominiously thrown over her horns. He also took it into his head to get into a washing-tub, and take a cruise in the horse-pond; but lost his balance at the sudden appearance of the master, and was overturned into the muddy water.

The whole of the account of his Tudhoe school experiences is given in a collected volume of his *Essays and Letters* (F. Warne & Co.), edited by Mr. N Moore, who had the sad privilege of being with him when he met with his fatal accident, and by his sofa when he died, about thirty-eight hours afterwards.

Tudhoe then being only a preliminary school, though it has since developed into Ushaw College, Waterton was removed at fourteen years of age to Stonyhurst, where he was one of the first pupils. This establishment, then a comparatively small one, was conducted by the English Jesuits who had been driven from their home at Liége. Of them Waterton always spoke with reverence and affection, and his life at Stonyhurst was a singularly happy one.

At first, his ingrained propensity for enterprise led him into trouble, and one adventure is too good not to be narrated in his own words. His account of it is another example of the way in which he enjoyed telling an anecdote against himself.

" At Stonyhurst there are boundaries marked out to the students, which they are not allowed to pass; and there are prefects always pacing to and fro within the lines to prevent any unlucky boy from straying on the other side of them.

" Notwithstanding the vigilance of the lynx-eyed guardians, I would now and then manage to escape, and would bolt into a very extensive labyrinth of yew and holly trees close at hand. It was the chosen place for animated nature. Birds, in particular, used to frequent the spacious enclosure, both to obtain food and enjoy security. Many a time have I hunted the foumart and the squirrel. I once took a cut through it to a neighbouring wood, where I knew of a carrion-crow's nest. The prefect missed me; and judging that I had gone into the labyrinth, he gave chase without loss of time. After eluding him in cover for nearly half an hour, being hard pressed, I took away down a hedgerow.

"Here (as I learned afterwards) he got a distant sight of me; but it was not sufficiently distinct for him to know to a certainty that I was the fugitive. I luckily succeeded in reaching the outbuildings which abutted on the college, and lay at a considerable distance from the place where I had first started. I had just time to enter the postern gate of a pigsty, when, most opportunely, I found old Joe Bowren, the brewer, bringing straw into the sty. He was more attached to me than to any other boy, for I had known him when I was at school in the North, and had made him a present of a very fine terrier.

"'I've just saved myself, Joe,' said I; 'cover me up with litter.'

"He had hardly complied with my request, when in bounced the prefect by the same gate through which I had entered.

"'Have you seen Charles Waterton?' said he, quite out of breath.

"My trusty guardian answered, in a tone of voice which would have deceived anybody, 'Sir, I have not spoken a word to Charles Waterton these three days, to the best of my knowledge.'

"Upon this, the prefect, having lost all scent of me,

gave up the pursuit, and went his way. When he had disappeared, I stole out of cover, as strongly perfumed as was old Falstaff when they had turned him out of the buck basket.

"Once I had gone into the labyrinth to look into a magpie's nest, which was in a high hollow tree; and hearing the sound of voices near, I managed to get a resting-place in the tree just over the nest, and there I squatted, waiting the event. Immediately the President, two other Jesuits, and the present Mr. Salvin of Croxdale Hall, passed close under the tree without perceiving me.

"The good fathers were aware of my predominant propensity. Though it was innocent in itself, nevertheless it was productive of harm in its consequences, by causing me to break the college rules, and thus to give a bad example to the community at large. Wherefore, with a magnanimity, and excellent exercise of judgment, which are only the province of those who have acquired a consummate knowledge of human nature, and who know how to turn to advantage the extraordinary dispositions of those intrusted to their care, they sagaciously managed matters in such a way as to enable me to ride my hobby to a certain extent, and still, at the same time, to prevent me from giving a bad example.

"As the establishment was very large, and as it contained an abundance of prey, the Hanoverian rat, which fattens so well on English food, and which always contrives to thrust its nose into every man's house when there is anything to be got, swarmed throughout the vast extent of this antiquated mansion. The ability which I showed in curtailing the career of this voracious intruder did not fail to bring me into considerable notice. The cook, the baker, the gardener, and my friend old Bowren, could all bear testimony to my progress in this line. By a mutual understanding I was made rat-catcher to the establishment, and also fox-taker, foumart-killer, and crossbow-charger at the time when the young rooks were fledged. Moreover, I fulfilled the duties of organ-blower and football-maker with entire satisfaction to the public.

"I was now at the height of my ambition. I followed up my calling with great success. The vermin disappeared by the dozen; the books were moderately well thumbed; and, according to my notion of things, all went on perfectly right."

One of those wise teachers did him an inestimable service. He called the lad into his room, told him that his roving disposition would carry him into distant countries, and asked him to promise that from that time he would not touch either wine or spirits. Waterton gave the promise, and kept it to the hour of his death, more than sixty years afterwards. Once, when returning from one of his foreign expeditions, he took a glass of beer at dinner, but, finding the taste, from long disuse, unpleasantly bitter, he put down the glass and never touched beer again.

At the age of eighteen he left Stonyhurst with much regret, and after a year spent at Walton Hall amid the pleasures of the field, he started on the first of his journeys abroad. It was during the Peace of Amiens, and Spain was chosen as the country which he should visit. After staying a short time at Cadiz, he sailed for Malaga, and had the good fortune to visit Gibraltar just in time to see the celebrated apes.

Gibraltar was the last place in Europe where apes lived wild. How they got there no one knows, but Waterton suggests in one of his Essays that they belonged originally to Africa.

"Let us imagine that, in times long gone by, the present Rock of Gibraltar was united to the corresponding mountain called Ape's Hill, on the coast of Barbary; and that, by some tremendous convulsion of nature, a channel had been made between them, and had thus allowed the vast Atlantic Ocean to mix its waves with those of the Mediterranean Sea.

"If apes had been on Gibraltar when the sudden shock occurred, these unlucky mimickers of man would have seen their late intercourse with Africa quite at an end. A rolling ocean, deep and dangerous, would have convinced them that there would never again be a highway overland from Europe into Africa at the Straits of Gibraltar.

"Now as long as trees were allowed to grow on the Rock of Gibraltar, these prisoner-apes would have been pretty well off. But, in the lapse of time and change of circumstances, forced by 'necessity's supreme command,' for want of trees, they would be obliged to take to the ground on all-fours, and to adopt a very different kind of life from that which they had hitherto pursued."

The animal here mentioned is the Barbary Ape, or Magot, a species of Macacque. At Gibraltar it feeds largely on the scorpions that have their habitations under the loose stones. I do not think that Waterton's suggestion as to its altered habits is carried out by facts, for the magot is quite as much at home among rocks or among trees, as are the great baboons of Southern Africa. I have seen a number of magots in a large cage, or rather, apartment, in the open air. They were supplied with rock-work and trees, and of the two seemed to prefer the former. Their colours harmonised so completely with that of the rough stones on which they sat, that many persons passed the cage, thinking it to be untenanted, while five or six magots were seated among the rocks, and almost as motionless as the stones themselves.

Generally, the Gibraltar magots keep themselves so

much aloof, that they cannot be seen without the aid of a telescope, but Waterton was fortunate enough to see the whole colony on the move, they being forced to leave their quarters by a change of wind. He counted between fifty and sixty of them, some having young on their backs.

After staying for more than a year in Malaga, and having apparently in the meantime acquired the Spanish language, of which he was totally ignorant when he entered Cadiz, but in which he was afterwards a proficient, he projected a visit to Malta, but was checked by a terrible obstacle. This was the " black-vomit," which broke out with irresistible force, accompanied with cholera and yellow fever.

The population died by thousands, and so many were the victims of these diseases that graves could not be dug fast enough to keep pace with the mortality. Large pits were dug—much like our plague-pits—and as they could not accommodate the coffins, the bodies of the dead were flung promiscuously into the pits. An uncle of Waterton died of the disease, his body was taken out of its coffin and thrown into the pit, and just beneath him lay the body of a Spanish marquis. No less than fourteen thousand people died in Malaga, notwithstanding that fifty thousand persons had fled from the city.

Waterton did not escape scatheless. He was seized with the black-vomit, but, although it was thought that he could not live until the following day, his great strength of constitution, aided by his simple mode of life, enabled him to conquer in the struggle. As if to add to the terrors of the time, earthquakes followed the plague, and every one who possessed another home was anxious to leave a spot which had been stricken with such plagues, and among them was Waterton. But the authorities had meanwhile laid an embargo on the shipping, and it was next to

impossible to get away. At last, at the risk of imprison-
ment for life, he escaped by the daring and forethought
of a Swedish captain.

He took on board Waterton and his younger brother,
the former being entered on the ship's books as a Swedish
carpenter, and the latter as a passenger. How carefully
the escape was planned, and how skilfully it was executed,
must be told in Waterton's own words :—

" We slept on board for many successive nights, in hopes
of a fair wind to carry us through the Straits. At last, a
real east wind did come, and it blew with great violence.
The captain, whose foresight and precautions were truly
admirable, had given the strictest orders to the crew that
not a word should be spoken whilst we were preparing to
escape. We lay in close tier amongst forty sail of mer-
chantmen. The harbour-master having come his usual
rounds and found all right, passed on without making any
observations.

" At one o'clock, P.M., just as the governor had gone to
the eastward to take an airing in his carriage, as was his
custom every day, and the boats of two Spanish brigs-of-
war at anchor in the harbour had landed their officers for
the afternoon's amusements, our vessel worked out clear
of the rest, and instantly became a cloud of canvas. The
captain's countenance, which was very manly, exhibited a
portrait of cool intrepidity rarely seen : had I possessed
the power, I would have made him an admiral on the spot.

" The vessel drove through the surf with such a press of
sail that I expected every moment to see her topmasts
carried away. Long before the brigs-of-war had got their
officers on board, and had weighed in chase of us, we were
far at sea ; and when night had set in we lost sight of them
for ever, our vessel passing Gibraltar at the rate of nearly
eleven knots an hour."

It was indeed fortunate for Waterton that he succeeded in making his escape, for in the following spring the plague returned with increased violence, and no less than thirty-six thousand more victims perished. Waterton never dwells on the hardships and sufferings which he underwent in his travels, but he remarks that his constitution was much shaken by the Malaga illness, and that in all probability he would not have survived a second attack. He had tried to persuade another uncle to take part in the escape, but he declined, and was carried off by the second outbreak of the pestilence.

So ended Waterton's first experience of foreign travel. It was not by any means an encouraging tour, for he had lost relatives, friends, and health, while he had gained little except a knowledge of travel, and the sight of flamingos, vultures, and apes at liberty.

It was characteristic of Waterton that when he found himself at Hull, forty-four years after he started on his travels, he made inquiries about the captain of the ship in which he took his first voyage, discovered that he was alive, sought him out, and renewed the acquaintance begun so many years before.

His weakened state caused him to take cold as he was sailing up the Channel ; the cold settled on the lungs, and he was scarcely in less danger in England than he had been in Malaga. However, he again rallied, and was able once more to join the hunting-field. Still, the shock to the system had been very great, and to the end of his life, though he could endure almost any amount of heat, he was painfully sensitive to cold, and especially to cold winds. The chilly climate of England did not agree with his health, and he found himself again obliged to go abroad. He longed, he said, " to bask in a warmer sun."

Some estates in Demerara being in possession of the

family, Waterton went to superintend them, and in the interval before starting, made the personal acquaintance of Sir Joseph Banks, who at once appreciated the powers which the young traveller was afterwards to develop. He gave Waterton a piece of most excellent advice, namely, to come home for a time at least once in three years.

He continued to administer the estates for eight years, when, as both his father and uncle, the proprietors of the estates, were dead, he handed over the property to those who had a right to it, and thence began his world-famed *Wanderings*, the account of which will be given exactly as he wrote it; without the change or omission of a syllable, or the addition of a note.

CHAPTER II.

DURING his stay in Demerara, he was selected as the
bearer of despatches to the Spanish Government in
Orinoco, and received the first commission which had
been held by any one bearing the name of Waterton
since the days of Queen Mary ; the commission being
dated August 2, 1808.

While passing up the Orinoco river in the fulfilment
of this mission, an adventure occurred which had well-
nigh deprived the world of the *Wanderings*.

" During the whole of the passage up the river, there was
a grand feast for the eyes and ears of an ornithologist. In
the swampy parts of the wooded islands, which abound in
this mighty river, we saw waterfowl innumerable ; and

when we had reached the higher grounds it was quite charming to observe the immense quantities of parrots and scarlet aras which passed over our heads. The loud harsh screams of the bird called the horned screamer were heard far and near; and I could frequently get a sight of this extraordinary bird as we passed along; but I never managed to bring one down with the gun, on account of the difficulty of approaching it.

"While we were wending our way up the river, an accident happened of a somewhat singular nature. There was a large labarri snake coiled up in a bush, which was close to us. I fired at it, and wounded it so severely that it could not escape. Being wishful to dissect it, I reached over into the bush, with the intention to seize it by the throat, and convey it aboard. The Spaniard at the tiller, on seeing this, took the alarm, and immediately put his helm aport. This forced the vessel's head to the stream, and I was left hanging to the bush with the snake close to me, not having been able to recover my balance as the vessel veered from the land. I kept firm hold of the branch to which I was clinging, and was three times overhead in the water below, presenting an easy prey to any alligator that might have been on the look-out for a meal.

"Luckily a man who was standing near the pilot, on seeing what had happened, rushed to the helm, seized hold of it, and put it hard a-starboard, in time to bring the head of the vessel back again. As they were pulling me up, I saw that the snake was evidently too far gone to do mischief; and so I laid hold of it and brought it aboard with me, to the horror and surprise of the crew. It measured eight feet in length. As soon as I had got a change of clothes, I killed it, and made a dissection of the head.

"I would sometimes go ashore in the swamps to shoot

maroudies, which are somewhat related to the pheasant; but they were very shy, and it required considerable address to get within shot of them. In these little excursions I now and then smarted for my pains. More than once I got among some hungry leeches, which made pretty free with my legs. The morning after I had had the adventure with the Labarri snake, a cayman slowly passed our vessel. All on board agreed that this tyrant of the fresh waters could not be less than thirty feet long."

I ought to state that the Labarri snake here mentioned is one of the most venomous serpents of Guiana, but as it will be fully described in a subsequent page, I shall say no more about it at present. Waterton never feared snakes, even though knowing that their bite is certain death, but the coxswain of the boat, not having such nerve, might well be excused for taking alarm.

A rather amusing incident took place when he had reached his destination.

" On arriving at Angostura, the capital of the Orinoco, we were received with great politeness by the Governor. Nothing could surpass the hospitality of the principal inhabitants. They never seemed satisfied unless we were partaking of the dainties which their houses afforded. Indeed, we had feasting, dancing, and music in super-abundance.

"The Governor, Don Felipe de Ynciarte, was tall and corpulent. On our first introduction, he told me that he expected the pleasure of our company to dinner every day during our stay in Angostura. We had certainly every reason to entertain very high notions of the plentiful supply of good things which Orinoco afforded ; for, at the first day's dinner, I counted more than forty dishes of fish and flesh. The governor was superbly

attired in a full uniform of gold and blue, the weight
of which alone, in that hot climate, and at such a
repast, was enough to have melted him down. He had
not half got through his soup before be began visibly
to liquefy. I looked at him, and bethought me of the
old saying, 'How I sweat! said the mutton-chop to the
gridiron.'

" He now became exceedingly uneasy; and I myself
had cause for alarm; but our sensations arose from very
different causes. He, no doubt, already felt that the
tightness of his uniform, and the weight of the ornaments upon it, would never allow him to get through
that day's dinner with any degree of comfort to himself; I, on the other hand (who would have been amply
satisfied with one dish well done) was horrified at the
appalling sight of so many meats before me. Good-
breeding whispered to me, and said; 'Try a little of
most of them.' Temperance replied, 'Do so at your
peril; and for your over-strained courtesy, you shall
have yellow-fever before midnight.'

" At last the Governor said to me, in Spanish, 'Don
Carlos, this is more than man can bear. *No puedo sufrír
tanto.* Pray pull off your coat, and tell your companions to
do the same; and I'll show them the example.' On saying
this, he stripped to the waistcoat; and I and my friends
and every officer at table did the same. The next day,
at dinner-time, we found his Excellency clad in a uniform
of blue Salempore, slightly edged with gold lace."

His tropical *Wanderings* came to an end in 1825, in
which year he published the now famous volume. At
first, he received from the critics much the same treatment as did Bruce and Le Vaillant. Critics would not
believe that Bruce ever saw a living ox cut up for food, oı

that the Abyssinians ate beef raw in preference to cooked. Neither would they believe that Le Vaillant ever chased a giraffe, because, as they said, there was no such animal, and that therefore, Le Vaillant could not have seen it.

Similarly, some of Waterton's statements were received with a storm of derision, more especially his account of the sloth and its strange way of living; of the mode of handling deadly serpents, and above all, his ride on the back of a cayman. There is however one honourable exception in the person of Sydney Smith, who devoted one of his wittiest and happiest essays to a review of the *Wanderings* and fully recognized the extraordinary powers of Waterton.

According to Sydney Smith, Waterton " appears in early life to have been seized with an unconquerable aversion to Piccadilly, and to that train of meteorological questions and answers which forms the great staple of polite conversation. . .

" The sun exhausted him by day, the mosquitos bit him by night, but on went Mr. Charles Waterton. . . . . happy that he had left his species far away, and is at last in the midst of his blessed baboons."

Nothing can be better than Sydney Smith's summary of the life of a sloth, who " moves suspended, rests suspended, sleeps suspended, and passes his whole life in suspense, like a young clergyman distantly related to a bishop." Or, than his simile of the box-tortoise and the boa, who " swallows him shell and all, and consumes him slowly in the interior, as the Court of Chancery does a large estate."

Or, what can be happier than the turn he gives to Waterton's account of the toucan ?

" How astonishing are the freaks and fancies of nature ! To what purpose, we say, is a bird placed in the forests of

Cayenne, with a bill a yard long, making a noise like a puppy dog, and laying eggs in hollow trees ? The Toucans, to be sure, might retort—to what purpose were gentlemen in Bond Street created? To what purpose were certain foolish, prating members of Parliament created? pestering the House of Commons with their ignorance and folly, and impeding the business of the country. There is no end of such questions. So we will not enter into the metaphysics of the toucan."

Perhaps the oddest thing to be found in criticism is that which is given in Lardner's *Cabinet Cyclopedia.* Waterton's statements having been proved to be true, the writer now turns round, and tries to show that after all there was nothing very wonderful in the achievement.

"The crocodile in fact, is only dangerous when in the water. Upon land it is a slow-paced and even timid animal, so that an active boy armed with a small hatchet might easily despatch one. There is no great prowess therefore required to ride on the back of a poor cayman after it has been secured, or perhaps wounded ; and a modern writer might well have spared the recital of his feats in this way upon the cayman of Guiana, had he not been influenced in this and numberless other instances by the greatest possible love of the marvellous, and a constant propensity to dress truth in the garb of fiction."

Putting aside the fact that the writer received some of his earliest instructions from Waterton, who was always ready to impart his knowledge to those who seemed likely to make a good use of it, the assertion is absolutely unaccountable. No man was less influenced by a love of the marvellous, and none less likely to " dress truth in the garb of fiction."

His knowledge of Nature was almost wholly obtained

from personal observation, and not one single statement of his has ever been proved to be exaggerated, much less shown to be false. He might sometimes discredit the statements of others. For example, he never could believe that any races of men could be cannibals from choice, and not from necessity or superstition. But, whether at home or abroad, his investigations were so close and patient, and his conclusions so just, that he is now acknowledged to be a guide absolutely safe in any department of Natural History which came within his scope. No one now would think of disputing Waterton's word. If he denied or even doubted the statements of others, his doubts would have great weight, and could lead to a closer investigation of the subject. But, if he asserted anything to be a fact, his assertion would be accepted without scruple.

As to the meaning of the sentence about truth and fiction, I fail to understand it, except as a poetical way of rounding a paragraph. In the first place, if truth be truth, it is essentially opposed to fiction, and cannot borrow her garb. In the next place, the writer gives no instance of this remarkable performance, except a reference to the capture of the cayman. Now, nothing can be simpler or more straightforward than Waterton's account of the whole transaction. He does not glorify himself, nor boast of his courage. He leaped astride the animal, being sure, from a knowledge of its structure, that he could not be reached by the cayman's only weapons, namely, its teeth and its tail, and he never repeated the feat.

Even the peculiar style in which Waterton wrote, could not justify such a charge as was made by Swainson.

It was, perhaps unconsciously, formed on that of Sterne, many of whose phrases are employed almost verbatim. Then, his mind was saturated with Horace, Virgil, Ovid,

Cervantes, Washington Irving (himself a disciple of Sterne), *Chevy Chase*, and literature of a similar character. In the days when he first took up the pen, it was the rather pedantic custom to introduce frequent quotations from the classics into writings, speeches, and sermons, and Waterton followed the custom of the day. Moreover, it is an old Stonyhurst custom to employ such quotations both in conversation and writing, and Waterton could never shake it off. But, when he came to descriptions of scenes in which he had taken part, nothing could be more simple, terse, and graphic, than his style, especially when his sense of humour was aroused. Take for example the very scene which Swainson assailed. There is no fine language in it. There are a few of the inevitable quotations, which might be omitted with advantage, but all the description is couched in the simplest and most forcible English, without a redundant word. A better word-picture does not exist in our language. We see before us the captured cayman struggling in the water, the mixed assembly of South American savages, African negroes, a Creole, and an Englishman, all puzzled to know how to get the beast ashore without damaging it, or being wounded themselves.

Then, there is the amusing cowardice of " Daddy Quashi," the negro, who ran away when suspecting danger, hung in the rear when forced to confront it, and, when it was over, " played a good finger and thumb at breakfast." Waterton's strong sense of humour prevails throughout the story, but there is not a tinge of vanity. He explains his firm seat on the furious animal's back by mentioning that he had hunted for several years with Lord Darlington's foxhounds, but he does not tell the reader that in that celebrated hunt he was considered, next to Lord Darlington, as the best horseman in the field.

It is illustrative of Waterton's character that when the reviewers impugned his veracity, he troubled himself very little about them, saying that the creatures which he had described would one day find their way to the Zoological Gardens, and then that everybody would see that he had but spoken the truth. So, when the first sloth arrived, Waterton had quite a little triumph over his detractors. Indeed, the probability was, that, after reading one of these reviews, he would invite the assailant to Walton Hall, offer him the good old English hospitality of that place, and settle the point of dispute in friendly controversy.

But, little as he cared for such attacks, he was deeply stung by the epithet 'eccentric' which one writer applied to him, and never could forget it.

Yet, had he not been eccentric, he could not have been the Charles Waterton so long known and loved. It was perhaps eccentric to have a strong religious faith, and act up to it. It was eccentric, as Thackeray said, to " dine on a crust, live as chastely as a hermit, and give his all to the poor." It was eccentric to come into a large estate as a young man and to have lived to extreme old age without having wasted an hour or a shilling. It was eccentric to give bountifully and never allow his name to appear in a subscription-list. It was eccentric to be saturated with the love of nature. It might be eccentric never to give dinner-parties, preferring to keep an always open house for his friends ; but it was a very agreeable kind of eccentricity. It was eccentric to be ever childlike, but never childish. We might multiply instances of his eccentricity to any extent, and may safely say that the world would be much better than it is if such eccentricity were more common.

It formed one of the peculiar charms of his society, and he was utterly unconscious of it. He thought himself the most common-place of human beings, and yet no one could be in his company for five minutes without feeling himself in the presence of no ordinary man. He had no idea that he was doing anything out of the general course of things if he asked a visitor to accompany him to the top of a lofty tree to look at a hawk's nest; or if he built his stables so that the horses might converse with each other after their work was over, or his kennel so that his hounds should be able to see everything that was going on.

Even the pigs came in for their share of his kindly thoughtfulness. He used to say that in a wild state, swine were not dirty beasts, but that when they are penned into small sties, as is usually the case, they have no opportunity of being clean. So he had his sties built of stone, with a stone platform in front, sloping and channelled so as to be easily and thoroughly cleansed, and having a southern aspect so that the pigs might enjoy the beams of that sun which their master loved so much himself.

On these warm stone slabs they used to lie in a half-dozing state, and Waterton often used to point out the multitudinous wasps that came flying into the sties and picked off the flies from the bodies of the drowsy pigs. If the sties at Tudhoe had been like those at Walton Hall, he would not have issued from them in the highly perfumed state which he so amusingly describes. See p. 7.

Some persons thought that his rooted abhorrence of mourning was eccentric. If so, the eccentricity is now shared by many, including myself, who have abandoned on principle the black crape, gloves, hat-bands, mutes, black feathers, black-edged writing paper, and other conventional signs of grief.

Waterton however carried the principle still further, and could never be induced to wear even a black coat of any kind on any occasion. He usually wore a blue body-coat with gold—not gilt buttons, but at the urgent request of the police, who told him that his costly buttons were a perpetual anxiety to them whenever he went to Wakefield, he at last consented to lay them aside, except at home, and have his buttons covered with blue cloth.

This peculiarity once caused him to lose the privilege of an introduction to the Pope (Gregory XVI.). Etiquette demanded that if uniform could not be worn, the presentee must appear in ordinary evening dress. Now, had Waterton qualified as Deputy-Lieutenant, he could have followed the usual custom and worn that uniform, but as he had refused to do so, evening-dress was the only alternative· But he would not wear ' frac-nero,' and so lost the presentation.

On another occasion however, the difficulty was evaded in a very characteristic manner. He bethought himself of his commission in the Demerara militia ; but he had no uniform, and there was no time to make one. Some naval friends were with him, Captain Marryatt being, I believe, one of them, and with Waterton's blue coat and gold buttons, surmounted with a pair of naval epaulettes, and with the addition of a naval captain's cocked hat and sword, they composed an amusingly miscellaneous uniform. One friend wickedly suggested that spurs would have an imposing effect in connection with the naval hat and epaulettes, but he was not to be caught in so palpable a snare.

Of his travels on the Continent, there is but little to say as they are related at some length in the three volumes of Essays. It is remarkable, by the way, that on the Continent, as well as in England, he met with injuries far more severe than any which he received in Guiana.

Twice he was nearly drowned.

On one occasion he was on board a vessel named the
Pollux, and bound from Civitá Vecchia to Leghorn. In
the night of the same day, an accident befell the *Pollux,*
almost exactly resembling that in which the ill-fated
Princess Alice was destroyed. The night was peculiarly
calm, the stars were shining brightly, and everything appeared to be in security, when all on board were startled
from their sleep by a violent shock. A steamer, named
the *Mongibello,* from Leghorn to Civitá Vecchia, had run
into the *Pollux,* and cut her nearly in two, the cutwater of
the *Mongibello* having actually forced its way into Waterton's cabin.

Fortunately for the passengers, most of them, including
Waterton and his family, were sleeping on deck. As is
too often the case under similar circumstances, the officials
on board the offending vessel lost their presence of mind,
and were actually sheering off from the wreck. Had it
not been for the courage and skill of Prince Canino (Charles
Bonaparte) the loss of life must have been very great.

He was a passenger on board the *Mongibello,* knocked
the steersman off the wheel, took the helm himself, and
laid the vessel alongside the sinking *Pollux.* Only one
life was lost, that of a man who had a large sum of gold
sewed in a belt round his waist, and was drawn under
water by the weight.

In this shipwreck, although Waterton's life was saved,
he and his party lost their wardrobes, money in cash, and
letters of credit, books, writings, passports, and works of
art ; the last mentioned loss being irreparable. Fever and
dysentery were the results of the shipwreck, and did not
loosen their hold until long afterwards.

Another time, he fell into Dover harbour while about to
embark on board the steamer. Any one who has walked on
cliffs on a dark night is aware of the difficulty of distinguish-

ing land from water. At Margate I was once within a single
step of falling over the cliff, whose edges corresponded so
exactly in colour with the sea and rocks below, that, had
it not been for the information conveyed by a stick, I
must have been instantly killed. Several persons, indeed,
have lately been killed at the same spot.

Thinking that he was at the gangway, he stepped over
the edge of the quay, and fell fifteen feet into the water,
sinking under the paddle-box, and only finding support
by catching at the wheel itself. Thence he was rescued ;
but the cold winds blowing on him as he stood wet and
dripping on the deck of the steamer, brought on a violent
attack of fever. He had recourse to his usual double
remedy, the lancet and calomel, and recovered sufficiently
to attend the great religious festival at Bruges, for the sake
of which he had left England.

His reliance on the lancet and calomel was almost incredible. In these times the former is hardly ever used,
and the latter has been abandoned by a great number of
medical men. But in Waterton's early days these were
the principal remedies, and he never lost faith in them.
When I last saw him in 1863, he told me that he had
been bled one hundred and sixty times, mostly by his own
hand.

The amount of blood which he would take at a time
from his spare and almost emaciated frame was positively
horrifying. On this occasion he lost twenty-five ounces
of blood, and next morning took twenty grains of jalap,
mixed with ten grains of calomel. It was no wonder that
the vampire bat of Guiana would never bite him, though
he left his foot invitingly out of the hammock in order to
attract it. He used to complain that the bat never could
be induced to bleed him, though it would attack a man
lying in the next hammock ; but he might have antici-

pated that the vampire would know better than to try to suck blood from a man who was constantly bleeding himself.

Besides these accidents by water, he twice suffered severe injuries when travelling by land.

In 1818, while returning over Mount Cenis, he fancied that the baggage on the top of the carriage was loose, and mounted on the wheel to examine it. Unfortunately his left knee broke the window, and two large pieces of glass ran into it just above the knee-joint. In spite of the darkness, he contrived to get out the two pieces of glass, bound up the wound with his cravat, cut off his coat pocket, and had it filled with poultice at the nearest house, and, although repeatedly attacked with fever, he reached Paris and there gained strength to return to England. The knee remained stiff for two years, but by continual exercise without the aid of a walking-stick, the limb recovered its normal flexibility.

The next accident might have been nearly as serious, and is here given in his own words :—

"I had a little adventure on the road from Baccano to Rome not worth relating, but which I deem necessary to be introduced here in order that some of my friends in the latter city, and others in England, may not give me credit for an affair which deserves no credit at all. These good friends had got it into their heads that I had reached Rome after walking barefoot for nearly twenty miles, in order to show my respect and reverence for the sacred capital of the Christian world. Would that my motive had been as pure as represented. The sanctity of the churches, the remains of holy martyrs which enrich them, the relics of canonised saints placed in such profusion throughout them, might well induce a Catholic traveller to adopt this easy and simple mode of showing his religious feeling. But, unfortunately, the idea never entered my mind at the time. I had no other motives than those of easy walking and self-enjoyment. The affair which caused the talk took place as follows :—

" We had arrived at Baccano in the evening, and whilst we were at tea, I proposed to our excellent friend Mr. Fletcher, who had joined us at Cologne, that we should leave the inn at four the next morning on foot to Rome, and secure lodgings for the ladies, who would follow us in the carriage after a nine-o'clock breakfast. Having been accustomed to go without shoes month after month in the rugged forests of Guiana, I took it for granted that I could do the same on the pavement of his Holiness Pope Gregory the Sixteenth, never once reflecting that some fifteen years had elapsed from the time that I could go barefooted with comfort and impunity ; during the interval, however, the sequel will show that the soles of my feet had undergone a considerable alteration.

" We rose at three the morning after, and having put a shoe and a sock or half-stocking into each pocket of my coat, we left the inn at Baccano for Rome just as the hands of our watches pointed to the hour of four. Mr. Fletcher, having been born in North Britain, ran no risk of injuring his feet by an act of imprudence. The sky was cloudless and the morning frosty, and the planet Venus shone upon us as though she had been a little moon.

" Whether the severity of the frost, which was more than commonly keen, or the hardness of the pavement, or perhaps both conjoined, had deprived my feet of sensibility, I had no means of ascertaining ; but this is certain, I went on merrily for several miles without a suspicion of anything being wrong, until we halted to admire more particularly the transcendent splendour of the morning planet, and then I saw blood on the pavement ; my right foot was bleeding apace, and, on turning the sole uppermost, I perceived a piece of jagged flesh hanging by a string. Seeing that there would be no chance of replacing the damaged part with success, I twisted it off, and then took a survey of the foot by the light which the stars afforded.

"Mr. Fletcher, horror-struck at what he saw, proposed immediately that I should sit down by the side of the road, and there wait for the carriage, or take advantage of any vehicle which might come up. Aware that the pain would be excessive so soon as the lacerated parts would become stiff by inaction, I resolved at once to push on to Rome, wherefore, putting one shoe on the sound foot, which, by the way, had two unbroken blisters on it, I forced the wounded one into the other, and off we started for Rome, which we reached after a very uncomfortable walk. The injured foot had two months' confinement to the sofa before the damage was repaired.

"It was this unfortunate adventure which gave rise to the story of my walking barefooted into Rome, and which gained me a reputation by no means merited on my part."

Two more serious accidents occurred within his own domains.

He was out shooting in 1824, when the gun exploded just as he was ramming the wad on the powder. Fortunately the charge of shot had not been put into the gun. As it was, the ramrod was driven completely through the forefinger of the right hand, between the knuckle and first joint, severing the tendons, but not breaking the bone, though the ignited wadding and powder followed the ramrod through the wound. He procured some warm water at a neighbouring house, washed the wound quite clean, replaced the tendons in their proper positions, and bound up the finger, taking care to give it its proper form.

Of course the lancet was used freely, and by dint of

poulticing and constant care, the full use of the finger was restored.

The other accident might have caused his death on the spot, and was a far more severe one than that by which he afterwards lost his life.

In 1850, he being then in his sixty-ninth year, he was mounted on a ladder for the purpose of pruning the branches of a pear-tree. The ladder, which was merely propped against a machine of his own invention, slipped sideways, and came to the ground, Waterton having fallen nearly twenty feet.

He had been repeatedly warned that the machine, not having side stays, must fall if the weight were thrown on one side. But he still persisted in using it, although, shortly before the accident, his son had left the spot, saying that he would not be responsible for an accident which he foresaw but could not prevent. He was partially stunned, and his arm greatly injured, the heavy ladder and machine having fallen into the hollow and smashed the elbow-joint.

His first act on recovering himself was to use his lancet and take away thirty ounces of blood. Unfortunately a second accident happened almost immediately after the first, a servant having thoughtlessly withdrawn a chair just as he was seating himself, and so causing a second shock, and the loss of thirty ounces more blood.

For some time, he lay insensible and was apparently dying fast, but his iron constitution at length prevailed, and he was restored to life, though not to health. The injured arm was gradually dwindling in size, and gave continual pain, causing loss of sleep and appetite. He had at last resolved on having the arm amputated, when his gamekeeper advised him to try a certain bone-setter living at Wakefield, who was celebrated for his cures.

Waterton took his advice and sent for the practitioner, Mr. J. Crowther, who decided that he could cure the injured limb, but at the expense of great pain. The wrist was much injured, a callus had formed in the elbow-joint, and the shoulder was partially dislocated. After a time spent in rubbing, pulling, and twisting, he got the shoulder and wrist into their places, and then, grasping the arm "just above the elbow with one hand, and below it with the other, he smashed to atoms, by main force, the callus which had formed in the dislocated joint, the elbow itself cracking as though the interior parts of it had consisted of tobacco-pipe shanks."

The process was rough, and gave inexpressible pain, but it was effectual, sleep and appetite returned, and health was soon restored.

From this accident Waterton drew a characteristic warning, namely, never to use ladders when climbing trees.

One, if not the principal reason of his cessation from tropical explorations, was his marriage. In 1829, he married Anne, a daughter of the Charles Edmonstone, of Demerara, who is often mentioned in the *Wanderings* as a kind and true friend.

His marriage has a curiously romantic history.

Mr. Charles Edmonstone, one of the Edmonstones of Broich in Scotland, had previously gone to Demerara, where he met a fellow-countryman, William Reid of Banffshire, who had settled there, and had married Minda (generally called Princess Minda), daughter of an Arowak chief. Charles Edmonstone married Helen, daughter of William Reid and Minda, and they had several children, one of whom, Anne Mary, became the wife of Waterton. He met her in Demerara, while she was yet a child, and made up his mind that she should be his wife.

Mr. Edmonstone afterwards returned with his family to

Scotland, and purchased Cardross Park, an old family estate that had formed a portion of the dower of one of his royal ancestors; Sir John Edmonstone, who married the Princess Isabel, daughter of Robert II. of Scotland; and Sir William Edmonstone his son, who married his cousin, the Princess Mary, daughter of Robert III.

Through this branch, Edmund Waterton, the present head of the family, is descended lineally from Leofric and Godiva, whose romantic legend is, I regret to say, wholly a myth. It was impossible that she could have ridden through Coventry, for the same reason that, according to the old song, prevented Guy Faux from crossing Vauxhall Bridge on his way " to perpetrate his guilt." Coventry was not in existence at the time.

There is, however, some foundation for the legend. Godiva was a lady possessing vast wealth, with which she determined to found and endow an abbey. This she did, " stripping herself of all that she had," and thence the legend. Coventry gradually arose round the abbey, and had no streets, and consequently no tolls, until Godiva had been dead at least a century.

On the death of Charles Edmonstone and his wife, their three daughters, Eliza, Anne Mary, and Helen, were sent to the well-known convent of Bruges, for the purpose of completing their education, and, in the Convent Church, Waterton ·was married to Anne, on May 11, 1829, she being then only seventeen, and he forty-eight. There is an old Scotch proverb to the effect that a bride of one May will never see a second. It was but too true in this case, for Anne Mary Waterton died on April 27, 1830, twenty-one days after giving birth to a son.

Through him it is to be hoped that a line so interwoven with ancient history, and so prominent in modern times, will not be broken. He married Josephine, second daughter

of Sir John Ennis, Bart., of Ballinahown Court, Co. West-
meath, Ireland. He has issue,—Two sons, Charles Edmund,
now a student at Stonyhurst, and Thomas More. Four
daughters, Mary, Agnes, Amabil (who died a few months
after her birth), and Josephine.

Waterton could never bear to speak of his wife, but he
needed help in the care of his infant son. For this purpose,
he asked her two sisters, the Misses Eliza and Helen Edmonstone to take up their abode with him. This they did
to the hour of his death, and he often wrote with affec-
tionate gratitude of their devotion to him.

He yearned to go back again to the wilds of Guiana, but
considered that his child had prior claims upon him, and
so, according to his invariable custom, he sacrificed inclination to duty.

CHAPTER III.

WATERTON AT HOME, and, what a home !

It was not magnificent in the ordinary sense of the word.
Such magnificence may be the result of mere wealth, without either taste, imagination, or appreciation. The veriest
boor in existence, who happens by some turn of fortune to
be put in possession of enormous wealth, need only give
the word, and he may revel in more than royal
magnificence.

As for the house itself, no expenditure could give it the
least pretence to beauty or stateliness. It is one of the
worst specimens of the worst era of architecture, and is
nothing but a stone box perforated with rows of oblong
holes by way of windows.

I tried on all sides to obtain a view of it which would
soften down its ugliness, but could not succeed. The

front of the house is, strange to say, the worst part of it,
being a flat, smooth, stone wall, with three rows of oblong
windows, eight in a row. The only specimen of architecture which could approach it in this respect is a work-
house of the same date, those of modern times being
infinitely superior in architectural effect.

Why the grand old house should have been pulled down
to make way for such an edifice is quite inexplicable.

WALTON HALL, FROM THE LAKE.

Very few houses will be found with an oak-panelled hall
ninety feet in length. Yet all this was destroyed ; part of
the oak-panelling was used in building a pigeon-house, and
the rest was burned. Such was the state of architecture
in the days "when George the Third was king."

Unfortunately, no paintings or engravings of this most
memorable house are in existence, though there are innumerable plates of the "Seats of the Nobility and

Gentry," most of them in the style satirized by Hogarth
in his " Marriage à la Mode."

In fact, the architecture of that era is on a par with the
classical costumes of the stage. I have possessed for
many years a volume of Shakspeare in which there is a
portrait of an actor in the part of Troilus. He is
classically costumed as a Trojan in a tight scale cuirass,
a short cloak, knee breeches and silk stockings, Roman
buskins, a tie wig, a helmet with a vast plume of ostrich
feathers, and he is bidding defiance to Diomedes with a
toy Moorish sword which would hardly cut off the head
of a wax doll.

So if Waterton had desired architectural magnificence,
he could not have obtained it, except by pulling the
house down, and building another. But, he had no taste
for such magnificence, his life being one of rigid, not to say
severe, simplicity.

His personal expenses were such as could have been
covered by the wages of one of the labourers on his own
estate. His single room had neither bed nor carpet. He
always lay on the bare boards with a blanket wrapped
round him, and with an oaken block by way of a pillow.
As has been mentioned, he never touched fermented liquids
of any kind, and he took but very little meat.

When I knew him, he always retired to his room
at 8 P.M. Few men of his age would have chosen a
room at the very top of a large house; but stairs were
nothing to Waterton, whose limbs were strengthened by
perpetual tree climbing. Punctually at three A.M., being
roused by the crowing of a huge Cochin China cock, which
he called his ' morning gun,' he rose from his plank couch,
lighted his fire, lay down for half an hour, and was always
dressed and closely, or as he called it, ' clean ' shaven, by
four, when he went into the private chapel which was

next door to his room, and where he usually spent an hour in prayer.

I had several friendly altercations with him upon shaving, but he would as soon give up the lancet as the razor. He would not even wear a particle of whisker, and kept his thick, snowy hair within half an inch of length. He had not lost a hair, in spite of his advanced age, and I have often thought that if he had allowed his hair and beard to grow to their full luxuriance, a nobler figure could not have visited an artist's dreams.

Then came reading Latin and Spanish books (Don Quixote being always one), and then writing, receiving bailiff's report, &c., until eight, when, at the stroke of Sir Thomas More's clock, breakfast was served. So, he had done a fair day's work and finished breakfast at the time when most persons of his position in life had scarcely awoke.

In the next place, he was not a rich man.

As a rule, the old Yorkshire families are wealthy, and the Watertons would have been among the wealthiest of them, but for the shameful oppressions to which they were subjected. That most accomplished robber, Henry VIII., had confiscated the greater part of the estates, and what with direct robberies, double taxation, fines, and so forth, the estates were terribly reduced when he came into possession of them. Even if he had wished it, magnificence would not have been attainable, but he achieved more than magnificence, and with the restricted means at his command, converted a Yorkshire valley into a veritable wonder-land.

In this congenial task he was favoured by circumstances which are not likely to occur again. He possessed the requisite knowledge, a constitution of iron, and a frame of astonishing endurance and activity. He came into possession of the estate as a very young man, only twenty-

four years of age, and remained absolute master for nearly
sixty years.

It was a pity that he did not bestow as much pains on
his estate as on his birds. But he was no practical
agriculturist as his father had been. He could not do
anything which looked like oppressing his tenants, and
the consequence was, that they were habitually in heavy
arrears, and often threw up their farms without paying
rent, having impoverished the land and enriched themselves.

He loved natural history in all its forms, but his chief
pursuit was the study of bird-life, and he modified the
grounds to the use of the birds, caring much more for their
comfort than his own. For this purpose the grounds were
admirably adapted by Nature, and he aided her by art.
There were a large moat and a succession of ponds for the
accommodation of aquatic birds. There were swampy
places where the birds could feed. There were ruined edifices
for such birds as chose them for a residence, and the whole
of the park was covered with stately trees. Moreover, the
house stood on a stone island in the moat, and, as may be
seen from the illustration on page 36, permitted the habits
of the water-birds to be closely watched.

The first need was obviously to allow the birds to be undisturbed by boys and other intruders, and to prohibit the
firing of guns—the only sound which birds seem instinc-
tively to dread. But, as there was a public pathway running in front of the house, he had great difficulty in
obtaining permission to close it. This object, however.
was at last attained, and he then began his wall. It is of
a roughly circular form, the house being near the centre.
Nowhere is it less than eight feet high, and where it runs
along the canal, it is more than double that height, in order
to protect the birds from the guns of bargees.

These men, by the way, used to be most determined poachers, and, on account of their mode of life, even if detected and chased, they could escape by means of their barges. They were chary, however, of venturing inside a sixteen feet wall, and after a while ceased from troubling. Such a work was necessarily very expensive, costing at least ten thousand pounds. It was too large a sum to be paid at once, and Waterton would not run in debt. So, every year, he put aside as much money as could be spared for the wall, went on building until the money was expended, and then stopped the work, and waited until the following year to continue it. The wall was three miles in total length, and inclosed an area of two hundred and fifty-nine acres.

The value of this wall was shown by the fact that the very year after it was finished the herons came and established themselves within it. At my last visit in 1863, there were nearly forty nests.

How should they know that a wall could protect them against man ? It was no obstacle to them, and how they could have known, as they evidently did, that it was an obstacle to mankind is one of the yet unsolved problems which puzzle students of zoology. Moreover, they knew that those few specimens of humanity who came within the wall would do them no harm. I have often been in the heronry, with the blue fragments of broken eggs lying on the ground, and seen the herons going to and from their home with perfect unconcern. Even on the ground, the herons had no fear of man. Provided that a man approached them slowly and quietly, he could come close enough to see their eyes, and even to notice the reflection of the rippling water upon their grey plumage.

Not only in the heronry, but in other parts of the park near the water, the birds would allow themselves to be approached quite closely, so that their peculiar habits could be watched. I was able to secure slight sketches of the characteristic, and almost grotesque attitudes assumed by the heron, and have selected three as examples.

1   2   3

Fig. 1 shows the bird in a position which, in common with the flamingo, stork, and other long-legged wading birds, it is fond of assuming. It doubles its legs under the body, thrusts the feet forward, sinks its head upon its shoulders, so as to conceal the long neck, and remains so motionless and so unlike a heron that it might easily be passed without notice.

Fig. 2 shows the heron standing on one leg at rest. By moving cautiously round the bird, I succeeded in getting a back view, so as to show the perfect balance of the body on the single leg (Fig. 3).

Waterton had a special love for the heron, and frequently alludes to the services which it renders to the owners of fish-ponds.

"Formerly we had a range of fish-ponds here, one above the other, covering a space of about three acres of ground. Close by them ran a brook, from which the water-rats made regular passages through the intervening bank into the ponds. These vermin were engaged in never-ceasing mischief. No sooner was one hole repaired than another was made ; so that we had the mortification to see the ponds generally eight or ten inches below water-mark. This encouraged the growth of weeds to a most incommodious extent, which at last put an end to all pleasure in fishing. Finding that the 'green mantle from the standing pool' was neither useful nor pleasant, I ordered the ponds to be drained, and a plantation to be made in the space of ground which they had occupied.

"Had I known as much then as I know now of the valuable services of the heron, and had there been a good heronry near the place, I should not have made the change. The draining of the ponds did not seem to lessen the number of rats in the brook; but soon after the herons had settled here to breed, the rats became extremely scarce; and now I rarely see one in the place, where formerly I could observe numbers sitting on the stones at the mouth of their holes, as soon as the sun had gone down below the horizon. I often watch the herons on the banks of some other store-ponds with feelings of delight; and nothing would grieve me more than to see the lives of these valuable and ornamental birds sacrificed to the whims and caprices of man."

A portion of one of these now dry fish-ponds may be seen in the illustration of the " Grotto," on page 68. On such a rich soil as that afforded by the bed of an old fish-pond, the trees grew with great rapidity, and the spot is now a singularly picturesque one, with bold effects of light and shade, and shelter from the wind and sun.

The next important work was the extension of the moat, a long and costly operation.

The present house is comparatively modern, standing well clear of the water. But, the original house extended to the water on the south side, and was a fortified building of sufficient strength to justify a siege under Cromwell's personal direction.

Unfortunately, Waterton's father destroyed this historical building to make room for the present house, and almost the only relic of this fortification is the old gateway, with its central tower and flanking turrets, and said to be more than a thousand years of age.

The gate itself is of very thick oak planking, pierced with loopholes for musketry, and bearing tangible evidences

GATEWAY AND IVY TOWER

of the siege in the shape of many bullet marks. In the left portion of the gate there is a ball still remaining, which is distinguished by an iron ring round it bearing an inscription to the effect that it was fired by Oliver Cromwell himself. That he took an active part in the siege is well known, but it is difficult to identify any individual bullet which he fired. The tradition further states that the shot was fired at the lady of the house, who gallantly conducted the defence herself. The reader may be interested to hear that her defence was successful.

The sketch, representing the Gateway in its present condition, was taken on the opposite side of the water, from a spot close to the tall and lightning-shattered poplar-tree, shown on the right hand of the illustration on p. 36. The chief interest of this view lies in the gateway itself. Just behind it is an odd-looking tower, which was built by Waterton for the use of starlings, and the place is enclosed on the north by a thick and closely-clipped hedge of yew. The heavy masses of ivy which fall in thick clusters from the turrets and which serve as a refuge for many birds, have given to the structure the name of Ivy Tower, by which it is often mentioned in the Essays.

While still very young, I was familiar with the Ivy Tower from Waterton's Essays. They mostly appeared in Loudon's *Magazine of Natural History,* and as that valuable publication was taken in at the Ashmolean Society of Oxford, where I lived, I used to watch impatiently for each successive number, in the hope that it might contain an article from Waterton's pen. Thus, the gateway, the lake, the heronry, the starling towers, the fallen millstone, the shattered poplar, the holly hedges and the wooden pheasants, were all known to me, and when at last I had the privilege of visiting Walton Hall, there was not one of those spots that I did not joyfully recognize.

In the old times, the only approach to the mainland was by a drawbridge, opening on to the gateway, which was then three stories high. This has long been destroyed, and at present the approach is made by a light iron bridge, rather to the right of the gateway. This bridge is not shown in the sketch.

As to the siege, there are other reminiscences beside the gateway itself.

While the soldiers of Cromwell were occupying the hill nearly opposite the gateway, one of the soldiers started off with a keg on his shoulder to fetch beer from the village. Thinking that he would return by the same route, one of the garrison aimed a little gun which was mounted on the topmost story, so as to command the path. The soldier did return by the same way, and was struck down by the ball, which passed through his thigh.

The tradition of this lucky shot was handed down from father to son, until it reached Waterton's father. He had the curiosity to dig at the spot where the man was said to have fallen, and there he found the ball, a little iron one. This he gave to his son, with a request that it should always remain in the family.

In 1857, while dredging away the drift mud which had accumulated round the gateway, a small iron cannon was discovered. As the ball fitted it, and it was found exactly below the turret from which the fatal shot had been fired, there could be no doubt that it was the identical gun

CULVERIN.

mentioned in the tradition; so Waterton had the pleasure of placing the cannon and the ball together in his house, where every visitor could see them.

Beside the gun, there were found a sword-blade, a spear, daggers, axe, many coins, keys, and some silver plate. For their presence in the mud Waterton accounts by suggesting that they were flung into the moat, when the house was ransacked for arms after the battle of Culloden. He told me that he believed that if the lake were completely drained, many more such articles would be recovered.

The view on page 36 is taken from a spot on the northern bank. At some hundreds of yards distance from the house there are a couple of splendid sycamores, and close to them is a large block of ironstone, called the Echo Stone. Any one standing by it, and speaking towards the house, will hear every syllable returned with wonderful clearness. Sitting on this stone, I made the sketch from which this illustration is taken. On it is engraved the word ECHO.

On the western side of the gateway there had been a curious old chapel formerly attached to the mansion. Waterton, however, disliked it and took it down, against the remonstrances of the then Duke of Norfolk, his godfather.

The lake is widest near the house, and then proceeds almost due west, narrowing as it goes, and taking a turn northwards towards the end, where it passes round a hill, and becomes shallower, allowing the sedges and reeds to appear, and so affording shelter for the aquatic birds.

Another view of the lake is now given, looking westward, and taken from the right-hand first-floor window of the house as seen on page 36.

On the ground-floor may be seen a large window, flanked by a smaller one on either side. These are the west windows of the drawing-room. The central window is a large sheet of plate glass, and behind it is mounted a large telescope, commanding nearly the whole of the lake.

On the left, before coming to the wood, are a few willows, and between them and the wood is a favourite resort of the herons. The low bank looks as if it would be endangered by the water, but it is perfectly firm, even to the very edge. It is made of large stones, not squared, but heaped loosely together. Seeds of various trees, especially those of the sycamore, fell into the water, floated on its surface, and were arrested by the bank, where they took root. They were never allowed to grow into trees, and were constantly cut down. But their roots twined themselves among the stones, and bound them together so firmly, that a stronger wall could not be desired.

LAKE, LOOKING WESTWARD.

The holes under these stones are favourite resorts of pike, with which the lake abounds.

I am no angler, but I have caught many pike near the willows by trolling, using nothing but a willow stick by way of rod, a hank of whipcord for a line, a gorge hook, and a minnow for bait. The largest that I ever took there weighed rather over ten pounds, and very proud I was of the fish, though it was a heavy and inconvenient article to carry to the house.

Some of the pike, including the ten-pounder, were for

the table, but the fish were generally used for the purpose
of feeding the cats, of which there were many about the
stables and cattle-yards, for the purpose of keeping down
the rats.   It is now well known that a well-fed cat is the
best mouser, seldom eating its prey, but killing it for the
mere sport.

When the cats were fed, the fish were chopped up on a
wooden block near the stables.   It was very amusing to
watch the operation.   Although at first not a cat might be
visible, half a dozen blows had not been struck with the
chopper before impatient cries were heard, and cats came
swarming round the block, just as they do round a cat's-
meat man's barrow in London.

On the right, just above the tall tree near the edge of
the lake, a heron is seen flying in the distance.   It was
near the bank at the further end of the lake that Waterton
met with his fatal accident at a spot nearly below the
flying heron.

CHAPTER IV.

WATERTON'S love of trees almost amounted to veneration. He studied their ways as minutely and as accurately as he did those of the animal world, and in consequence he could do more with trees than any one else. By patient observation of their modes of growth, he knew how to plant them in the locality best suited for themselves, how to encourage them, and, if they were injured, to reduce their damage to a minimum.

Many a fine tree has he shown me which would have been long ago condemned by ignorant men, but which was then flourishing in full growth, and in such renewed health that scarcely a scar was left in the bark to show the spot on which the injury had occurred.

One of his triumphs in this art was to be seen by a splendid poplar situated nearly opposite the picturesque gateway, and especially favoured by Waterton as having been planted by his father. It was twice struck by lightning, and the trunk split open for many feet.

However, Waterton filled up the breaches, and in course of time the tree recovered itself (see p. 36). It was in full growth during my last visit, but it was blown down by a severe gale in 1869, having succumbed, not to the lightning, but to age. To heal a tree by filling it with bricks and mortar may appear to be rather a singular method, but it is a very effectual one; the chief object being to keep rain out of the tree, and so to guard it against rotting.

How thoroughly Waterton had studied the ways of trees may be seen from the following extract from his essay on the Titmouse and the Woodpecker, in which he combated the popular opinion that these birds were injurious to trees:—

"Would you inspect the nest of a carrion crow? Brittle are the living branches of the ash and sycamore; while, on the contrary, those which are dead on the Scotch pine are tough, and will support your weight. The arms of the oak may safely be relied on; but, I pray you, trust with extreme caution those of the quick-growing alder. Neither press heavily on the linden tree; though you may ascend the beech and the elm without any fear of danger. But let us stop here for the present. On some future day, should I be in a right frame for it, I may pen down a few remarks, which will possibly be useful to the naturalist when roving in quest of ornithological knowledge. I will now confine myself to the misfortunes and diseases of trees; and I will show that neither the titmouse nor the woodpecker ever bore into the hard and live wood.

"Trees, in general, are exposed to decay by two different processes, independent of old age. The first is that of a broken branch, which, when neglected, or not cut off close to the parent stem, will, in the course of time, bring utter ruin on the tree. The new wood, which is annually formed, cannot grow over the jutting and fractured part, into which the rain enters, and gradually eats deeper and deeper, till at last it reaches the trunk itself. There it makes sad havoc ; and the tree, no longer able to resist the fury of the tempest, is split asunder, and falls in ponderous ruins. But ere it comes to this, the titmouse will enter the cavity in a dry spring, and rear its young ones here. Now, if the diseased or fractured branches were carefully cut off close to the bole, you would see the new accession of wood gradually rolling over the flat surface, which, in time, would be entirely covered by it ; and then the tree would be freed for ever from all danger in that quarter. The second process towards decay is exceedingly curious, and cannot well be accounted for. If it takes place to a serious extent, no art of man can possibly save the tree ; and sooner or later, according to the magnitude of the disease with which it has been tainted, it will fall before the force of the raging winds. Should this disease be slight, the timely prevention of rain from penetrating the injured part will secure the tree from further mischief.

" I must here observe that, in animated nature, the vital functions are internal ; so that, if the part within be mortally wounded, death is the inevitable consequence. With most trees, and with all those of Britain, it is otherwise. Their vitality is at the periphery, connected with the bark, under which an annual increase of wood takes place, so long as the tree is alive. Should, however, the bark be cut away, the tree will die upwards from the place where all the bark has been destroyed. Not so with its internal parts. You may entirely excavate the interior of a tree ; and provided you leave a sufficient strength of wood, by way of wall, in order that it may be able to resist the fury of the tempest without, taking care at the same time to exclude the rain, your tree will remain in vigour from generation to generation.

" The internal texture of a tree will perish without any notice by which we may be forewarned of the coming ruin. The disease which causes the destruction takes place in the oak ; but more frequently in the sycamore, and most commonly of all in the ash. We will select this last tree by way of elucidation.

" Often, when arrayed in all the bloom of vegetable beauty, the ash-tree is seen to send forth from its bole, or from some principal branch, a small fungus, which, during the summer, increases to a considerable size. It ripens in the autumn, and falls to the ground when winter's rain sets in. The bark through which this fungus sprouted is now completely dead, though it still retains its colour; and that part of the wood from which it proceeded is entirely changed in its nature, the whole of its vitiated juices having been expended in forming and nourishing the fungus. Nothing remains of its once firm and vigorous texture. It is become what is commonly called touch-wood, as soft and frangible as a piece of cork, which, when set on fire, will burn like tinder. In the meantime, the tree shows no sign of sickness, and its annual increase goes on as usual, till at last the new swelling wood closes over the part from which the fungus had grown, and all appears to go on right again. But ere the slow process arrives at this state the titmouse or the woodpecker will have found an entrance and a place of safety for their incubation. They quickly perforate the distempered bark, and then the tainted wood beneath it yields to their pointed bills, with which they soon effect a spacious cavity.

" Here, then, we have the whole mystery unfolded. These

birds, which never perforate the live wood, find in this diseased part of the tree, or of the branch, a place suitable to their wants. They make a circular hole large enough to admit their bodies, and then they form a cavity within sufficiently spacious to contain their young. Thus does nature kindly smooth the way in order that all her creatures may prosper and be happy. Whenever I see these sylvan carpenters thus employed I say to them, 'Work on, ye pretty birds; you do no harm in excavating there. I am your friend, and I will tell the owner of the tree that you are not to blame. But his woodman deserves a severe reprimand. He ought to have cut down the tree in the autumn, after the appearance of the fungus.'"

Even when the tree was hopelessly destroyed by the fungus, Waterton would still find uses for the stump. He would clothe it with ivy so as to render it picturesque, and he would manipulate it so that it should be a home for birds.

Many of these stumps are in the grounds, and of them I have selected one or two as examples.

The first shows the "brick and mortar" system which has already been mentioned. Several habitations for birds are constructed in it, and the stone in front is intended to aid the observer in looking into the nests. I tried to sketch this stump so as not to make it look like a grotesque human face. But exactness was the first consideration, and it is represented precisely as it was in 1863.

The second sketch was chosen because it represents one of the fungus-visited ash-trees described by Waterton.

The tree has been broken off some ten feet from the ground, at a spot weakened by a fungus. Of the tree itself little remains except the broken stump and a few small branches which still retain their leaves. Ivy has ascended

it, and is hanging in heavy clusters, so as to give the
fast-dying tree a verdure not its own.   And, as the reader
may observe, two more masses of fungus are projecting
from the tree and extracting the life from its fibres.

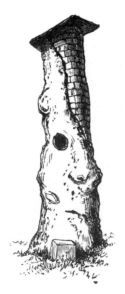

DECAYED ASH AND BRICK.

Just above the upper fungus and on its right is a small
door, with a hole near the top, and this little door has
rather a curious history.

In the spot where the door is shown there is a fungus,
proving that the wood from which it has sprung was
decayed.   Now, Waterton had for some time wanted the
Cole-titmouse to breed in his park, and, in accordance with
this notion, provided it with a home.   First, he separated an
oblong piece of wood about an inch in thickness so as to
form a door.   Next, he cut away the soft decayed wood
until he had formed a considerable cavity.   He then

replaced the door, fastening it with two little hinges and a hasp, and bored a hole in it about an inch in diameter.

In fulfilment of his expectations, the very bird which he wanted soon discovered the locality, examined it carefully, and then built in the chamber so thoughtfully provided

DECAYED ASH AND FUNGUS.

for it. I was never at Walton Hall while the bird was sitting, but have often seen the nest.

The last of these sketches represents a singularly ingenious combination of accommodation for man and bird. The trunk of an old oak-tree has been hollowed out, and the interior is divided into two stories.

In the upper there are nesting-places for birds, especially for owls, and in the lower there is a seat where the occupant can remain unseen. It is placed on the brow of the hill which borders the lake, and is so arranged that not only can the observer watch from its shelter the habits of the various aquatic beings which frequent the lake, but can actually look into the nests built on the tops of lofty

OWL HOUSE AND SEAT.

trees without the birds suspecting that their movements could be seen.

With regard to the decay of wood after it had been felled, Waterton was not long in coming to the conclusion that the "dry-rot," as it is oddly named, was caused not so much by external moisture as by the natural sap of the tree which had not been thoroughly expelled. When its juices have been completely dried and it is thoroughly "seasoned," wood is as lasting as stone. We have in the British Museum specimens of woodwork which, although more than three thousand years have elapsed since the trees were felled, are as sound as when they were first carved. Waterton used to say that paint was the chief cause of dry rot, especially when it was used to cover the deficiencies of ill-seasoned wood, because it closed the pores and did not allow the sap to escape. As a proof

that weather does not injure well-seasoned wood, he was
wont to point to certain posts, gates, and other articles
made of oak, which had never been painted, and which
had been in the open air for some seven hundred years,
and were perfectly sound. The oak doors of the gateway
are fully seven hundred years old. They are pierced and
torn with musket-balls, but are still free from decay.

When he had new doors made which would be exposed
to the weather he used every precaution to keep the wet
from lodging in them. No panels were seen on the outer
side, which was as smooth as it could be made. The
corners were bound with strong iron, painted before it was
put on.

No matter how well-seasoned the wood might be, if the
doors were made of deal, three years were allowed to
elapse before painting, while, if of oak, it was never
painted until six years had passed, and very often was not
painted at all. It is also found that if holes were bored
transversely into posts, so as to allow free entrance of air,
the dry-rot scarcely ever made its appearance. If modern
builders would act upon a knowledge of this fact they
would render our houses, roofs of buildings, &c., far more
enduring than they are at present.

DID we wish to show the wonderful command which
Waterton had over trees, we need only point to the holly-
trees in his park. The holly was a great favourite of his,
as it is very hardy when properly planted, possesses a
remarkable beauty of its own, affords shelter for birds in
winter as well as summer, and can be formed into a hedge
impenetrable to man and beast.

As to laurel hedges, Waterton never would plant them,
and he had found by experience that in ordinary hawthorn
hedges a bush would often die without any apparent

reason, leaving an unsightly gap which could not be filled up. In most hands the holly is a slow-growing tree, but Waterton made it grow with astonishing rapidity.

How he managed to "force" the holly may be seen from his own words.

"People generally imagine that the holly is of tardy growth. It may be so in ordinary cases, but means may be adopted to make this plant increase with such effect as to repay us amply for all our labour and expense.

"Thus, let us dig the ground to a full yard in depth, and plant the hollies during the last week of May, taking care to puddle their roots well into the pulverized soil. We shall find by the end of September that many of the plants will have shot nearly a foot in length, and that not one of them has failed, let the ·summer have been never so dry.

"Small plants, bought in a nursery, and placed in your own garden for a couple of years, will be admirably adapted for the purpose of transplanting. Had I been aware in early life of this increasing growth of the holly, it should have formed all my fences in lieu of hawthorn."

I tried this plan with perfect success upon a stony and ungrateful soil. The *rationale* of the process is, that the young rootlets, which ought to be carefully spread by the fingers, are able to draw nourishment rapidly from the earth, and in consequence throw up branches in proportion. Waterton advised me to cut down the young hollies at first, and his advice was most valuable, although it cost some pangs when followed.

I mentioned just now that a good holly hedge is impervious to man and beast. So it is; and not even the rat, stoat, weasel, or even that worst of poachers, the cat, can get through it. True, they might push their way between the stems, but there is one obstacle which prevents them, namely, that they cannot put their feet to the ground.

The holly is perpetually shedding its leaves, especially in summer-time, in order to make way for the new leafage. The old leaves fall, become dry, and curl up, with their sharp spikes projecting in all directions. These points, sharp as needles, prick the feet of the prowling animals, and so prevent them from passing.

Of this property Waterton took advantage. Like many landed gentlemen he had a preserve of pheasants, and was consequently harassed by poachers. Now he hated prosecution, and always evaded it if possible. On one occasion, for example, when eight men and a boy were captured on Sunday morning, while trespassing in his rookery, he released them on finding that they were tailors, saying that he could not think of prosecuting eight-ninths and a half of a man.

So with the poachers in his preserves. He would not expose them to be shot by keepers, nor would he prosecute them if he could help himself, but he could circumvent them, and did so effectually by means of the holly.

The preserves were situated at some distance from the house, so that the poachers could make a rapid inroad and carry off their booty before they could be seized. So Waterton laid a deep scheme. First he planted near the house, and just opposite his window, a clump of yews, on which trees pheasants are fond of perching. Next he surrounded them with a thick holly hedge, leaving only one little gap, which could be closed by a strong padlocked gate. Then, leaving the trees to grow, he set about the other preparations.

He made a number of wooden pheasants, and did it in the simplest manner imaginable. He got some small scaffolding poles and cut them diagonally into pieces about

as long as a pheasant's body. A lath fastened to one end
made a capital tail, and all that was needed was to trim
the shoulder to the neck, and put a head on the other end,
a nail doing duty for a beak.

STRUCTURE OF WOODEN PHEASANT.

By the time that the trees had grown sufficiently for his
purpose he had made about a couple of hundred of dummy
pheasants. He then threw a few sacks full of beans
inside the holly hedge, and laid a train of beans into the
preserve. The birds, finding the beans on the ground,
naturally followed the trail, and reaching so abundant a
supply of food as they saw inside the hedge, flew over it
and feasted to their heart's content. Then, not caring to
fly, after having gorged themselves, they settled for the
night in the yews.

Meanwhile the wooden pheasants were nailed on the
trees in the preserve, and so exactly did they resemble the
actual birds that in the dark no one could detect the
imposition. Even in daylight the dummy so closely represents the bird that a second glance is necessary in
order to make sure that it is only an imitation. The accompanying sketch represents one of these dummies on
the outskirts of the preserve.

The poachers were completely deceived, and Waterton used to enjoy the reports of their guns, knowing that they were only wasting their shot upon the wooden images,

WOODEN PHEASANT IN TREE.

while the real birds were comfortably asleep under his eye.

If the reader will refer to the illustration on page 36, he will see that on the right hand, and near the poplar, is a rather curious circular object. This represents the pheasant fortress in question, and, although the small size prohibits any detail, the general shape and appearance are sufficiently shown. It will also be seen how close to the house is the fortress, so as to be under the master's eye.

He made several more of these ingenious refuges, of which other birds besides the pheasants took full advantage.

There was not a tree in the park that Waterton did not know, and, if the smallest damage were done, he would be sure to find it out. One day I found the keeper much disturbed, having discovered some shot in a tree trunk, and being quite sure that he would be called to account for it. The man was right enough, for Waterton found the shot, before many hours had passed, and the keeper had to undergo a severe cross-examination.

Not only did he know the trees individually, and had distinctive names for them, but there was scarcely one which he had not climbed and in the topmost branches of which he had not sat, pursuing his favourite amusements of watching birds, and reading Horace or Virgil. There are not many men who at the age of sixty would have either the power or nerve to climb a tall tree, but Waterton retained his powers of tree-climbing until his death, and very shortly before his fatal accident had ascended one of the largest trees in the park, he being then in his eighty-third year.

Such a spot for study may seem a remarkable one, but Waterton was never affected by heights, and the man who had scrambled up the cross of St. Peter's at Rome, climbed the lightning conductor, and stood with one foot on the head of the colossal angel of St. Angelo, was not likely to be made giddy by the view from the top of an oak-tree.

In part of his autobiography, Waterton mentions that he climbed to the top of the conductor, and left his glove on it, but he does not tell the sequel of the story.

All Rome rang with the exploit, which reached the ears of the Pope, Pius VII. Knowing that the glove would spoil the conductor, he ordered it to be removed at once Not a man could be found in Rome whose nerves were equal to such a task, and so Waterton had to repeat the ascent and fetch his glove down again, to the amusement of his friends, and the delight of the populace.

No one could have given the advice in tree-climbing which is quoted on page 50, without having experienced the comparative strength of the different trees. Perhaps the reader may not know that coming down a tree is a far more difficult task than ascending it. In the latter case, the climber can see his course, and note beforehand where he shall place his hands and feet, while in descending he has to trust partly to memory, and partly to touch.

It is easy enough, for example, to spring for a few inches from a lower to a higher branch, but to drop those few inches is a very nervous business. I have more than once seen a climber ascend a tree very boldly, and then be so frightened that he could not be induced to come down without some one to guide his feet. The same rule holds good with precipices, where a man can always ascend where he has descended without jumping, but not *vice versâ*.

Even with trees, Waterton must needs have his joke. All the important trees in the park had their names. There were, for example, the Twelve Apostles standing in a group, all starting from one root, the Eight Beatitudes, the Seven Deadly Sins, &c. Then there were an oak and a Scotch fir twined together, and going by the name of Church and State (see p. 64).

YEW was one of Waterton's favourite trees, and he was accustomed to say that it would be perfect if its leaves were only furnished with spikes sharp enough to keep out the cats, stoats, weasels, and his pet abhorrence, the brown rat, which he always called the Hanoverian rat, and stoutly believed was imported into England by the same ship that brought William of Orange to our shores. I rather fancy that the Hanoverian origin of the brown rat must have been one of Waterton's early jokes, and that he gradually came to consider it as a fact. The yew furnishes harborage for many birds, which after all do not seem to suffer much from four-footed enemies. The well-known yew-hedge in the garden of Merton College, Oxford, is full of little birds, though their domiciles are not easily seen through the dense foliage.

Waterton made great use of this valuable tree, and formed with it evergreen walls, impermeable to the north wind, the one foe which he dreaded, and which seemed quite to benumb him. I have seen him with his lips so

CHURCH AND STATE.

paralysed by the north wind that he could scarcely frame a word. He spent most of his waking time out of doors, and his yew hedges were a great advantage to him in sheltering him from the north wind, and forming pleasant nooks which received the cheering rays of the southern sun.

He wrote as follows in his Essay on the Yew-tree: " It

has already repaid me for the pains which I have taken in its cultivation ; and when I resort to my usual evening stand, in order to watch the flocks of sparrows, finches, and starlings, whilst they are dropping in upon the neighbouring hollies, I feel not the wintry blast, as the yew-trees, which are close at hand, are to me a shield against its fury ; and in fact, they offer me a protection little inferior to that of the house itself."

There is a magnificent crescent-shaped yew-hedge, which partly surrounds the stables, and shuts them out from sight so effectually, that no one could suspect their presence unless informed of it. Another yew-hedge forms a sort of wall behind the Ivy Tower, and aids in keeping it quiet for the many birds which breed in it.

I have given the land view of the gateway (sometimes called the " Ivy Tower " in the Essays) because it shows how admirably Waterton adapted existing objects to his chief pursuit at Walton Hall, namely, the cherishing of birds and study of their habits.

The view is taken from the southern window of the guest-chamber, and is one of the first objects that meets the visitor's eyes on rising in the morning.

One portion of this illustration requires notice. Just above the yew-hedge may be seen a curious - looking circular tower ; with a conical roof. This was built expressly for the use of starlings, and is appropriately named the Starling Tower. Many starlings found a home in the Ivy Tower, but wishing to accommodate these birds still further, Waterton built this tower for them, and a very interesting structure it is, uniting several advantages.

In the first place, it is raised upon a smooth stone pillar, on which rests a large circular, flattened stone, considerably larger than the pillar. The object of this arrangement is to keep out rats, the worst foes of the

starling. Even the most active and sharpest-clawed rat
could hardly climb up the pillar, and if it did, would
be stopped by the flat stone. In fact, this pillar and
stone are similar in design to the "staddles" on which
wheat-stacks ought to be built, if farmers wish to preserve
their grain. Cats are also foes to the starling, but the flat
stone is too high for most cats to reach by jumping, and if

GATEWAY—BACK VIEW.

they tried to do so, the upper surface of the stone is
made with a slope, and is so smooth, that the claws could
not retain their hold.

The tower is circular, and is built in regular layers of
stones. Each alternate stone is loose, and when pulled
out, discloses a chamber behind, to which the bird obtains
access by means of a channel cut in the corner of the
stone. The birds took possession of the tower at once,

as well they might, and it is very interesting to remove
the stones and see the birds sitting on their eggs without
being in the least alarmed at the intrusion. In consequence of the protection which they enjoy, the starlings
are to be found in great numbers around the house, and
will assemble on the lawn in front of the sitting-room
windows, where they feed without fear, notwithstanding

STARLING TOWER.

that they may be within a few yards of the window from
which they are being watched. A second tower was afterwards built and placed in another portion of the grounds.

THE reader may remember that Waterton drained some
fish-ponds and planted them with trees, which grew with
great rapidity. By means of the ever-useful yew, various
sheltering-places were made in it, and there was a little
single-roomed cottage where Waterton could sit by a fire

in cold weather, and yet be able to watch the birds, for
whose benefit the door was always left open.　This cottage
is not shown in the illustration, but on the right hand
is seen a heap of rough stones.　These were piled up for
the benefit of the weasel, which loves such localities, and
is tolerably sure to take possession of them.

THE GROTTO.

The whole of this corner of the park goes by the general
name of the "Grotto," on account of a cave which forms
part of it.　In this beautiful place Waterton used to allow
parties to congregate, on the understanding that they
would do no injury, and, for their benefit, he had erected
swings, &c., among the trees.　For this reason, the place
was often called the "Picnic," and this name was used
indifferently with that of Grotto.

"The Squire," as he was invariably called, was, after his usual fashion, too trustful when he thought that he was doing a kindness to others. During his later years, the privilege became shamefully abused, and when, after his death, a party of picnic-makers set fire to the magnificent yew hedge enclosing the stables, and destroyed a considerable portion of it, his son took the opportunity of prohibiting picnics for the future.

By the way, Waterton was scarcely ever mentioned by name, and just as the Duke of Wellington was known as "the Duke," so was Waterton known far and wide as " the Squire." Even his nearest relatives invariably addressed him as " Squire," and it would be perfectly possible for a visitor to be at Walton Hall for a week and never hear the name of Waterton.

To EXHAUST all the objects of interest within the park wall would require a large volume, and space is valuable. There are one or two, however, which ought not to be passed over without notice, and one of them is figured in the illustration on page 70.

In former days there had been a water-mill, but time, which, as Waterton quaintly says, is " the great annihilator of all human inventions saving taxation and the national debt," destroyed the mill, and nothing of it is left except a single millstone, measuring between five and six feet in diameter. " The ground where the mill stood having been converted into meadow, this stone lay there unnoticed and unknown (save by the passing haymaker), from the period of the mill's dissolution to the autumn of the year 1813, when one of our nut-eating wild animals, probably by way of winter store, deposited a few nuts under its protecting cover.

" In the course of the following summer, a single nut.

having escaped the teeth of the destroyer, sent up its verdant shoot through the hole in the centre of the procumbent millstone.

" One day I pointed out this rising tree to a gentleman who was standing by, and I said ' If this young plant escape destruction, some time or other it will support the millstone, and raise it from the ground. He seemed to doubt this. In order, however, that the plant might have

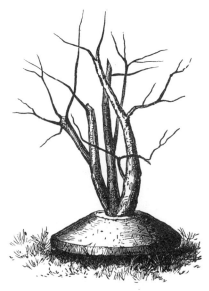

NUT-TREE AND MILL-STONE.

a fair chance of success, I directed that it should be defended from accident and harm by means of a wooden paling.

" Year after year it increased in size and beauty, and when its expansion had entirely filled up the hole in the centre of the millstone, it gradually began to raise up the millstone itself from the seat of its long repose. This huge mass of stone is now eight inches above the ground and is entirely supported by the stem of the nut-tree, which has risen to the height of twenty-five feet, and bears excellent fruit."

When I saw it in 1862, however, the tree had been dead for some time, the millstone having evidently killed it, not by its weight, but by preventing the flow of sap through the bark. It would, of course, have been more picturesque to have drawn the tree in a living state and of its full height, but I thought it better to give it exactly as I saw it. Mr. Edmund Waterton once told me that when a boy he often climbed the tree in search of nuts, which it then bore plentifully.

It is a most valuable object, inasmuch as it shows in a striking manner the tremendous powers of Nature, which are continually being exerted, and which we, as a rule, do not even suspect. The late Charles Kingsley mentions that he has seen a large flat stone raised off the ground in a single night by a crop of tiny mushrooms, and I quite lately saw some weighty kerbstones in a crowded London thoroughfare, which had been forced completely out of their places by grass-blades which had grown between their junctions.

CHAPTER V.

Now we must cast a glance at some of those ingenious arrangements which I called "the Squire's dodges" on first seeing them.

There never was a place so full of 'dodges' as Walton Hall. The Starling Tower, described on page 67, was one of them, being so arranged as to keep out rats and cats. Now, Waterton wished to make a place which cats could enter, but would keep out rats, and he achieved his object by remembering that cats and rats could both climb, but that rats were no great jumpers.

As may be remembered, the flat stone of the starling tower was just out of reach of a cat's jump, which Waterton calculated at five feet for an ordinarily active cat. So he had a large, smooth, flat stone let into the wall, and an aperture made in it, which he called the "cat's hole." It was just five feet from the ground, so that pussy could jump into it, while the stone was made so smooth that no rat could climb it.

Having securely protected the starlings by their towers, and the pheasants by the holly fortress and wooden dummies—another dodge—he had to protect his pigeons.

He found that pigeons were stolen in great numbers, and almost invariably for one purpose, namely, to supply birds for pigeon-shooting matches, many of which took place thirty or forty miles from the spot whence the birds were stolen. Now, Waterton had a righteous indignation against pigeon-shooting, and had an ingenious mode of thwarting the thieves.

Their plan was to come at night, when the pigeons were all at home, and throw a net over the 'glover,' i.e. the opening at the top, through which the pigeons enter and leave the cote. Then if they can force an entrance into the cote they do so, but even if not, they frighten the birds by knocking at the walls, and so drive them into the net.

Pigeon-houses, however, constructed like those at Walton Hall, can set those nocturnal robbers at defiance. In the first place, the house is so high that thieves could scarcely find a ladder long enough to reach the roof, and then they would need a second ladder to lay on the roof before they could get at the glover. As to gaining admission by the door, it is almost impossible.

The building is in two storeys, the lower being for the reception of tools, chains, and the other multifarious requirements of a farm. The rest of the building is intended for the pigeons, and can only be approached by a door some twenty feet from the ground. The door, which is very strong, and bound with iron, fits flush into the wall, so that there is no hold for a tool, and moreover, only one man could work at a time, he having nothing but a ladder as a foothold.   So much for the outside of the pigeon-house.

If we wish to enter the building we must ascend to the door by a ladder and unlock it. We then find ourselves within a large and lofty chamber, well lighted and venti-

PIGEON-HOUSE.

lated, white-washed, and perfectly clean and neat. The whole place is scraped and white-washed at least twice in each year, November and February being recommended for these operations.

The interior walls are most curiously constructed. Parallel rows of pigeon-holes occupy each wall, and beneath each row is a ledge of brick. There are three rows of bricks between the ledges, which are each one brick in width. Twenty rows of nests occupy each wall. It is easy, therefore, for a man, without the aid of a ladder, to traverse the whole of the building, and to examine every nest as he goes along the ledges. On an average, to search three rows of holes occupies an hour. Waterton mentions in his Essay on the Dovecot Pigeon that this single cote furnished in one season seventy-three dozens of young pigeons. There is a stove, with flues in the building, but since it caught fire by over-heating, and endangered the whole structure, it has not been lighted.

There is another 'dodge' in feeding the pigeons. It was found that when their food was thrown down in the yard, the poultry, being stronger than the pigeons, drove them away, and ate the food themselves. So Waterton had a floor of close wattle-work laid under the roof of a shed at some height from the ground. The food for the pigeons was always thrown upon this floor, where the pigeons could easily reach it, while it was too high for the poultry.

Here are two more 'dodges' intended for the preservation of young peas, beans, &c., from the all-present rats and mice.

Poisoned food is one effectual plan, but it must be so laid that neither poultry nor game can get at it. This object was attained by means of a poison-bowl, *i.e.* a rounded bowl of earthenware, or even stone, through the centre of which is a hole just large enough to admit a rat·

POISON-BOWL AND SECTION.

The use of the poison-bowl was simple enough. A spoonful of poisoned meal was laid on the ground, and the bowl inverted over it. Rats could reach the meal by the hole, and did so, but neither pheasants nor poultry could so much as touch it with the tips of their beaks.

A section of the poison-bowl is given in the illustration, together with a view of its upper surface.

Next comes a trap of great efficacy, but which answers better for mice than rats. It is simply an earthen or glass jar, having its neck narrower than its shoulder, and buried until its mouth is exactly level with the ground. The inside of the shoulder is then rubbed with bacon fat—the ranker the better—and the trap is set, with scarcely any expenditure of bait.

The mice, prowling about in search of food, soon discover the jar, being attracted by the smell of the bacon.

SUNKEN JAR.

They crane over the mouth, try to reach the savoury food, and slip into the jar, from which there is no possibility of escape.

Yet two more 'dodges,' and we must leave the wonders of Walton Hall.

Waterton found that when cattle were placed in contiguous fields connected by a gate, nothing could keep them away from that gate. They came and leant against it on both sides, while they indulged in conversation after their own manner, very much as their masters and mistresses might do.

Now, the cattle which were in the field towards which the gate opened did no harm to it, because as they leant against it they only pressed against the posts. But the weight of those on the opposite side came heavily upon the catch and hinges, and sometimes even broke them down.

Waterton was much too kind-hearted to convert the open gates into doors, and so to shut out the cattle from social intercourse. So he suspended a stout chain on the weak side, so that the cattle might lean against it and rest upon the gate. As the chain was fastened by a staple at

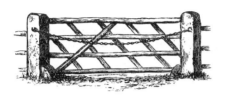

GATE AND CHAIN.

one end, and hitched over a strong hook at the other, it could easily be dropped when the gate had to be opened for traffic, and replaced after it was shut.

The last 'dodge' which we can mention is that of the carriage-pond. It was about four feet wider than an ordinary carriage, and edged with broad, flat stones. At each end it sloped gradually downwards until in the centre it was just deep enough to allow the water to reach rather above the axletrees. When a carriage or a cart had to be washed after being used it was gently wheeled into the pond at one end, while men with brooms washed the wheels as they turned. In the centre of the pond the men had command over every part of the carriage, which was then drawn gently out, the mops and brooms being at work until it came upon level ground.

Horses could thus be washed as well as carts and carriages, and very much they seemed to enjoy their bath.

It is impossible to conclude the memoir of this accomplished naturalist without allusion to his rooted abhorrence of scientific names. I do not think that this antipathy

was justified.   He was perfectly right in entering his
protest against the cumbrous pedantry which bade fair
to make science a mere question of memory for names,
and the language which he uses is not in the least too
strong.

Perhaps I may be pardoned for inserting a passage from
one of my own works, written twenty years ago, and long
before I knew Waterton, so that the reader may see how
completely I sympathise with him.

" Owing to the inordinate use of pseudo-classical phraseo-
logy, the fascinating study of animal life has been too long
considered as a profession or a science restricted to a
favoured few, and interdicted to the many until they have
undergone a long apprenticeship to its preliminary formulæ.
So deeply rooted is this idea, that the popular notion of a
scientific man is of one who possesses a fund of words,
and not of one who has gathered a mass of ideas.   There
is really not the least reason why any one of ordinary
capabilities and moderate memory should not be acquainted
with the general outlines of Zoology, and possess some
knowledge of the representative animals, which serve as
types of each group, tribe, or family ; for when relieved
of the cumbersome diction with which it is embarrassed,
the study of animal life can be brought within the comprehension of all who care to examine the myriad varieties
of form and colour with which the Almighty clothes His
living poems.

" The true object of Zoology is not, as some appear to
fancy, to arrange, to number, and to ticket animals in a
formal inventory, but to make the study an inquiry into
the life-nature, and not only an investigation of the lifeless
organism.   I must not, however, be understood to disparage
the outward form, thing of clay though it be.   For what
wondrous clay it is, and how marvellous the continuous

miracle by which the dust of earth is transmuted into the glowing colours and graceful forms which we most imperfectly endeavour to preserve after the soul has separated from them."

But Waterton certainly erred in his persistent rejection of scientific names, which form an universal language, and are needed for the purpose of identifying the creatures whose habits are being described. Even in England, there are thousands of animals which have no popular names, nor are likely to have them, and we are therefore driven to use the names by which they are known to science all over the world.

It is true that such names are often unintelligible, especially to those who do not know Greek as well as Latin, and the words Lophophorus, Tachipetes, Pachycephala, Ptilonorhynchus, Palæornis, Meliphagidæ, &c., which are selected by Waterton as 'shocking examples,' certainly cannot be understood by persons who know nothing of Greek or ornithology.

But the local words which he himself employs are far less intelligible than the scientific terms. If a very moderate Greek scholar were asked the meaning of these words, he could at all events tell the inquirer that one word referred to swiftness, another to the crest of the bird, another to the size of its head, another to its fruit-eating habits, and so forth, even though he should know nothing of the birds themselves. But suppose the same inquirer to have read the *Wanderings*, and to have asked the meaning of Hannaquoi, Camoudi, Salempenta, Maroudi, Coulacanara, Sakawinki, Wallababa, Houtou, Karabimiti, Sawari, &c., I very much doubt whether one scholar in a thousand could have given an answer. Consequently, the otherwise delightful *Wanderings* has been in many points a sealed book.

Sometimes the acceptance of local names is misleading,

as for example, when the jaguar is called 'tiger' (which
Waterton explains, using either term indifferently), or
when he applies the familiar name of chameleon to one of
the Anolis lizards, the chameleons being exclusively inhabitants of the Old World.   Similarly, in North America the
bison is called the buffalo, and the puma is termed the lion.
In Australia the nomenclature of the colonists looks like
Zoology gone mad.   In that country, the mammalia are,
with one doubtful example, marsupials.   Yet, we read of
the monkey, the bear, the wolf, the tiger, the cat, the rat,
the mouse, the badger, the jerboa, the hare, the sloth, the
mole, and the hedgehog, not one of these animals really
belonging to Australia.   So, in these cases, unless we have
the scientific as well as the local names, whether native or
imported, we shall find ourselves entirely bewildered.

With Waterton's views concerning what he happily terms
'complimentary nomenclature,' I unreservedly agree, and
have often written strongly on the subject.   Waterton,
after noticing that in a single volume on birds, no less
than thirteen species have the names of men, makes the
following witty remarks.

" In the plates to the first volume of his work, I find
that a hawk is called the 'Black Warrior,' and that the
Latin name which he has given it is 'Falco Harlani.'
Pray, who or what is 'Harlani'?   A man, a mountain,
or a mud-flat?   Is 'Black Warrior' a Negro of pugnacious propensities ? "

Now we come to the last scenes of Waterton's life, for
which we are indebted to his friend Dr. N. Moore, who
was staying with him at the time.   The full account may be
seen in the volume of Essays to which reference has been
made, and is well worth reading.   Briefly, it is as follows.

He had gone, accompanied by Dr. Moore, to the further

end of the park for the purpose of directing some carpenters, when he caught his foot in an overhanging bramble, and fell, with his side upon a log. He knew at once the extent of the injury, but contrived to reach the boat. On arriving at the island, he walked to the house, changed his clothes as usual, and, in spite of terrible pain, walked up stairs without help. He would have gone on to his own room at the top of the house, but consented to stop half way, and lie on the sofa of Miss Edmonstone's (his sister-in-law's) sitting room, for the sake of saving trouble to others.

Here he died, and I must borrow Dr. Moore's own words.

" The end was now at hand, and he died at twenty-seven minutes past two in the morning of May 27, 1865. The window was open. The sky was beginning to grow grey, a few rooks had cawed, the swallows were twittering, the landrail was craking from the Ox-close, and a favourite cock, which he used to call his morning-gun, leaped out from some hollies, and gave his accustomed crow. The ear of his master was deaf to the call. He had obeyed a sublimer summons, and had woke up to the glories of the eternal world."

So passed away Charles Waterton, a man who was, perhaps, more thoroughly missed and more widely mourned than any other of his time.

It is much to be regretted that he would never sit for his portrait since 1823. As far as the head without the dress goes, Mr. Waterhouse Hawkins's bust gives a good idea of "The Squire," but marble could not give his sweet, kindly smile, or the animated expressions which flitted over his face as he recurred to his former travels, or pointed out the many wonders of the park and lake. A good painter might have succeeded, provided that he knew Waterton thoroughly.

and, for such a memorial, thousands who never saw him would have been grateful.

The following account of the funeral is taken from the *Illustrated London News* of June 17, 1865.

" On the 3rd inst. (the anniversary of Mr. Waterton's birth) his remains were laid amidst the scenes he loved so well. He had selected the spot, and left minute instructions for the funeral ceremony, which commenced at nine o'clock in the morning.

" The entrance-hall had been converted into a temporary chapel, which was draped with black. Before the door, on a catafalque, rested the coffin, of polished oak, with brass inscription plates. Mr. Waterton was an eminent member of the Roman Catholic Church, and fourteen priests took part at his burial. First, ' the Office for the Dead ' was said, and then requiem high mass, the Bishop of Beverley singing, Canon Walker assisting as Deacon, and the Rev. G. Waterton as Sub-Deacon.

" The invited guests having arrived soon after ten o'clock, the coffin was borne in procession through the ancient portcullis gate, accompanied by mourners and priests, bearing tapers, and followed by Edmund Waterton, Esq., son of the deceased, and chief mourner. At the landing-stairs the body was placed on a floating bier. Thence, preceded by a barge, containing the Bishop and officiating priests, chanting the office, and followed by mourners and friends in attendant boats—Mr. Waterton's own boat, un-occupied, bringing up the rear,—the author of the *Wanderings* made his last voyage. The boats were all draped with black, and boats containing the friends of the family flanked the three central ones : the tenantry went by land.

" At the head of the lake, beneath the shade of two noble oaks, is the vault, into which the coffin having been lowered, the mourners and others took their place, the

Bishop of Beverley at the head, the blessing of the grave took place, and the ceremony terminated with the canticle ' Benedictus ;' during which a linnet in one of the oaks overhead joined its song to the chanting of the clergy. And here, ' buried in silence, broken only by the cry of the heron, and in a solitude almost as deep as that in which he had lived so long in the swamps of the Orinoco and the forests of the Amazon,' rest the remains of Charles Waterton.

" Eighty-three being his age, that number of aged persons had been invited to attend at the funeral, and had a dole, each a loaf of bread and sixpence, distributed to them at the park gate."

The very appropriate spot which received his remains had been long fixed upon by him, but it was not until a year before his death that he caused to be erected the plain stone cross the base of which bears the inscription written by himself.

ORATE PRO ANIMA

CAROLI WATERTON.

CUJUS FESSA

JUXTA HANC CRUCEM

SEPELIUNTUR OSSA.

Natus 1782.   *Obiit* 1865.

The actual day of his birth was not known until June 3, 1864, when he asked the Misses Edmonstone to come and see a new cross which he had put up between two magnificent oaks near the head of the lake. There are many crosses in different parts of the park. The most conspicuous one is on the top of the Ivy Tower, and another is on the wall of the Grotto, both of which are shown in illustrations on pages 43, 66, 68. Another is upon a favourite resting-place nearly opposite the Gateway, but there was a peculiar significance about this last cross.

"He rowed his sisters-in-law," writes Mr. Moore, "in his boat to the far end of the lake which surrounds Walton Hall, and when they arrived at the spot, he told them he intended to be buried there, and put his arms round the cross. 'Squire,' said Miss Edmonstone in Italian, for there was a man at work within hearing, 'it is your birth-day.' He smiled and bowed assent." And on the 3rd of June in the following year he was laid in the spot which he had indicated.

The remains of his grandfather lie beneath an elm-tree in another part of the park.

It is noteworthy that the spot where he fell is only a stone's-throw from the cross, and just half-way between it and the group of trees called the "Twelve Apostles." It is now marked with a cross.

Originally, his son intended to build a memorial chapel over the grave, but he afterwards, and rightly, relin-quished the intention, thinking that the plain stone cross erected by Waterton himself, engraved with his own simple inscription, was a more fitting memorial than any chapel, however beautiful it might be.

[Note.—The Bust of Waterton has now been reproduced with the dress according to his invariable costume. Copies and Photographs may be procured from F. W. Wilson, Westgate House, Kirk-Dale, Sydenham.]

WANDERINGS IN SOUTH AMERICA.

WANDERINGS IN SOUTH AMERICA.

FIRST JOURNEY.

CHAPTER I.

—————— " nec herba, nec latens in asperis
Radix fefellit me locis."

Object of the *Wanderings.* — Demerara R. — Saba. — Toucan.— Forest trees.—Parasites.—Bush-rope.—Red monkey.—Wild animals.—Sloths. —Venomous snakes.—Lizards.—Bell-bird.—Houtou.—Insects.—Dog poisoned with Wourali.--Falls.—Essequibo R.—Rapid decay.—Falls of the Essequibo.—Macoushia.—A white recluse.—The Watermamma. —A savage financier.—The Jabiru.—Ants' nests.—Fort St. Joachim. —Lake Parima.

In the month of April, 1812, I left the town of Stabroek, to travel through the wilds of Demerara and Essequibo, a part of *ci-devant* Dutch Guiana, in South America.

The chief objects in view were to collect a quantity of the strongest Wourali poison; and to reach the inland frontier fort of Portuguese Guiana.

It would be a tedious journey for him who wishes to travel through these wilds, to set out from Stabroek on foot. The sun would exhaust him in his attempts to wade through the swamps, and the Mosquitos at night would deprive him of every hour of sleep.

The road for horses runs parallel to the river, but it extends a very little way, and even ends before the cultivation of the plantation ceases.

The only mode then that remains is to proceed by water; and when you come to the high lands, you may make your way through the forest on foot, or continue your route on the river.

After passing the third island in the river Demerara, there are few plantations to be seen, and those not joining on to one another, but separated by large tracts of wood.

The Loo is the last where the Sugar-cane is growing. The greater part of its negroes have just been ordered to another estate; and ere a few months shall have elapsed all signs of cultivation will be lost in underwood.

Higher up stand the sugar-works of Amelia's Waard, solitary and abandoned! and after passing these there is not a ruin to inform the traveller that either coffee or sugar have ever been cultivated.

From Amelia's Waard an unbroken range of forest covers each bank of the river, saving here and there where a hut discovers itself, inhabited by free people of colour, with a rood or two of bared ground about it; or where the wood-cutter has erected himself a dwelling, and cleared a few acres for pasturage. Sometimes you see level ground on each side of you for two or three hours at a stretch; at other times a gently sloping hill presents itself; and often, on turning a point, the eye is pleased with the contrast of an almost perpendicular height jutting into the water. The trees put you in mind of an eternal spring, with summer and autumn kindly blended into it.

Here you may see a sloping extent of noble trees, whose foliage displays a charming variety of every shade, from the lightest to the darkest green and purple. The tops of some are crowned with bloom of the loveliest hue; while the boughs of others bend with a profusion of seeds and fruits.

Those whose heads have been bared by time, or blasted by the thunder-storm, strike the eye, as a mournful sound does the ear in music ; and seem to beckon to the sentimental traveller to stop a moment or two, and see that the forests which surround him, like men and kingdoms, have their periods of misfortune and decay.

The first rocks of any considerable size that are observed on the side of the river are at a place called Saba, from the Indian word, which means a stone. They appear sloping down to the water's edge, not shelvy, but smooth, and their exuberances rounded off, and, in some places, deeply furrowed, as though they had been worn with continual floods of water.

There are patches of soil up and down, and the huge stones amongst them produce a pleasing and novel effect. You see a few Coffee-trees of a fine luxuriant growth; and nearly on the top of Saba stands the house of the postholder.

He is appointed by government to give in his report to the protector of the Indians of what is going on amongst them, and to prevent suspicious people from passing up the river.

When the Indians assemble here the stranger may have an opportunity of seeing the Aborigines dancing to the sound of their country music, and painted in their native style. They will shoot their arrows for him with an unerring aim, and send the poisoned dart from the blow-pipe true to its destination ; and here he may often view all the different shades, from the red savage to the white man, and from the white man to the sootiest son of Africa.

Beyond this post there are no more habitations of white men, or free people of colour.

In a country so extensively covered with wood as this is, having every advantage that a tropical sun and the richest mould, in many places, can give to vegetation, it is natural to look for trees of very large dimensions; but it is rare to meet with them above six yards in circumference. If larger have ever existed, they have fallen a sacrifice either to the axe or to fire.

If, however, they disappoint you in size, they make ample amends in height. Heedless and bankrupt in all curiosity must he be who can journey on without stopping to take a view of the towering Mora. Its topmost branch, when naked with age or dried by accident, is the favourite resort of the Toucan. Many a time has this singular bird felt the shot faintly strike him from the gun of the fowler beneath, and owed his life to the distance betwixt them.

The trees which form these far-extending wilds are as useful as they are ornamental. It would take a volume of itself to describe them.

The Green-heart, famous for its hardness and durability; the Hackea, for its toughness; the Ducalabali, surpassing mahogany; the Ebony and Letter-wood, vying with the choicest woods of the old world; the Locust-tree, yielding copal; and the Hayawa and Olou-trees, furnishing a sweet-smelling resin, are all to be met with in the forest, betwixt the plantations and the rock Saba.

Beyond this rock the country has been little explored; but it is very probable that these, and a vast collection of other kinds, and possibly many new species, are scattered up and down, in all directions, through the swamps, and hills, and savannas of *ci-devant* Dutch Guiana.

On viewing the stately trees around him the naturalist will observe many of them bearing leaves, and blossoms, and fruit, not their own.

The Wild Fig-tree, as large as a common English apple-

tree, often rears itself from one of the thick branches at
the top of the mora; and when its fruit is ripe, to it the
birds resort for nourishment.   It was to an undigested
seed, passing through the body of the bird which had
perched on the mora, that the fig-tree first owed its elevated station there.   The sap of the mora raised it into full
bearing; but now, in its turn, it is doomed to contribute a
portion of its own sap and juices towards the growth of
different species of vines, the seeds of which, also, the
birds deposited on its branches.   These soon vegetate, and
bear fruit in great quantities; so what with their usurpa-
tion of the resources of the fig-tree, and the fig-tree of the
mora, the mora, unable to support a charge which nature
never intended it should, languishes and dies under its
burden; and then the fig-tree, and its usurping progeny
of vines, receiving no more succour from their late foster-
parent, droop and perish in their turn.

A vine, called the Bush-rope by the wood-cutters, on
account of its use in hauling out the heaviest timber, has
a singular appearance in the forests of Demerara.   Sometimes you see it nearly as thick as a man's body, twisted
like a corkscrew round the tallest trees, and rearing its
head high above their tops.   At other times three or four
of them, like strands in a cable, join tree and tree and
branch and branch together.   Others, descending from on
high, take root as soon as their extremity touches the
ground, and appear like shrouds and stays supporting
the mainmast of a line-of-battle ship; while others,
sending out parallel, oblique, horizontal, and perpendicular shoots in all directions, put you in mind of what
travellers call a matted forest.   Oftentimes a tree, above a
hundred feet high, uprooted by the whirlwind, is stopped
in its fall by these amazing cables of nature; and hence
it is that you account for the phenomenon of seeing trees

not only vegetating, but sending forth vigorous shoots, though far from their perpendicular, and their trunks inclined to every degree from the meridian to the horizon.

Their heads remain firmly supported by the bush-rope; many of their roots soon refix themselves in the earth, and frequently a strong shoot will sprout out perpendicularly from near the root of the reclined trunk, and in time become a fine tree. No grass grows under the trees; and few weeds, except in the swamps.

The high grounds are pretty clear of underwood, and with a cutlass to sever the small bush-ropes, it is not difficult walking among the trees.

The soil, chiefly formed by the fallen leaves and decayed trees, is very rich and fertile in the valleys. On the hills, it is little better than sand. The rains seem to have carried away, and swept into the valleys, every particle which nature intended to have formed a mould.

Four-footed animals are scarce, considering how very thinly these forests are inhabited by men.

Several species of the animal, commonly called Tiger, though in reality it approaches nearer to the leopard, are found here; and two of their diminutives, named Tiger-cats. The Tapir, the Labba, and Deer, afford excellent food, and chiefly frequent the swamps and low ground, near the sides of the river and creeks.

In stating that four-footed animals are scarce, the Peccari must be excepted. Three or four hundred of them herd together, and traverse the wilds in all directions, in quest of roots and fallen seeds. The Indians mostly shoot them with poisoned arrows. When wounded, they run about one hundred and fifty paces; they then drop, and make wholesome food.

The Red Monkey, erroneously called the baboon, is heard

oftener than it is seen; while the common Brown Monkey, the Bisa, and Sacawinki, rove from tree to tree, and amuse the stranger as he journeys on.

A species of the Polecat, and another of the Fox, are destructive to the Indian's poultry; while the Opossum, the Guana, and Salempenta, afford him a delicious morsel.

The small Ant-bear, and the large one, remarkable for his long, broad, bushy tail, are sometimes seen on the tops of the wood-ants' nests; the Armadillas bore in the sand-hills, like rabbits in a warren; and the Porcupine is now and then discovered in the trees over your head.

This, too, is the native country of the Sloth. His looks, his gestures, and his cries, all conspire to entreat you to take pity on him. These are the only weapons of defence which nature hath given him. While other animals assemble in herds, or in pairs range through these boundless wilds, the sloth is solitary, and almost stationary; he cannot escape from you. It is said, his piteous moans make the tiger relent, and turn out of the way. Do not then level your gun at him, or pierce him with a poisoned arrow; —he has never hurt one living creature. A few leaves, and those of the commonest and coarsest kind, are all he asks for his support. On comparing him with other animals, you would say that you could perceive deficiency, deformity, and superabundance in his composition. He has no cutting teeth, and though four stomachs, he still wants the long intestines of ruminating animals. He has only one inferior aperture, as in birds. He has no soles to his feet, nor has he the power of moving his toes separately. His hair is flat, and puts you in mind of grass withered by the wintry blast. His legs are too short; they appear deformed by the manner in which they are joined to the body; and when he is on the ground, they seem as if only calculated to be of use in climbing trees. He has forty-six ribs, while the elephant has only forty; and his claws are disproportionably long. Were you to mark down, upon a graduated scale, the different claims to superiority amongst the four-footed animals, this poor ill-formed creature's claim would be the last upon the lowest degree.

Demerara yields to no country in the world in her wonderful and beautiful productions of the feathered race. Here the finest precious stones are far surpassed by the vivid tints which adorn the birds. The naturalist may exclaim, that nature has not known where to stop in forming new species, and painting her requisite shades. Almost every one of those singular and elegant birds described by Buffon as belonging to Cayenne, are to be met with in Demerara; but it is only by an indefatigable naturalist that they are to be found.

The Scarlet Curlew breeds in innumerable quantities in the muddy islands on the coasts of Pomauron; the Egrets and Crabiers in the same place. They resort to the mud-flats at ebbing water, while thousands of Sandpipers and Plovers, with here and there a Spoonbill and Flamingo, are seen amongst them. The Pelicans go farther out to sea, but return at sundown to the Courada-trees. The Humming-birds are chiefly to be found near the flowers at which each of the species of the genus is wont to feed. The pie, the gallinaceous, the columbine, and passerine tribes, resort to the fruit-bearing trees.

You never fail to see the common Vulture where there is carrion. In passing up the river there was an opportunity of seeing a pair of the King of the Vultures; they were sitting on the naked branch of a tree, with about a dozen of the common ones with them. A Tiger had killed a Goat the day before; he had been driven away in the act of sucking the blood, and not finding it safe or prudent to return, the goat remained in the same place where he had killed it; it had begun to putrefy, and the vultures had arrived that morning to claim the savoury morsel.

At the close of day, the Vampires leave the hollow trees, whither they had fled at the morning's dawn, and scour along the river's banks in quest of prey. On waking from sleep, the astonished traveller finds his hammock all stained with blood. It is the vampire that hath sucked him. Not man alone, but every unprotected animal, is exposed to his depredations : and so gently does this nocturnal surgeon draw the blood, that instead of being roused, the patient is lulled into a still profounder sleep. There are two species of vampire in Demerara, and both suck living animals ; one is rather larger than the common bat; the other measures above two feet from wing to wing extended.

Snakes are frequently met with in the woods betwixt the sea-coast and the rock Saba, chiefly near the creeks and on the banks of the river. They are large, beautiful, and formidable. The Rattlesnake seems partial to a tract of ground known by the name of Canal Number-three ; there the effects of his poison will be long remembered.

The Camoudi snake has been killed from thirty to forty feet long; though not venomous, his size renders him destructive to the passing animals. The Spaniards in the Oroonoque positively affirm that he grows to the length of seventy or eighty feet, and that he will destroy the strongest and largest bull. His name seems to confirm this ; there he is called " matatoro," which literally means " bull-killer." Thus he may be ranked amongst the deadly snakes ; for it comes nearly to the same thing in the end, whether the victim dies by poison from the fangs, which corrupts his blood and makes it stink horribly, or whether his body be crushed to mummy, and swallowed by this hideous beast.

The Whipsnake, of a beautiful changing green, and the
Coral, with alternate broad transverse bars of black and
red, glide from bush to bush, and may be handled with
safety; they are harmless little creatures.

The Labarri snake is speckled, of a dirty brown colour,
and can scarcely be distinguished from the ground or stump
on which he is coiled up; he grows to the length of about
eight feet, and his bite often proves fatal in a few minutes.

Unrivalled in his display of every lovely colour of the
rainbow, and unmatched in the effects of his deadly poison,
the Couanacouchi glides undaunted on, sole monarch of
these forests; he is commonly known by the name of the
bush-master. Both man and beast fly before him, and
allow him to pursue an undisputed path. He sometimes
grows to the length of fourteen feet.

A few small Caimen, from two to twelve feet long, may
be observed now and then in passing up and down the
river; they just keep their heads above the water, and a
stranger would not know them from a rotten stump.

Lizards of the finest green, brown, and copper colour,
from two inches to two feet and a half long, are ever and
anon rustling among the fallen leaves, and crossing the
path before you; whilst the Chameleon is busily employed
in chasing insects round the trunks of the neighbouring
trees.

The fish are of many different sorts, and well-tasted, but
not, generally speaking, very plentiful. It is probable that
their numbers are considerably thinned by the Otters,
which are much larger than those of Europe. In going
through the overflowed savannas, which have all a communication with the river, you may often see a dozen or
two of them sporting amongst the sedges before you.

This warm and humid climate seems particularly adapted
to the producing of insects; it gives birth to myriads,

beautiful past description in their variety of tints, astonishing in their form and size, and many of them noxious in their qualities.

He whose eye can distinguish the various beauties of uncultivated nature, and whose ear is not shut to the wild sounds in the woods, will be delighted in passing up the river Demerara. Every now and then, the Maam or Tinamou sends forth one long and plaintive whistle from the depths of the forest, and then stops ; whilst the yelping of the toucan, and the shrill voice of the bird called Pi-pi-yo, is heard during the interval. The Campanero never fails to attract the attention of the passenger : at a distance of nearly three miles, you may hear this snow-white bird tolling every four or five minutes, like the distant convent bell. From six to nine in the morning, the forests resound with the mingled cries and strains of the feathered race ; after this, they gradually die away. From eleven to three all nature is hushed as in a midnight silence, and scarce a note is heard, saving that of the campanero and the pi-pi-yo ; it is then that, oppressed by the solar heat, the birds retire to the thickest shade, and wait for the refreshing cool of evening.

At sundown the Vampires, Bats, and Goat-suckers dart from their lonely retreat, and skim along the trees on the river's bank. The different kinds of Frogs almost stun the ear with their coarse and hollow-sounding croaking, while the Owls and goat-suckers lament and mourn all night long.

About two hours before daybreak, you will hear the red monkey moaning as though in deep distress ; the Houtou, a solitary bird, and only found in the thickest recesses of the forest, distinctly articulates, " houtou, houtou," in a low and plaintive tone, an hour before sunrise ; the maam whistles about the same hour ; the Hannaquoi, Pataca, and Maroudi announce his near approach to the eastern horizon, and the Parrots and Parroquets confirm his arrival there.

The Crickets chirp from sunset to sunrise, and often during the day, when the weather is cloudy. The Bete-rouge is exceedingly numerous in these extensive wilds, and not only man, but beasts and birds, are tormented by it. Mosquitos are very rare after you pass the third island in the Demerara, and Sand-flies but seldom appear.

Courteous reader, here thou hast the outlines of an amazing landscape given thee; thou wilt see that the principal parts of it are but faintly traced, some of them scarcely visible at all, and that the shades are wholly wanting. If thy soul partakes of the ardent flame which the persevering Mungo Park's did, these outlines will be enough for thee: they will give thee some idea of what a noble country this is; and if thou hast but courage to set about giving the world a finished picture of it, neither materials to work on, nor colours to paint it in its true shades, will be wanting to thee. It may appear a difficult task at a distance; but look close at it, and it is nothing at all; provided thou hast but a quiet mind, little more is necessary, and the genius which presides over these wilds will kindly help thee through the rest. She will allow thee to slay the fawn, and cut down the Mountain-cabbage for thy support, and to select from every part of her domain whatever may be necessary for the work thou art about; but having killed a pair of Doves in order to enable thee to give mankind a true and proper description of them, thou must not destroy a third through wantonness, or to show what a good marksman thou art; that would only blot the picture thou art finishing, not colour it.

Though retired from the haunts of men, and even without a friend with thee, thou wouldst not find it solitary. The crowing of the hannaquoi will sound in thine ears like the daybreak town-clock; and the Wren and the Thrush will join with thee in thy matin hymn to thy Creator, to thank Him for thy night's rest.

At noon thy Genius will lead thee to the Troely, one leaf of which will defend thee from both sun and rain. And if, in the cool of the evening, thou hast been tempted to stray too far from thy place of abode, and art deprived of light to write down the information thou hast collected, the Firefly, which thou wilt see in almost every bush around thee, will be thy candle. Hold it over thy pocket-book, in any position which thou knowest will not hurt it, and it will afford thee ample light. And when thou hast done with it, put it kindly back again on the next branch to thee. It will want no other reward for its services.

When in thy hammock, should the thought of thy little crosses and disappointments, in thy ups and downs through life, break in upon thee, and throw thee into a pensive mood, the Owl will bear thee company. She will tell thee that hard has been her fate too; and at intervals, "Whip-poor-Will," and "Willy come go," will take up the tale of sorrow. Ovid has told thee how the owl once boasted the human form, and lost it for a very small offence; and were the poet alive now, he would inform thee, that "Whip-poor-Will," and "Willy come go," are the shades of those poor African and Indian slaves, who died worn out and brokenhearted. They wail and cry, "Whip-poor-Will," and "Willy come go," all night long; and often, when the moon shines, you see them sitting on the green turf, near the houses of those whose ancestors tore them from the bosom of their helpless families, which all probably perished through grief and want, after their support was gone.

About an hour above the rock of Saba, stands the habitation of an Indian, called Simon, on the top of a hill.

The side next the river is almost perpendicular, and you may easily throw a stone over to the opposite bank. Here there was an opportunity of seeing man in his rudest state. The Indians who frequented this habitation, though living in the midst of woods, bore evident marks of attention to their persons. Their hair was neatly collected, and tied up in a knot; their bodies fancifully painted red, and the paint was scented with hayawa. This gave them a gay and animated appearance. Some of them had on necklaces, composed of the teeth of wild boars slain in the chase; many wore rings, and others had an ornament on the left arm, midway betwixt the shoulder and the elbow. At the close of day, they regularly bathed in the river below; and the next morning seemed busy in renewing the faded colours of their faces.

One day there came into the hut a form which literally might be called the wild man of the woods. On entering, he laid down a ball of wax, which he had collected in the forest. His hammock was all ragged and torn; and his bow, though of good wood, was without any ornament or polish; " erubuit domino, cultior esse suo." His face was meagre, his looks forbidding, and his whole appearance neglected. His long black hair hung from his head in matted confusion; nor had his body, to all appearance, ever been painted. They gave him some Cassava bread and boiled fish, which he ate voraciously, and soon after left the hut. As he went out you could observe no traces in his countenance or demeanour, which indicated that he was in the least mindful of having been benefited by the society he was just leaving.

The Indians said that he had neither wife, nor child, nor friend. They had often tried to persuade him to come and live amongst them; but it was of no avail. He went roving on, plundering the Wild Bees of their honey, and

picking up the fallen nuts and fruits of the forest.   When
he fell in with game, he procured fire from two sticks, and
cooked it on the spot.   When a hut happened to be in his
way, he stepped in, and asked for something to eat, and
then months elapsed ere they saw him again.   They did
not know what had caused him to be thus unsettled ; he
had been so for years ; nor did they believe that even old
age itself would change the habits of this poor, harmless,
solitary wanderer.

From Simon's, the traveller may reach the large fall,
with ease, in four days.

The first falls that he meets are merely rapids, scarce a
stone appearing above the water in the rainy season ; and
those in the bed of the river, barely high enough to arrest
the water's course, and by causing a bubbling, show that
they are there.

With this small change of appearance in the stream,
the stranger observes nothing new till he comes within
eight or ten miles of the great fall.   Each side of the
river presents an uninterrupted range of wood, just as
it did below.   All the productions found betwixt
the plantations and the rock Saba, are to be met with
here.

From Simon's to the great fall there are five habitations
of the Indians—two of them close to the river's side ; the
other three a little way in the forest.   These habitations
consist of from four to eight huts, situated on about an
acre of ground which they have cleared from the surrounding woods.   A few Pappaw, Cotton, and mountain
cabbage-trees, are scattered round them.

At one of these habitations a small quantity of the
Wourali poison was procured.   It was in a little gourd.
The Indian who had it said that he had killed a number
of Wild Hogs with it, and two Tapirs. Appearances seemed

to confirm what he said; for on one side it had been nearly taken out to the bottom, at different times, which probably would not have been the case had the first or second trial failed.

Its strength was proved on a middle-sized dog. He was wounded in the thigh, in order that there might be no possibility of touching a vital part. In three or four minutes he began to be affected, smelt at every little thing on the ground around him, and looked wistfully at the wounded part. Soon after this he staggered, laid himself down, and never rose more. He barked once, though not as if in pain. His voice was low and weak; and in a second attempt it quite failed him. He now put his head betwixt his fore-legs, and raising it slowly again, he fell over on his side. His eye immediately became fixed, and though his extremities every now and then shot convulsively, he never showed the least desire to raise up his head. His heart fluttered much from the time he lay down, and at intervals beat very strong; then stopped for a moment or two, and then beat again; and continued faintly beating several minutes after every other part of his body seemed dead.

In a quarter of an hour after he had received the poison he was quite motionless.

A few miles before you reach the great fall, and which, indeed, is the only one which can be called a fall, large balls of froth come floating past you. The river appears beautifully marked with streaks of foam, and on your nearer approach the stream is whitened all over.

At first, you behold the fall rushing down a bed of rocks, with a tremendous noise, divided into two foamy streams, which at their junction again form a small island covered with wood. Above this island, for a short space, there appears but one stream, all white with froth, and fretting and boiling amongst the huge rocks which obstruct its course.

Higher up it is seen dividing itself into a short channel or two, and trees grow on the rocks which caused its separation. The torrent in many places has eaten deep into the rocks, and split them into large fragments by driving others against them. The trees on the rocks are in bloom and vigour, though their roots are half bared, and many of them bruised and broken by the rushing waters.

This is the general appearance of the fall from the level of the water below to where the river is smooth and quiet above. It must be remembered that this is during the periodical rains. Probably in the dry season it puts on a very different appearance. There is no perpendicular fall of water of any consequence throughout it, but the dreadful roaring and rushing of the torrent down a long, rocky, and moderately sloping channel, has a fine effect; and the stranger returns well pleased with what he has seen. No animal, nor craft of any kind, could stem this downward flood. In a few moments the first would be killed, the second dashed in pieces.

The Indians have a path alongside of it, through the forest, where prodigious Crabwood-trees grow. Up this path they drag their canoes, and launch them into the river above; and on their return bring them down the same way.

About two hours below this fall is the habitation of an Acoway chief called Sinkerman. At night you hear the roaring of the fall from it. It is pleasantly situated on the top of a sand-hill. At this place you have the finest view the river Demerara affords: three tiers of hills rise in slow gradation, one above the other, before you, and present a grand and magnificent scene, especially to him who has been accustomed to a level country.

Here, a little after midnight on the first of May, was heard a most strange and unaccountable noise; it seemed as though several regiments were engaged, and musketry firing with great rapidity. The Indians, terrified beyond description, left their hammocks, and crowded all together, like sheep at the approach of the wolf. There were no soldiers within three or four hundred miles. Conjecture was of no avail, and all conversation next morning on the subject was as useless and unsatisfactory as the dead silence which succeeded to the noise.

He who wishes to reach the Macoushi country had better send his canoe over land from Sinkerman's to the Essequibo.

There is a pretty good path, and meeting a creek about three-quarters of the way, it eases the labour, and twelve Indians will arrive with it in the Essequibo in four days.

The traveller need not attend his canoe; there is a shorter and a better way. Half an hour below Sinkerman's he finds a little creek on the western bank of the Demerara. After proceeding about a couple of hundred yards up it, he leaves it, and pursues a west-north-west direction by land for the Essequibo. The path is good, though somewhat rugged with the roots of trees, and here and there obstructed by fallen ones; it extends more over level ground than otherwise. There are a few steep ascents and descents in it, with a little brook running at the bottom of them; but they are easily passed over, and the fallen trees serve for a bridge.

You may reach the Essequibo with ease in a day and a half; and so matted and interwoven are the tops of the trees above you, that the sun is not felt once all the way, saving where the space which a newly-fallen tree occupied lets in his rays upon you. The forest contains an abundance of Wild Hogs, Labbas, Acouries, Powisses, Maams,

Maroudis, and Waracabas, for your nourishment, and there are plenty of leaves to cover a shed whenever you are inclined to sleep.

The soil has three-fourths of sand in it, till you come within half an hour's walk of the Essequibo, where you find a red gravel and rocks. In this retired and solitary tract, nature's garb, to all appearance, has not been injured by fire, nor her productions broken in upon by the exterminating hand of man.

Here the finest Green-heart grows, and Wallaba, Purple-heart, Siloabali, Sawari, Buletre, Tauronira, and Mora, are met with in vast abundance, far and near, towering up in majestic grandeur, straight as pillars, sixty or seventy feet high, without a knot or branch.

Traveller, forget for a little while the idea thou hast of wandering farther on, and stop and look at this grand picture of vegetable nature; it is a reflection of the crowd thou hast lately been in, and though a silent monitor, it is not a less eloquent one on that account. See that noble Purple-heart before thee! Nature has been kind to it. Not a hole, not the least oozing from its trunk, to show that its best days are past. Vigorous in youthful blooming beauty, it stands the ornament of these sequestered wilds, and tacitly rebukes those base ones of thine own species who have been hardy enough to deny the existence of Him who ordered it to flourish here.

Behold that one next to it!—Hark! how the hammerings of the Red-headed Woodpecker resound through its distempered boughs! See what a quantity of holes he has made in it, and how its bark is stained with the drops which trickle down from them. The lightning, too, has blasted one side of it. Nature looks pale and wan in its leaves, and her resources are nearly dried up in its extremities; its sap is tainted; a mortal sickness, slow as a consumption, and as sure in its consequences, has long since entered its frame, vitiating and destroying the wholesome juices there.

Step a few paces aside, and cast thine eye on that remnant of a Mora behind it. Best part of its branches, once so high and ornamental, now lie on the ground in sad confusion one upon the other, all shattered and fungus-grown, and a prey to millions of insects, which are busily employed in destroying them. One branch of it still looks healthy! Will it recover? No, it cannot; nature has already run her course, and that healthy-looking branch is only as a fallacious good symptom in him who is just about to die of a mortification when he feels no more pain, and fancies his distemper has left him; it is as the momentary gleam of a wintry sun's ray close to the western horizon.—See! while we are speaking, a gust of wind has brought the tree to the ground, and made room for its successor.

Come further on, and examine that apparently luxuriant Tauronira on thy right hand. It boasts a verdure not its own; they are false ornaments it wears; the Bush-rope and Bird-vines have clothed it from the root to its topmost branch. The succession of fruit which it hath borne, like good cheer in the houses of the great, has invited the birds to resort to it, and they have disseminated beautiful, though destructive, plants on its branches, which, like the distempers vice brings into the human frame, rob it of all its health and vigour; they have shortened its days, and probably in another year they will finally kill it, long before nature intended that it should die.

Ere thou leavest this interesting scene, look on the ground around thee, and see what everything here below must come to.

Behold that newly fallen Wallaba! The whirlwind has

uprooted it in its prime, and it has brought down to the ground a dozen small ones in its fall. Its bark has already begun to drop off! And that heart of Mora close by it is fast yielding, in spite of its firm, tough texture.

The tree which thou passedst but a little ago, and which perhaps has lain over yonder brook for years, can now hardly support itself, and in a few months more it will have fallen into the water.

Put thy foot on that large trunk thou seest to the left. It seems entire amid the surrounding fragments. Mere outward appearance, delusive phantom of what it once was! Tread on it, and like the fuss-ball, it will break into dust.

Sad and silent mementos to the giddy traveller as he wanders on! Prostrate remnants of vegetable nature, how incontestably ye prove what we must all at last come to, and how plain your mouldering ruins show that the firmest texture avails us nought when Heaven wills that we should cease to be!—

> " The cloud-capt towers, the gorgeous palaces,
> The solemn temples, the great globe itself,
> Yea, all which it inhabit, shall dissolve,
> And, like the baseless fabric of a vision,
> Leave not a wreck behind."

Cast thine eye around thee, and see the thousands of nature's productions. Take a view of them from the opening seed on the surface, sending a downward shoot, to the loftiest and the largest trees, rising up and blooming in wild luxuriance; some side by side, others separate; some curved and knotty, others straight as lances; all, in beautiful gradation, fulfilling the mandates they had received from Heaven, and though condemned to die, still never failing to keep up their species till time shall be no more.

Reader, canst thou not be induced to dedicate a few months to the good of the public, and examine with thy scientific eye the productions which the vast and well-stored colony of Demerara presents to thee?

What an immense range of forest is there from the rock Saba to the great fall! and what an uninterrupted extent before thee from it to the banks of the Essequibo! No doubt, there is many a balsam and many a medicinal root yet to be discovered, and many a resin, gum, and oil yet unnoticed. Thy work would be a pleasing one, and thou mightest make several useful observations in it.

Would it be thought impertinent in thee to hazard a conjecture, that with the resources the government of Demerara has, stones might be conveyed from the rock Saba to Stabroek, to stem the equinoctial tides, which are for ever sweeping away the expensive wooden piles round the mounds of the fort? Or would the timber-merchant point at thee in passing by, and call thee a descendant of La Mancha's knight, because thou maintainest that the stones which form the rapids might be removed with little expense, and thus open the navigation to the woodcutter from Stabroek to the great fall? Or wouldst thou be deemed enthusiastic or biassed, because thou givest it as thy opinion that the climate in these high lands is exceedingly wholesome, and the lands themselves capable of nourishing and maintaining any number of settlers? In thy dissertation on the Indians, thou mightest hint, that possibly they could be induced to help the new settlers a little; and that finding their labours well requited, it would be the means of their keeping up a constant communication with us, which probably might be the means of laying the first stone towards their Christianity. They are a poor, harmless, inoffensive set of people, and their wandering and ill-provided way of living seems more to ask for pity from us, than to fill our heads with thoughts that they would be hostile to us.

What a noble field, kind reader, for thy experimental philosophy and speculations, for thy learning, for thy perseverance, for thy kind-heartedness, for everything that is great and good within thee!

The accidental traveller who has journeyed on from Stabroek to the rock Saba, and from thence to the banks of the Essequibo, in pursuit of other things, as he told thee at the beginning, with but an indifferent interpreter to talk to, no friend to converse with, and totally unfit for that which he wishes thee to do, can merely mark the outlines of the path he has trodden, or tell thee the sounds he has heard, or faintly describe what he has seen in the environs of his resting-places; but if this be enough to induce thee to undertake the journey, and give the world a description of it, he will be amply satisfied.

It will be two days and a half from the time of entering the path on the western bank of the Demerara till all be ready, and the canoe fairly afloat on the Essequibo. The new rigging it, and putting every little thing to rights and in its proper place, cannot well be done in less than a day.

After being night and day in the forest impervious to the sun's and moon's rays the sudden transition to light has a fine heart-cheering effect. Welcome as a lost friend, the solar beam makes the frame rejoice, and with it a thousand enlivening thoughts rush at once on the soul, and disperse, as a vapour, every sad and sorrowful idea which the deep gloom had helped to collect there. In coming out of the woods, you see the western bank of the Essequibo before you, low and flat. Here the river is two-thirds as broad as the Demerara at Stabroek.

To the northward there is a hill higher than any in the

Demerara ; and in the south-south-west quarter a mountain.
It is far away, and appears like a bluish cloud in the
horizon.   There is not the least opening on either side·
Hills, valleys, and lowlands, are all linked together by a
chain of forest.   Ascend the highest mountain, climb
the loftiest tree, as far as the eye can extend, whichever way it directs itself, all is luxuriant and unbroken
forest.

In about nine or ten hours from this, you get to an
Indian habitation of three huts, on the point of an island.
It is said that a Dutch post once stood here.   But there is
not the smallest vestige of it remaining, and, except that
the trees appear younger than those on the other islands,
which shows that the place has been cleared some time
or other, there is no mark left by which you can conjecture that ever this was a post.

The many islands which you meet with in the way,
enliven and change the scene, by the avenues which they
make, which look like the mouths of other rivers, and
break that long-extended sameness which is seen in the
Demerara.

Proceeding onwards, you get to the falls and rapids.   In
the rainy season they are very tedious to pass, and often
stop your course.   In the dry season, by stepping from
rock to rock, the Indians soon manage to get a canoe over
them.   But when the river is swollen, as it was in May,
1812, it is then a difficult task, and often a dangerous one
too.   At that time many of the islands were overflowed,
the rocks covered, and the lower branches of the trees in
the water.   Sometimes the Indians were obliged to take
everything out of the canoe, cut a passage through the
branches, which hung over into the river, and then drag
up the canoe by main force.

At one place, the falls form an oblique line quite across

the river, impassable to the ascending canoe, and you are forced to have it dragged four or five hundred yards by land.

It will take you five days, from the Indian habitation, on the point of the island, to where these falls and rapids terminate.

There are no huts in the way. You must bring your own cassava-bread along with you, hunt in the forest for your meat, and make the night's shelter for yourself.

Here is a noble range of hills, all covered with the finest trees, rising majestically one above the other, on the western bank, and presenting as rich a scene as ever the eye would wish to look on. Nothing in vegetable nature can be conceived more charming, grand, and luxuriant.

How the heart rejoices in viewing this beautiful landscape! when the sky is serene, the air cool, and the sun just sunk behind the mountain's top.

The Hayawa-tree perfumes the woods around; pairs of Scarlet Aras are continually crossing the river. The Maam sends forth its plaintive note, the Wren chants its evening song. The Caprimulgus wheels in busy flight around the canoe, while "Whip-poor-Will" sits on the broken stump near the water's edge, complaining as the shades of night set in.

A little before you pass the last of these rapids two immense rocks appear, nearly on the summit of one of the many hills which form this far-extending range, where it begins to fall off gradually to the south.

They look like two ancient stately towers of some Gothic potentate, rearing their heads above the surrounding trees. What with their situation and their shape together, they strike the beholder with an idea of antiquated grandeur which he will never forget. He may travel far and near and see nothing like them. On looking at them through a glass, the summit of the southern one appeared crowned with bushes. The one to the north was quite bare. The Indians have it from their ancestors that they are the abode of an evil genius, and they pass in the river below with a reverential awe.

In about seven hours from these stupendous sons of the hill, you leave the Essequibo, and enter the river Apoura-poura, which falls into it from the south. The Apoura-poura is nearly one-third the size of the Demerara at Stabroek. For two days you see nothing but level ground, richly clothed in timber. You leave the Siparouni to the right hand, and on the third day come to a little hill. The Indians have cleared about an acre of ground on it, and erected a temporary shed. If it be not intended for provision-ground alone, perhaps the next white man who travels through these remote wilds will find an Indian settlement here.

Two days after leaving this, you get to a rising ground on the western bank, where stands a single hut; and about half a mile in the forest there are a few more; some of them square, and some round with spiral roots.

Here the fish called Pacou is very plentiful : it is perhaps the fattest and most delicious fish in Guiana. It does not take the hook, but the Indians decoy it to the surface of the water by means of the seeds of the Crab-wood-tree, and then shoot it with an arrow.

You are now within the borders of Macoushia, inhabited by a different tribe of people, called Macoushi Indians ; uncommonly dexterous in the use of the blow-pipe, and famous for their skill in preparing the deadly vegetable poison, commonly called Wourali.

It is from this country that those beautiful parroquets named Kessi-kessi are procured. Here the crystal mountains are found; and here the three different species of the

Ara are seen in great abundance. Here, too, grows the tree from which the gum-elastic is got: it is large, and as tall as any in the forest. The wood has much the appearance of sycamore. The gum is contained in the bark: when that is cut through, it oozes out very freely: it is quite white, and looks as rich as cream: it hardens almost immediately as it issues from the tree; so that it is very easy to collect a ball, by forming the juice into a globular shape as fast as it comes out: it becomes nearly black by being exposed to the air, and is real India-rubber without undergoing any process.

The elegant crested bird called Cock of the Rock, admirably described by Buffon, is a native of the woody mountains of Macoushia. In the daytime, he retires amongst the darkest rocks, and only comes out to feed a little before sunrise, and at sunset: he is of a gloomy disposition, and, like the houtou, never associates with the other birds of the forest.

The Indians, in the just-mentioned settlement, seemed to depend more on the wourali-poison for killing their game than upon anything else. They had only one gun, and it appeared rusty and neglected; but their poisoned weapons were in fine order. Their blow-pipes hung from the roof of the hut, carefully suspended by a silk-grass cord; and on taking a nearer view of them, no dust seemed to have collected there, nor had the spider spun the smallest web on them; which showed that they were in constant use. The quivers were close by them, with the jaw-bone of the fish Pirai tied by a string to their brim, and a small wicker-basket of wild cotton, which hung down to the centre; they were nearly full of poisoned arrows. It was with difficulty these Indians could be persuaded to part with any of the wourali-poison, though a good price was offered for it; they gave me to understand that it was powder and shot to them, and very difficult to be procured.

On the second day after leaving the settlement, in passing along, the Indians show you a place where once a white man lived. His retiring so far from those of his own colour and acquaintance seemed to carry something extraordinary along with it, and raised a desire to know what could have induced him to do so. It seems he had been unsuccessful, and that his creditors had treated him with as little mercy as the strong generally show to the weak. Seeing his endeavours daily frustrated, and his best intentions of no avail, and fearing that when they had taken all he had they would probably take his liberty too, he thought the world would not be hard-hearted enough to condemn him for retiring from the evils which pressed so heavily on him, and which he had done all that an honest man could do to ward off. He left his creditors to talk of him as they thought fit, and, bidding adieu for ever to the place in which he had once seen better times, he penetrated thus far into those remote and gloomy wilds, and ended his days here.

According to the new map of South America, Lake Parima, or the White Sea, ought to be within three or four days' walk from this place. On asking the Indians whether there was such a place or not, and describing that the water was fresh and good to drink, an old Indian, who appeared to be about sixty, said that there was such a place, and that he had been there. This information would have been satisfactory in some degree, had not the Indians carried the point a little too far. It is very large, said another Indian, and ships come to it. Now these unfortunate ships were the very things which were not wanted : had he kept them out, it might have done, but his introducing them was sadly against the lake.

Thus you must either suppose that the old savage and his companion had a confused idea of the thing, and that probably the Lake Parima they talked of was the Amazons, not far from the city of Para, or that it was their intention to deceive you. You ought to be cautious in giving credit to their stories, otherwise you will be apt to be led astray.

Many a ridiculous thing concerning the interior of Guiana has been propagated and received as true, merely because six or seven Indians questioned separately, have agreed in their narrative.

Ask those who live high up in the Demerara, and they will, every one of them, tell you that there is a nation of Indians with long tails; that they are very malicious, cruel, and ill-natured; and that the Portuguese have been obliged to stop them off in a certain river, to prevent their depredations. They have also dreadful stories concerning a horrible beast, called the Watermamma, which, when it happens to take a spite against a canoe, rises out of the river, and in the most unrelenting manner possible carries both canoe and Indians down to the bottom with it, and there destroys them. Ludicrous extravagances; pleasing to those fond of the marvellous, and excellent matter for a distempered brain.

The misinformed and timid court of policy in Demerara was made the dupe of a savage, who came down the Esse-quibo, and gave himself out as king of a mighty tribe. This naked wild man of the woods seemed to hold the said court in tolerable contempt, and demanded immense supplies, all which he got; and moreover, some time after, an invitation to come down the ensuing year for more, which he took care not to forget.

This noisy chieftain boasted so much of his dynasty and domain, that the government was induced to send up an expedition into his territories to see if he had spoken the truth, and nothing but the truth. It appeared, however, that his palace was nothing but a hut, the monarch a needy savage, the heir-apparent nothing to inherit but his father's club, and bow and arrows, and his officers of state wild and uncultivated as the forests through which they strayed.

There was nothing in the hut of this savage, saving the presents he had received from government, but what was barely sufficient to support existence; nothing that indicated a power to collect a hostile force; nothing that showed the least progress towards civilization. All was rude and barbarous in the extreme, expressive of the utmost poverty and a scanty population.

You may travel six or seven days without seeing a hut, and when you reach a settlement it seldom contains more than ten.

The farther you advance into the interior the more you are convinced that it is thinly inhabited.

The day after passing the place where the white man lived you see a creek on the left hand, and shortly after the path to the open country. Here you drag the canoe up into the forest, and leave it there. Your baggage must now be carried by the Indians. The creek you passed in the river intersects the path to the next settlement: a large Mora has fallen across it, and makes an excellent bridge. After walking an hour and a half you come to the edge of the forest, and a savanna unfolds itself to the view.

The finest park that England boasts falls far short of this delightful scene. There are about two thousand acres of grass, with here and there a clump of trees, and a few bushes and single trees scattered up and down by the hand of Nature. The ground is neither hilly nor level, but diversified with moderate rises and falls, so gently running into one another that the eye cannot distinguish where they begin, nor where they end, while the distant black rocks have the appearance of a herd at rest.   Nearly in the middle there is an eminence, which falls off gradually on every side; and on this the Indians have erected their huts.

To the northward of them the foremost forms a circle, as though it had been done by art; to the eastward it hangs in festoons ; and to the south and west it rushes in abruptly, disclosing a new scene behind it at every step as you advance along.

This beautiful park of nature is quite surrounded by lofty hills, all arrayed in superbest garb of trees; some in the form of pyramids, others like sugar-loaves towering one above the other, some rounded off, and others as though they had lost their apex.   Here two hills rise up in spiral summits, and the wooded line of communication betwixt them sinks so gradually that it forms a crescent; and there the ridges of others resemble the waves of an agitated sea.   Beyond these appear others, and others past them ; and others still farther on, till they can scarcely be distinguished from the clouds.

There are no sand-flies, nor bete-rouge, nor mosquitos, in this pretty spot.   The fire-flies during the night vie in numbers and brightness with the stars in the firmament above; the air is pure, and the north-east breeze blows a refreshing gale throughout the day.   Here the White-crested Maroudi, which is never found in the Demerara, is pretty plentiful; and here grows the tree which produces the Moran, sometimes called Balsam-capivi.

Your route lies south from this place ; and at the extremity of the savanna you enter the forest, and journey along a winding path at the foot of a hill.   There is no habitation within this day's walk.   The traveller, as usual, must sleep in the forest; the path is not so good the following day. The hills over which it lies are rocky, steep, and rugged, and the spaces betwixt them swampy, and mostly knee-deep in water. After eight hours' walk you find two or three Indian huts, surrounded by the forest; and in little more than half an hour from these you come to ten or twelve others, where you pass the night. They are prettily situated at the entrance into a savanna. The eastern and western hills are still covered with wood; but on looking to the south-west quarter you perceive it begins to die away. In these forests you may find plenty of the trees which yield the sweet-smelling resin called Acaiari, and which, when pounded and burnt on charcoal, gives a delightful fragrance.

From hence you proceed, in a south-west direction, through a long swampy savanna. Some of the hills which border on it have nothing but a thin coarse grass and huge stones on them; others quite wooded; others with their summits crowned, and their base quite bare; and others, again, with their summits bare, and their base in thickest wood.

Half of this day's march is in water, nearly up to the knees. There are four creeks to pass: one of them has a fallen tree across it. You must make your own bridge across the other three. Probably, were the truth known, these apparently four creeks are only the meanders of one.

The Jabiru, the largest bird in Guiana, feeds in the marshy savanna through which you have just passed. He is wary and shy, and will not allow you to get within gun-shot of him.

You sleep this night in the forest, and reach an Indian settlement about three o'clock the next evening, after walking one-third of the way through wet and miry ground.

But, bad as the walking is through it, it is easier than where you cross over the bare hills, where you have to tread on sharp stones, most of them lying edgewise.

The ground gone over these two last days seems condemned to perpetual solitude and silence. There was not one four-footed animal to be seen, nor even the marks of one. It would have been as silent as midnight, and all as still and unmoved as a monument, had not the Jabiru in the marsh, and a few Vultures soaring over the mountain's top, shown that it was not quite deserted by animated nature. There were no insects, except one kind of fly, about one-fourth the size of the common house-fly. It bit cruelly, and was much more tormenting than the mosquito on the sea-coast.

This seems to be the native country of the Arrowroot. Wherever you passed through a patch of wood in a low situation, there you found it growing luxuriantly.

The Indian place you are now at is not the proper place to have come to in order to reach the Portuguese frontiers. You have advanced too much to the westward. But there was no alternative. The ground betwixt you and another small settlement (which was the right place to have gone to) was overflowed; and thus, instead of proceeding southward, you were obliged to wind along the foot of the western hills, quite out of your way.

But the grand landscape this place affords makes you ample amends for the time you have spent in reaching it. It would require great descriptive powers to give a proper idea of the situation these people have chosen for their dwelling.

The hill they are on is steep and high, and full of immense rocks. The huts are not all in one place, but dispersed wherever they have found a place level enough for a lodgement. Before you ascend the hill you see at

intervals an acre or two of wood, then an open space, with
a few huts on it   then wood again, and then an open space,
and so on, till the intervening of the western hills, higher
and steeper still, and crowned with trees of the loveliest
shades, closes the enchanting scene.

At the base of this hill stretches an immense plain,
which appears to the eye, on this elevated spot, as level
as a bowling-green. The mountains on the other side are
piled one upon the other in romantic forms, and gradually
retire, till they are undiscernible from the clouds in which
they are involved.   To the south-south-west this far-
extending plain is lost in the horizon.   The trees on it,
which look like islands on the ocean, add greatly to the
beauty of the landscape ; while the rivulet's course is
marked out by the Æta-trees which follow its meanders.

Not being able to pursue the direct course from hence
to the next Indian habitation on account of the floods of
water that fall at this time of the year, you take a circuit
westerly along the mountain's foot.

At last a large and deep creek stops your progress: it is
wide and rapid, and its banks very steep. There is neither
curial nor canoe, nor purple-heart tree in the neighbourhood to make a Wood-skin to carry you over, so that you
are obliged to swim across ; and by the time you have
formed a kind of raft, composed of boughs of trees and
coarse grass, to ferry over your baggage, the day will be
too far spent to think of proceeding. You must be very
cautious before you venture to swim across this creek, for
the alligators are numerous, and near twenty feet long. On
the present occasion the Indians took uncommon precautions lest they should be devoured by this cruel and voracious reptile. They cut long sticks, and examined closely
the side of the creek for half a mile above and below the
place where it was to be crossed ; and as soon as the

boldest had swum over, he did the same on the other side, and then all followed.

After passing the night on the opposite bank, which is well wooded, it is a brisk walk of nine hours before you reach four Indian huts, on a rising ground a few hundred paces from a little brook, whose banks are covered over with Coucourite and Æta-trees.

This is the place you ought to have come to two days ago had the water permitted you. In crossing the plain at the most advantageous place you are above ankle-deep in water for three hours; the remainder of the way is dry, the ground gently rising. As the lower parts of this spacious plain put on somewhat the appearance of a lake during the periodical rains, it is improbable but that this is the place which hath given rise to the supposed existence of the famed Lake Parima, or El Dorado; but this is mere conjecture.

A few Deer are feeding on the coarse rough grass of this far-extending plain; they keep at a distance from you, and are continually on the look-out.

The Spur-winged Plover, and a species of the Curlew, black, with a white bar across the wings, nearly as large again as the scarlet curlew on the sea-coast, frequently rise before you. Here, too, the Moscovy Duck is numerous; and large flocks of two other kinds wheel round you as you pass on, but keep out of gun-shot. The milk-white Egrets and Jabirus are distinguished at a great distance; and in the æta and coucourite trees you may observe flocks of scarlet and blue Aras feeding on the seeds.

It is to these trees that the largest sort of Toucan resorts. He is remarkable by a large black spot on the point of his fine yellow bill. He is very scarce in Demerara, and never seen except near the sea-coast.

The Ants' Nests have a singular appearance on this plain,

They are in vast abundance on those parts of it free from water, and are formed of an exceedingly hard yellow clay. They rise eight or ten feet from the ground, in a spiral form, impenetrable to the rain, and strong enough to defy the severest tornado.

The wourali-poison, procured in these last-mentioned huts, seemed very good, and proved afterwards to be very strong.

There are now no more Indian settlements betwixt you and the Portuguese frontiers. If you wish to visit their fort, it would be advisable to send an Indian with a letter from hence, and wait his return. On the present occasion a very fortunate circumstance occurred. The Portuguese commander had sent some Indians and soldiers to build a canoe, not far from this settlement ; they had just finished it, and those who did not stay with it had stopped here on their return.

The soldier who commanded the rest, said, he durst not, upon any account, convey a stranger to the fort; but he added, as there were two canoes, one of them might be despatched with a letter, and then we could proceed slowly on in the other.

About three hours from this settlement there is a river called Pirarara ; and here the soldiers had left their canoes while they were making the new one. From the Pirarara you get into the river Maou, and then into the Tacatou ; and just where the Tacatou falls into the Rio Branco, there stands the Portuguese frontier fort, called Fort. St. Joachim. From the time of embarking in the river Pirarara, it takes you four days before you reach this fort.

There was nothing very remarkable in passing down these rivers. It is an open country, producing a coarse grass, and interspersed with clumps of trees. The banks have some wood on them, but it appears stinted and crooked, like that on the bleak hills in England.

The Tapir frequently plunged into the river ; he was by no means shy, and it was easy to get a shot at him on land. The Kessi-kessi paroquets were in great abundance ; and the fine scarlet Aras innumerable in the coucourite-trees at a distance from the river's bank. In the Tacatou was seen the Troupiale. It was charming to hear the sweet and plaintive notes of this pretty songster of the wilds. The Portuguese call it the Nightingale of Guiana.

Towards the close of the fourth evening, the canoe, which had been sent on with a letter, met us with the commander's answer. During its absence, the nights had been cold and stormy, the rain had fallen in torrents, the days cloudy, and there was no sun to dry the wet hammocks. Exposed thus, day and night, to the chilling blast and pelting shower, strength of constitution at last failed, and a severe fever came on. The commander's answer was very polite. He remarked, he regretted much to say, that he had received orders to allow no stranger to enter the frontier, and this being the case, he hoped I would not consider him as uncivil : "however," continued he, "I have ordered the soldier to land you at a certain distance from the fort, where we can consult together."

We had now arrived at the place, and the canoe which brought the letter returned to the fort, to tell the commander I had fallen sick.

The sun had not risen above an hour the morning after when the Portuguese officer came to the spot where we had landed the preceding evening. He was tall and spare, and appeared to be from fifty to fifty-five years old ; and though thirty years of service under an equatorial sun had burnt and shrivelled up his face, still there was some-

thing in it so inexpressibly affable and kind, that it set
you immediately at your ease. He came close up to the
hammock, and taking hold of my wrist to feel the pulse,
" I am sorry, sir," said he, " to see that the fever has taken
such hold of you. You shall go directly with me," continued he, " to the fort ; and though we have no doctor
there, I trust," added he, " we shall soon bring you about
again. The orders I have received forbidding the admission of strangers were ·never intended to be put in
force against a sick English gentleman."

As the canoe was proceeding slowly down the river
towards the fort, the commander asked, with much more
interest than a question in ordinary conversation is asked,
where was I on the night of the first of May ? On telling
him that I was at an Indian settlement a little below the
great fall in the Demerara, and that a strange and sudden
noise had alarmed all the Indians, he said the same
astonishing noise had roused every man in Fort St.
Joachim, and that they remained under arms till morning.
He observed, that he had been quite at a loss to form any
idea what could have caused the noise ; but now learning
that the same noise had been heard at the same time far
away from the Rio Branco, it struck him there must have
been an earthquake somewhere or other.

Good nourishment and rest, and the unwearied attention
and kindness of the Portuguese commander, stopped the
progress of the fever, and enabled me to walk about in six
days.

Fort St. Joachim was built about five and forty years
ago, under the apprehension, it is said, that the Spaniards
were coming from the Rio Negro to settle there. It has
been much neglected; the floods of water have carried
away the gate, and destroyed the wall on each side of it;
but the present commander is putting it into thorough

repair.   When finished, it will mount six nine and six twelve pounders.

In a straight line with the fort, and within a few yards of the river, stand the commander's house, the barracks, the chapel, the father confessor's house, and two others, all at little intervals from each other ; and these are the only buildings at Fort St. Joachim.   The neighbouring extensive plains afford good pasturage for a fine breed of cattle, and the Portuguese make enough of butter and cheese for their own consumption.

On asking the old officer if there were such a place as Lake Parima, or El Dorado, he replied, he looked upon it as imaginary altogether. " I have been above forty years," added he, " in Portuguese Guiana, but have never yet met with anybody who has seen the lake."

So much for Lake Parima, or El Dorado, or the White Sea.   Its existence at best seems doubtful ; some affirm that there is such a place, and others deny it.

CHAPTER II.

"Grammatici certant, et adhuc sub judice lis est."

The Macoushi Indians—Poison vendors—Apparent failure of poison—
Collecting materials for wourali-poison—Preparing the poison—Super-
stitions—The blow-pipe gun—The Ourah—The Samourah—Silk-grass
—Acuero fruit—Coucourite palm—Wild Cotton—Arrows—Quivers—
Jaw of Pirai—Packing the arrows—Cotton basket—Gun sight made
of Acouri teeth—Poisoned fowl—Suspending the guns—The bow—
Ingenious arrows—Small quivers—A wild hog shot—Utilization of
indigenous products.

HAVING now reached the Portuguese inland frontier, and
collected a sufficient quantity of the wourali-poison,
nothing remains but to give a brief account of its composition, its effects, its uses, and its supposed antidotes.

It has been already remarked, that in the extensive wilds
of Demerara and Essequibo, far away from any European
settlement, there is a tribe of Indians who are known by
the name of Macoushi.

Though the wourali-poison is used by all the South
American savages betwixt the Amazons and the Oroonoque,
still this tribe makes it stronger than any of the rest.
The Indians in the vicinity of the Rio Negro are aware of
this, and come to the Macoushi country to purchase it.

Much has been said concerning this fatal and extraordinary poison. Some have affirmed that its effects are
almost instantaneous, provided the minutest particle of

it mixes with the blood; and others again have maintained that it is not strong enough to kill an animal of the size and strength of a man.   The first have erred by lending a too willing ear to the marvellous, and believing assertions without sufficient proof.   The following short story points out the necessity of a cautious examination.

One day, on asking an Indian if he thought the poison would kill a man, he replied, that they always go to battle with it; that he was standing by when an Indian was shot with a poisoned arrow, and that he expired almost immediately.   Not wishing to dispute this apparently satisfactory information, the subject was dropped.   However, about an hour after, having purposely asked him in what part of the body the said Indian was wounded, he answered without hesitation, that the arrow entered betwixt his shoulders, and passed quite through his heart. Was it the weapon, or the strength of the poison, that brought on immediate dissolution in this case?   Of course the weapon.

The second have been misled by disappointment, caused by neglect in keeping the poisoned arrows, or by not knowing how to use them, or by trying inferior poison. If the arrows are not kept dry, the poison loses its strength; and in wet or damp weather it turns mouldy, and becomes quite soft.   In shooting an arrow in this state, upon examining the place where it has entered, it will be observed that, though the arrow has penetrated deep into the flesh, still by far the greatest part of the poison has shrunk back, and thus, instead of entering with the arrow, it has remained collected at the mouth of the wound.   In this case the arrow might as well have not been poisoned.   Probably, it was to this that a gentleman, some time ago, owed his disappointment, when he tried the poison on a horse in the town of Stabroek, the capital of Demerara; the horse never betrayed the least symptom of being affected by it.

Wishful to obtain the best information concerning this poison, and as repeated inquiries, in lieu of dissipating the surrounding shade, did but tend more and more to darken the little light that existed, I determined to penetrate into the country where the poisonous ingredients grow, where this pernicious composition is prepared, and where it is constantly used. Success attended the adventure; and the information acquired made amends for one hundred and twenty days passed in the solitudes of Guiana, and afforded a balm to the wounds and bruises which every traveller must expect to receive who wanders through a thorny and obstructed path.

Thou must not, courteous reader, expect a dissertation on the manner in which the wourali-poison operates on the system; a treatise has been already written on the subject, and after all, there is probably still reason to doubt. It is supposed to affect the nervous system, and thus destroy the vital functions; it is also said to be perfectly harmless, provided it does not touch the blood. However, this is certain, when a sufficient quantity of it enters the blood, death is the inevitable consequence; but there is no alteration in the colour of the blood, and both the blood and flesh may be eaten with safety.

All that thou wilt find here is a concise, unadorned account of the wourali-poison. It may be of service to thee some time or other, shouldst thou ever travel through the wilds where it is used. Neither attribute to cruelty, nor to a want of feeling for the sufferings of the inferior animals, the ensuing experiments. The larger animals were destroyed in order to have proof positive of the strength of a poison which hath hitherto been doubted:

and the smaller ones were killed with the hope of substantiating that which has commonly been supposed to be an antidote.

It makes a pitying heart ache to see a poor creature in distress and pain ; and too often has the compassionate traveller occasion to heave a sigh as he journeys on. However, here, though the kind-hearted will be sorry to read of an unoffending animal doomed to death, in order to satisfy a doubt, still it will be a relief to know that the victim was not tortured.   The wourali-poison destroys life's action so gently, that the victim appears to be in no pain whatever; and probably, were the truth known, it feels none, saving the momentary smart at the time the arrow enters.

A day or two before the Macoushi Indian prepares his poison, he goes into the forest in quest of the ingredients. A vine grows in these wilds, which is called Wourali.   It is from this that the poison takes its name, and it is the principal ingredient.   When he has procured enough of this, he digs up a root of a very bitter taste, ties them together, and then looks about for two kinds of bulbous plants, which contain a green and glutinous juice.   He fills a little quake, which he carries on his back, with the stalks of these; and lastly, ranges up and down till he finds two species of ants.   One of them is very large and black, and so venomous, that its sting produces a fever ; it is most commonly to be met with on the ground.   The other is a little red ant, which stings like a nettle, and generally has its nest under the leaf of a shrub.   After obtaining these, he has no more need to range the forest.

A quantity of the strongest Indian pepper is used; but this he has already planted round his hut.   The pounded fangs of the Labarri snake, and those of the Counacouchi, are likewise added.   These he commonly has in store; for when he kills a snake, he generally extracts the fangs, and keeps them by him.

Having thus found the necessary ingredients, he scrapes the wourali vine and bitter root into thin shavings, and puts them into a kind of colander made of leaves : this he holds over an earthen pot, and pours water on the shavings : the liquor which comes through has the appearance of coffee. When a sufficient quantity has been procured, the shavings are thrown aside. He then bruises the bulbous stalks, and squeezes a proportionate quantity of their juice through his hands into the pot. Lastly, the snakes' fangs, ants, and pepper are bruised, and thrown into it. It is then placed on a slow fire, and as it boils, more of the juice of the wourali is added, according as it may be found necessary, and the scum is taken off with a leaf : it remains on the fire till reduced to a thick syrup of a deep brown colour. As soon as it has arrived at this state, a few arrows are poisoned with it, to try its strength. If it answer the expectations, it is poured out into a calabash, or little pot of Indian manufacture, which is carefully covered with a couple of leaves, and over them a piece of deer's skin, tied round with a cord. They keep it in the most dry part of the hut; and from time to time suspend it over the fire, to counteract the effects of dampness.

The act of preparing this poison is not considered as a common one: the savage may shape his bow, fasten the barb on the point of his arrow, and make his other implements of destruction, either lying in his hammock, or in the midst of his family ; but, if he has to prepare the wourali-poison, many precautions are supposed to be necessary.

The women and young girls are not allowed to be present, lest the Yabahou, or evil spirit, should do them harm. The shed under which it has been boiled is pronounced polluted, and abandoned ever after. He who makes the poison must eat nothing that morning, and must continue fasting as long as the operation lasts. The pot in which it is boiled must be a new one, and must never have held anything before, otherwise the poison would be deficient in strength: add to this, that the operator must take particular care not to expose himself to the vapour which arises from it while on the fire.

Though this and other precautions are taken, such as frequently washing the face and hands, still the Indians think that it affects the health; and the operator either is, or, what is more probable, supposes himself to be, sick for some days after.

Thus is appears that the making the wourali-poison is considered as a gloomy and mysterious operation; and it would seem that they imagine it affects others as well as him who boils it; for an Indian agreed one evening to make some for me, but the next morning he declined having anything to do with it, alleging that his wife was with child!

Here it might be asked, are all the ingredients just mentioned necessary, in order to produce the wourali-poison? Though our opinions and conjectures may militate against the absolute necessity of some of them, still it would be hardly fair to pronounce them added by the hand of superstition, till proof positive can be obtained.

We might argue on the subject, and, by bringing forward instances of Indian superstition, draw our conclusion by inference, and still remain in doubt on this head. You know superstition to be the offspring of ignorance, and of course that it takes up its abode amongst the rudest tribes of uncivilized man. It even too often resides with man in his more enlightened state.

The Augustan age furnishes numerous examples. A

bone snatched from the jaws of a fasting bitch, and a
feather from the wing of a night owl —" ossa ab ore rapta
jejunæ canis, plumamque nocturnæ strigis,"—were necessary for Canidia's incantations.   And in aftertimes. parson
Evans, the Welshman, was treated most ungenteelly by an
enraged spirit, solely because he had forgotten a fumiga-
tion in his witch-work.

If, then, enlightened man lets his better sense give way,
and believes, or allows himself to be persuaded, that certain substances and actions, in reality of no avail, possess
a virtue which renders them useful in producing the
wished-for effect; may not the wild, untaught, unen-
lightened savage of Guiana add an ingredient which, on
account of the harm it does him, he fancies may be useful
to the perfection of his poison, though in fact it be of no
use at all?   If a bone snatched from the jaws of a fasting
bitch be thought necessary in incantation; or if witchcraft
have recourse to the raiment of the owl, because it resorts
to the tombs and mausoleums of the dead, and wails and
hovers about at the time that the rest of animated nature
sleeps; certainly the savage may imagine that the ants,
whose sting causes a fever, and the teeth of the Labarri
and Couanacouchi snakes, which convey death in a very
short space of time, are essentially necessary in the composition of his poison; and being once impressed with
this idea, he will add them every time he makes the
poison, and transmit the absolute use of them to his pos-
terity.   The question to be answered seems not to be, if
it is natural for the Indians to mix these ingredients, but,
if they are essential to make the poison.

So much for the preparing of this vegetable essence;
terrible importer of death, into whatever animal it enters.
Let us now see how it is used; let us examine the weapons
which bear it to its destination, and take a view of the

poor victim, from the time he receives his wound till death comes to his relief.

When a native of Macoushia goes in quest of feathered game or other birds, he seldom carries his bow and arrows. It is the blow-pipe he then uses. This extraordinary tube of death is, perhaps one of the greates natural curiosities of Guiana. It is not found in the country of the Macoushi. Those Indians tel you that it grows to the south-west of them, in the wilds which extend betwixt them and the Rio Negro. The reed must grow to an amazing length, as the part the Indians use is from ten to eleven feet long, and no tapering can be perceived in it, one end being as thick as the other. It is of a bright yellow colour, perfectly smooth both inside and out. It grows hollow; nor is there the least appearance of a knot or joint throughout the whole extent. The natives call it Ourah. This, of itself, is too slender to answer the end of a blow-pipe; but there is a species of palma, larger and stronger, and common in Guiana, and this the Indians make use of as a case, in which they put the ourah. It is brown, susceptible of a fine polish, and appears as if it had joints five or six inches from each other. It is called Samourah, and the pulp inside is easily extracted, by steeping it for a few days in water.

Thus the ourah and samourah, one within the other, form the blow-pipe of Guiana. The end which is applied to the mouth is tied round with a small silk-grass cord, to prevent its splitting; and the other end, which is apt to strike against the ground, is secured by the seed of the Acuero fruit, cut horizontally through the middle, with a hole made in the end, through which is put the extremity of the blow-pipe. It is fastened on with string on the outside, and the inside is filled up with wild bees'-wax.

The arrow is from nine to ten inches long. It is made

out of the leaf of a species of palm-tree, called Coucourite, hard and brittle, and pointed as sharp as a needle. About an inch of the pointed end is poisoned. The other end is burnt to make it still harder, and wild cotton is put round it for about an inch and a half. It requires considerable practice to put on this cotton well. It must just be large enough to fit the hollow of the tube, and taper off to nothing downwards. They tie it on with a thread of the silk-grass, to prevent its slipping off the arrow.

The Indians have shown ingenuity in making a quiver to hold the arrows. It will contain from five to six hundred. It is generally from twelve to fourteen inches long, and in shape resembles a dice-box used at backgammon. The inside is prettily done in basket-work, with wood not unlike bamboo, and the outside has a coat of wax. The cover is all of one piece, formed out of the skin of the tapir. Round the centre there is fastened a loop, large enough to admit the arm and shoulder, from which it hangs when used. To the rim is tied a little bunch of silk-grass, and half of the jaw-bone of the fish called pirai, with which the Indian scrapes the point of his arrow.

Before he puts the arrows into the quiver, he links them together by two strings of cotton, one string at each end, and then folds them round a stick, which is nearly the length of the quiver. The end of the stick, which is uppermost, is guarded by two little pieces of wood crosswise, with a hoop round their extremities, which appears something like a wheel; and this saves the hand from being wounded when the quiver is reversed in order to let the bunch of arrows drop out.

There is also attached to the quiver a little kind of basket, to hold the wild cotton which is put on the blunt end of the arrow. With a quiver of poisoned arrows slung over his shoulder, and with his blow-pipe in his hand, in the same position as a soldier carries his musket, see the Macoushi Indian advancing towards the forest in quest of powises, maroudis, waracabas, and other feathered game.

These generally sit high up in the tall and tufted trees, but still are not out of the Indian's reach; for his blow-pipe, at its greatest elevation, will send an arrow three hundred feet. Silent as midnight he steals under them, and so cautiously does he tread the ground, that the fallen leaves rustle not beneath his feet. His ears are open to the least sound, while his eye, keen as that of the lynx, is employed in finding out the game in the thickest shade. Often he imitates their cry, and decoys them from tree to tree, till they are within range of his tube. Then taking a poisoned arrow from his quiver, he puts it in the blow-pipe, and collects his breath for the fatal puff.

About two feet from the end through which he blows there are fastened two teeth of the acouri, and these serve him for a sight. Silent and swift the arrow flies, and seldom fails to pierce the object at which it is sent. Sometimes the wounded bird remains in the same tree where it was shot, and in three minutes falls down at the Indian's feet. Should he take wing, his flight is of short duration, and the Indian, following the direction he has gone, is sure to find him dead.

It is natural to imagine that, when a slight wound only is inflicted, the game will make its escape. Far otherwise; the wourali-poison almost instantaneously mixes with blood or water, so that if you wet your finger, and dash it along the poisoned arrow in the quickest manner possible, you are sure to carry off some of the poison. Though three minutes generally elapse before the convulsions come on in the wounded bird, still a stupor evidently takes place sooner, and this stupor manifests itself by an apparent unwillingness in the bird to move. This was very visible in a dying fowl.

Having procured a healthy full-grown one, a short piece of a poisoned blow-pipe arrow was broken off and run up into its thigh, as near as possible betwixt the skin and the flesh, in order that it might not be incommoded by the wound. For the first minute it walked about, but walked very slowly, and did not appear the least agitated. During the second minute it stood still, and began to peck the ground; and ere half another had elapsed, it frequently opened and shut its mouth. The tail had now dropped, and the wings almost touched the ground. By the termination of the third minute, it had sat down, scarce able to support its head, which nodded, and then recovered itself, and then nodded again, lower and lower every time, like that of a weary traveller slumbering in an erect position; the eyes alternately open and shut. The fourth minute brought on convulsions, and life and the fifth terminated together.

The flesh of the game is not in the least injured by the poison, nor does it appear to corrupt sooner than that killed by the gun or knife. The body of this fowl was kept for sixteen hours, in a climate damp and rainy, and within seven degrees of the equator; at the end of which time it had contracted no bad smell whatever, and there were no symptoms of putrefaction, saving that, just round the wound, the flesh appeared somewhat discoloured.

The Indian, on his return home, carefully suspends his blow-pipe from the top of his spiral roof; seldom placing it in an oblique position, lest it should receive a cast.

Here let the blow-pipe remain suspended, while you take a view of the arms which are made to slay the larger beasts of the forest.

When the Indian intends to chase the peccari, or surprise the deer, or rouse the tapir from his marshy retreat, he carries his bow and arrows, which are very different from the weapons already described.

The bow is generally from six to seven feet long, and strung with a cord, spun out of the silk-grass. The forests of Guiana furnish many species of hard wood, tough and elastic, out of which beautiful and excellent bows are formed.

The arrows are from four to five feet in length, made of a yellow reed without a knot or joint. It is found in great plenty up and down throughout Guiana. A piece of hard wood, about nine inches long, is inserted into the end of the reed, and fastened with cotton well waxed. A square hole, an inch deep, is then made in the end of this piece of hard wood, done tight round with cotton to keep it from splitting. Into this square hole is fitted a spike of Coucourite wood, poisoned, and which may be kept there, or taken out at pleasure. A joint of bamboo, about as thick as your finger, is fitted on over the poisoned spike, to prevent accidents and defend it from the rain, and is taken off when the arrow is about to be used. Lastly, two feathers are fastened on the other end of the reed to steady it in its flight.

Besides his bow and arrows, the Indian carries a little box made of bamboo, which holds a dozen or fifteen poisoned spikes, six inches long. They are poisoned in the following manner: a small piece of wood is dipped in the poison, and with this they give the spike a first coat. It is then exposed to the sun or fire. After it is dry, it receives another coat, and is then dried again; after this a third coat, and sometimes a fourth.

They take great care to put the poison on thicker at the middle than at the sides, by which means the spike retains the shape of a two-edged sword. It is rather a tedious operation to make one of these arrows complete ; and as the Indian is not famed for industry, except when pressed by hunger, he has hit upon a plan of preserving his arrows which deserves notice.

About a quarter of an inch above the part where the Coucourite spike is fixed into the square hole, he cuts it half through; and thus, when it has entered the animal, the weight of the arrow causes it to break off there, by which means the arrow falls to the ground uninjured ; so that, should this be the only arrow he happens to have with him, and should another shot immediately occur, he has only to take another poisoned spike out of his little bamboo box, fit it on his arrow, and send it to its destination.

Thus armed with deadly poison, and hungry as the hyæna, he ranges through the forest in quest of the wild beasts' track. No hound can act a surer part. Without clothes to fetter him, or shoes to bind his feet, he observes the footsteps of the game, where an European eye could not discern the smallest vestige. He pursues it through all its turns and windings, with astonishing perseverance, and success generally crowns his efforts. The animal, after receiving the poisoned arrow, seldom retreats two hundred paces before it drops.

In passing overland from the Essequibo to the Demerara we fell in with a herd of wild hogs. Though encumbered with baggage, and fatigued with a hard day's walk, an Indian got his bow ready, and let fly a poisoned arrow at one of them. It entered the cheek-bone and broke off. The wild hog was found quite dead about one hundred and seventy paces from the place where he had been shot. He afforded us an excellent and wholesome supper.

Thus the savage of Guiana, independent of the common

weapons of destruction, has it in his power to prepare a
poison, by which he can generally ensure to himself a
supply of animal food; and the food so destroyed imbibes
no deleterious qualities. Nature has been bountiful to him.
She has not only ordered poisonous herbs and roots to grow
in the unbounded forests through which he strays, but has
also furnished an excellent reed for his arrows, and another,
still more singular, for his blow-pipe; and planted trees of
an amazing hard, tough, and elastic texture, out of which
he forms his bows. And in order that nothing might be
wanting, she has superadded a tree which yields him
a fine wax, and disseminated up and down, a plant not
unlike that of the pine-apple, which affords him capital
bow-strings.

CHAPTER III.

HAVING now followed the Indian in the chase, and described the poison, let us take a nearer view of its action,
and observe a large animal expiring under the weight of
its baneful virulence.

Many have doubted the strength of the wourali-poison.
Should they ever by chance read what follows, probably
their doubts on that score will be settled for ever.

In the former experiment on the hog, some faint resistance on the part of nature was observed, as if existence
struggled for superiority; but in the following instance of
the sloth, life sank in death without the least apparent
contention, without a cry, without a struggle, and without
a groan. This was an Ai, or three-toed Sloth. It was in
the possession of a gentleman who was collecting curiosities.
He wished to have it killed, in order to preserve the skin,
and the wourali-poison was resorted to as the easiest
death.

Of all animals, not even the toad and tortoise excepted, this poor ill-formed creature is the most tenacious of life. It exists long after it has received wounds which would have destroyed any other animal; and it may be said, on seeing a mortally-wounded sloth, that life disputes with death every inch of flesh in its body.

The Ai was wounded in the leg, and put down on the floor, about two feet from the table; it contrived to reach the leg of the table and fastened himself on it, as if wishful to ascend. But this was its last advancing step: life was ebbing fast, though imperceptibly; nor could this singular production of nature, which has been formed of a texture to resist death in a thousand shapes, make any stand against the wourali-poison.

First, one fore-leg let go its hold, and dropped down motionless by its side; the other gradually did the same. The fore-legs having now lost their strength, the sloth slowly doubled its body, and placed its head betwixt its hind-legs, which still adhered to the table; but when the poison had affected these also, it sank to the ground, but sank so gently, that you could not distinguish the movement from an ordinary motion; and had you been ignorant that it was wounded with a poisoned arrow, you would never have suspected that it was dying. Its mouth was shut, nor had any froth or saliva collected there.

There was no subsultus tendinum, or any visible alteration in its breathing. During the tenth minute from the time it was wounded it stirred, and that was all; and the minute after, life's last spark went out. From the time the poison began to operate, you would have conjectured that sleep was overpowering it, and you would have exclaimed, " Pressitque jacentem, dulcis et alta quies, placidæque simillima morti."

There are now two positive proofs of the effect of this

fatal poison ; viz. the death of the hog, and that of the sloth.
But still these animals were nothing remarkable for size;
and the strength of the poison in large animals might
yet be doubted, were it not for what follows.

A large well-fed ox, from nine hundred to a thousand
pounds weight, was tied to a stake by a rope sufficiently
long to allow him to move to and fro.   Having no large
Coucourite spikes at hand, it was judged necessary, on
account of his superior size, to put three wild-hog arrows
into him; one was sent into each thigh just above the
hock, in order to avoid wounding a vital part, and the
third was shot traversely into the extremity of the nostril.

The poison seemed to take effect in four minutes. Conscious as though he would fall, the ox set himself firmly
on his legs, and remained quite still in the same place,
till about the fourteenth minute, when he smelled the
ground, and appeared as if inclined to walk. He advanced
a pace or two, staggered, and fell, and remained extended
on his side with his head on the ground. His eye, a few
minutes ago so bright and lively, now became fixed and
dim, and though you put your hand close to it as if to
give him a blow there, he never closed his eyelid.

His legs were convulsed, and his head from time to time
started involuntarily ; but he never showed the least desire
to raise it from the ground ; he breathed hard, and emitted
foam from his mouth. The startings, or subsultus tendinum, now became gradually weaker and weaker; his
hinder parts were fixed in death; and in a minute or two
more his head and fore-legs ceased to stir.

Nothing now remained to show that life was still within
him, except that his heart faintly beat and fluttered at
intervals. In five-and-twenty minutes from the time of
his being wounded he was quite dead. His flesh was very
sweet and savoury at dinner.

On taking a retrospective view of the two different kinds of poisoned arrows, and the animals destroyed by them, it would appear that the quantity of poison must be proportioned to the animal, and thus those probably labour under an error who imagine that the smallest particle of it introduced into the blood has almost instantaneous effects.

Make an estimate of the difference in size betwixt the fowl and the ox, and then weigh a sufficient quantity of poison for a blow-pipe arrow with which the fowl was killed, and weigh also enough poison for three wild-hog arrows which destroyed the ox, and it will appear that the fowl received much more poison in proportion than the ox. Hence the cause why the fowl died in five minutes, and the ox in five-and-twenty.

Indeed, were it the case that the smallest particle of it introduced into the blood has almost instantaneous effects, the Indian would not find it necessary to make the large arrow; that of the blow-pipe is much easier made and requires less poison.

And now for the antidotes, or rather the supposed antidotes. The Indians tell you, that if the wounded animal be held for a considerable time up to the mouth in water, the poison will not prove fatal; also that the juice of the sugar-cane poured down the throat will counteract the effects of it. These antidotes were fairly tried upon full-grown healthy fowls, but they all died, as though no steps had been taken to preserve their lives. Rum was recommended and given to another, but with as little success.

It is supposed by some, that wind introduced into the lungs by means of a small pair of bellows would revive the poisoned patient, provided the operation be continued for a sufficient length of time. It may be so; but this is a difficult and a tedious mode of cure, and he who is wounded in the forest far away from his friends, or in the hut of the savages, stands but a poor chance of being saved by it.

Had the Indians a sure antidote, it is likely they would carry it about with them, or resort to it immediately after being wounded, if at hand; and their confidence in its efficacy would greatly diminish the horror they betray when you point a poisoned arrow at them.

One day, while we were eating a red monkey, erroneously called the baboon in Demerara, an Arowack Indian told an affecting story of what happened to a comrade of his. He was present at his death. As it did not interest this Indian in any point to tell a falsehood, it is very probable that his account was a true one. If so, it appears that there is no certain antidote, or at least an antidote that could be resorted to in a case of urgent need; for the Indian gave up all thoughts of life as soon as he was wounded.

The Arowack Indian said it was but four years ago that he and his companion were ranging in the forest in quest of game. His companion took a poisoned arrow, and sent it at a red monkey in a tree above him. It was nearly a perpendicular shot. The arrow missed the monkey, and in the descent, struck him in the arm, a little above the elbow. He was convinced it was all over with him. "I shall never," said he to his companion in a faltering voice, and looking at his bow as said it, "I shall never," said he, "bend this bow again." And having said that, he took off his little bamboo poison-box, which hung across his shoulder, and putting it together with his bow and arrows on the ground, he laid himself down close by them, bid his companion farewell, and never spoke more.

He who is unfortunate enough to be wounded by a poisoned arrow from Macoushia had better not depend upon the common antidotes for a cure. Many who have been in Guiana will recommend immediate immersion in water, or to take the juice of the sugar-cane, or to fill the mouth full of salt; and they recommend these antidotes because they have got them from the Indians. But were you to ask them if they ever saw these antidotes used with success, it is ten to one their answer would be in the negative.

Wherefore let him reject these antidotes as unprofitable, and of no avail. He has got an active and deadly foe within him, which, like Shakspeare's fell Sergeant Death, is strict in his arrest, and will allow him but little time— very—very little time. In a few minutes he will be numbered with the dead. Life ought, if possible, to be preserved, be the expense ever so great. Should the part affected admit of it, let a ligature be tied tight round the wound, and have immediate recourse to the knife :—

> " Continuo, culpam ferro compesce priusquam,
> Dira per infaustum serpant contagia corpus."

And now, kind reader, it is time to bid thee farewell. The two ends proposed have been obtained. The Portuguese inland frontier fort has been reached, and the Macoushi wourali-poison acquired. The account of this excursion through the interior of Guiana has been submitted to thy perusal, in order to induce thy abler genius to undertake a more extensive one. If any difficulties have arisen, or fevers come on, they have been caused by the periodical rains, which fall in torrents as the sun approaches the tropic of Cancer. In dry weather there would be no difficulties or sickness.

Amongst the many satisfactory conclusions which thou wouldest be able to draw during the journey, there is one which, perhaps, would please thee not a little ; and that is with regard to dogs. Many a time, no doubt, thou hast heard it hotly disputed, that dogs existed in Guiana previously to the arrival of the Spaniards in those parts. Whatever the Spaniards introduced, and which bore no resemblance to anything the Indians had been accustomed to see, retains its Spanish name to this day.

Thus the Warow, the Arowack, the Acoway, the Macoushi, and Carib tribes, call a hat, sombrero; a shirt, or any kind of cloth, camiso; a shoe, zapato; a letter, carta; a fowl, gallina; gunpowder, colvora, (Spanish, polvora;) ammunition, bala; a cow, vaca; and a dog, perro.

This argues strongly against the existence of dogs in Guiana before it was discovered by the Spaniards, and probably may be of use to thee, in thy next canine dispute.

In a political point of view this country presents a large field for speculation. A few years ago there was but little inducement for any Englishman to explore the interior of these rich and fine colonies, as the British Government did not consider them worth holding at the peace of Amiens. Since that period their mother-country has been blotted out from the list of nations, and America has unfolded a new sheet of politics. On one side, the crown of Braganza, attacked by an ambitious chieftain, has fled from the palace of its ancestors, and now seems fixed on the banks of the Janeiro. Cayenne has yielded to its arms. La Plata has raised the standard of independence, and thinks itself sufficiently strong to obtain a government of its own. On the other side, the Caraccas are in open revolt, and should Santa Fe join them in good earnest, they may form a powerful association.

Thus, on each side of the *ci-devant* Dutch Guiana, most unexpected and astonishing changes have taken place. Will they raise or lower it in the scale of estimation at the Court of St. James's? Will they be of benefit to these grand and extensive colonies? Colonies enjoying perpetual summer. Colonies of the richest soil. Colonies containing within themselves everything necessary for their support. Colonies, in fine, so varied in their quality and situation, as to be capable of bringing to perfection every tropical production; and only want the support of government, and an enlightened governor, to render them as fine as the finest portions of the equatorial regions. Kind reader, fare thee well.

LETTER TO THE PORTUGUESE COMMANDER.

Muy Señor,

Como no tengo el honor, de ser conocido de VM. lo pienso mejor, y mas decoroso, quedarme aqui, hastaque huviere recibido su respuesta.   Haviendo caminado hasta la chozo, adonde estoi, no quisiere volverme, antes de haver visto la fortaleza de los Portugueses; y pido licencia de VM. para que me adelante.   Honradissimos son mis motivos, ni tengo proyecto ninguno, o de comercio, o de la soldadesca, no siendo yo, o comerciante, o oficial.   Hidalgo catolico soy, de hacienda in Ynglatierra, y muchos años de mi vida he pasado en caminar.   Ultimamente, de Demeraria vengo, la qual dexé el 5 dia de Abril, para ver este hermoso pais, y coger unas curiosidades, especialmente, el veneno, que se llama wourali.   Las mas recentes noticias que tenian en Demeraria, antes de mi salida, eran medias tristes, medias alegres.   Tristes digo, viendo que Valencia ha caido en poder del enemigo comun, y le General Blake, y sus valientes tropas quedan prisioneros de guerra.   Alegres, al contrario, porque Milord Wellington se ha apoderado de Ciudad Rodrigo.   A pesar de la caida de Valencia, parece claro al mundo, que las cosas del enemigo, estan andando, de pejor a pejor cada dia.   Nosotros debemos dar gracias al Altissimo, por haver sido servido dexarnos castigar ultimamente, a los robadores de sus santas Yglesias.   Se vera VM. que yo no escribo Portugues ni aun lo hablo, pero, haviendo aprendido el Castellano, no nos faltara medio de communicar y tener conversacion.   Ruego se escuse esta carta escrita sin tinta, porque un Indio dexo caer mi tintero y quebrose.   Dios le dé a VM. muchos años de salud.   Entretanto, tengo el honor de ser

Su mas obedeciente servidor,

CARLOS WATERTON.

REMARKS.

"Incertus, quo fata ferant, ubi sistere detur."

KIND and gentle reader, if the journey in quest of the woutali-poison has engaged thy attention, probably thou mayest recollect that the traveller took leave of thee at Fort St. Joachim, on the Rio Branco. Shouldest thou wish to know what befell him afterwards, excuse the following uninteresting narrative.

Having had a return of fever, and aware that the farther he advanced into these wild and lonely regions, the less would be the chance of regaining his health ; he gave up all idea of proceeding onwards, and went slowly back towards the Demerara, nearly by the same route he had come.

On descending the falls in the Essequibo, which form an oblique line quite across the river, it was resolved to push through them, the downward stream being in the canoe's favour. At a little distance from the place, a large tree had fallen into the river, and in the meantime the canoe was lashed to one of its branches.

The roaring of the water was dreadful ; it foamed and dashed over the rocks with a tremendous spray, like breakers on a lee-shore, threatening destruction to whatever approached it. You would have thought, by the confusion it caused in the river, and the whirlpools it made, that Scylla and Charybdis, and their whole progeny, had left the Mediterranean, and come and settled here. The channel was barely twelve feet wide, and the torrent in rushing down formed traverse furrows, which showed how near the rocks were to the surface.

Nothing could surpass the skill of the Indian who steered the canoe. He looked steadfastly at it, then at the rocks, then cast an eye on the channel, and then looked at the canoe again. It was in vain to speak. The sound was lost in the roar of waters; but his eye showed that he had already passed it in imagination. He held up his paddle in a position, as much as to say, that he would keep exactly amid channel; and then made a sign to cut the bush rope that held the canoe to the fallen tree. The canoe drove down the torrent with inconceivable rapidity. It did not touch the rocks once all the way. The Indian proved to a nicety, " medio tutissimus ibis."

Shortly after this it rained almost day and night, the lightning flashing incessantly, and the roar of thunder awful beyond expression.

The fever returned, and pressed so heavy on him, that to all appearance his last day's march was over. However, it abated; his spirits rallied, and he marched again; and after delays and inconveniences he reached the house of his worthy friend, Mr. Edmonstone, in Mibiri Creek, which falls into the Demerara. No words of his can do justice to the hospitality of that gentleman, whose repeated encounters with the hostile negroes in the forest have been publicly rewarded, and will be remembered in the colony for years to come.

Here he learned that an eruption had taken place in St. Vincent's; and thus the noise heard in the night of the first of May, which had caused such terror amongst the Indians, and made the garrison at Fort St. Joachim remain under arms the rest of the night, is accounted for.

After experiencing every kindness and attention from Mr. Edmonstone, he sailed for Granada, and from thence to St. Thomas's, a few days before poor Captain Peake lost his life on his own quarter-deck, bravely fighting for his country on the coast of Guiana.

At St. Thomas's they show you a tower, a little distance from the town, which they say formerly belonged to a Bucanier chieftain. Probably the fury of besiegers has reduced it to its present dismantled state. What still remains of it bears testimony of its former strength, and may brave the attack of time for centuries. You cannot view its ruins without calling to mind the exploits of those fierce and hardy hunters, long the terror of the western world. While you admire their undaunted courage, you lament that it was often stained with cruelty; while you extol their scrupulous justice to each other, you will find a want of it towards the rest of mankind. Often possessed of enormous wealth, often in extreme poverty, often triumphant on the ocean, and often forced to fly to the forests, their life was an ever-changing scene of advance and retreat, of glory and disorder, of luxury and famine. Spain treated them as outlaws and pirates, while other European powers publicly disowned them. They, on the other hand, maintained that injustice on the part of Spain first forced them to take up arms in self-defence; and that, whilst they kept inviolable the laws which they had framed for their own common benefit and protection, they had a right to consider as foes those who treated them as outlaws. Under this impression they drew the sword, and rushed on as though in lawful war, and divided the spoils of victory in the scale of justice.

After leaving St. Thomas's a severe tertian ague every now and then kept putting the traveller in mind that his shattered frame, " starting and shivering in the inconstant

blast, meagre and pale—the ghost of what it was"—
wanted repairs. Three years elapsed after arriving in
England before the ague took its final leave of him.

During that time several experiments were made with
the wourali poison. In London an ass was inoculated
with it, and died in twelve minutes. The poison was
inserted into the leg of another, round which a bandage
had been previously tied a little above the place where
the wourali was introduced. He walked about as usual,
and ate his food as though all were right. After an hour
had elapsed the bandage was untied, and ten minutes
after death overtook him.

A she-ass received the wourali poison in the shoulder,
and died apparently in ten minutes. An incision was
then made in its windpipe, and through it the lungs were
regularly inflated for two hours with a pair of bellows.
Suspended animation returned. The ass held up her head,
and looked around; but the inflating being discontinued, she
sunk once more in apparent death. The artificial breathing was immediately recommenced, and continued without
intermission for two hours. This saved the ass from final
dissolution; she rose up, and walked about; she seemed
neither in agitation nor in pain. The wound, through
which the poison entered, was healed without difficulty.
Her constitution, however, was so severely affected that
it was long a doubt if ever she would be well again.
She looked lean and sickly for above a year, but began
to mend the spring after, and by Midsummer became fat
and frisky.

The kind-hearted reader will rejoice on learning that
Earl Percy, pitying her misfortunes, sent her down from
London to Walton Hall, near Wakefield. There she goes
by the name of Wouralia. Wouralia shall be sheltered
from the wintry storm; and when summer comes she

shall feed in the finest pasture. No burden shall be placed upon her, and she shall end her days in peace.[1]

For three revolving autumns the ague-beaten wanderer never saw, without a sigh, the swallow bend her flight towards warmer regions. He wished to go too, but could not; for sickness had enfeebled him, and prudence pointed out the folly of roving again too soon across the northern tropic. To be sure, the continent was now open, and change of air might prove beneficial; but there was nothing very tempting in a trip across the Channel, and as for a tour through England!—England has long ceased to be the land for adventures. Indeed, when good King Arthur re-appears to claim his crown he will find things strangely altered here; and may we not look for his coming? for there is written upon his grave-stone:—

> "Hic jacet Arturus, Rex quondam Rexque futurus,"
> "Here Arthur lies, who formerly
> Was king—and king again to be."

Don Quixote was always of opinion that this famous king did not die, but that he was changed into a raven by enchantment, and that the English are momentarily expecting his return. Be this as it may, it is certain that when he reigned here all was harmony and joy. The browsing herds passed from vale to vale, the swains sang from the bluebell-teeming groves, and nymphs with eglantine and roses in their neatly-braided hair went hand in hand to the flowery mead to weave garlands for their lambkins. If by chance some rude uncivil fellow dared to molest them, or attempted to throw thorns in their path, there was sure to be a knight-errant not far off ready to

[1] Poor Wouralia breathed her last on the 15th of February, 1839, having survived the operation nearly five and twenty years.

rush forward in their defence. But alas! in these de-
generate days it is not so. Should a harmless cottage
maid wander out of the highway to pluck a primrose or
two in the neighbouring field the haughty owner sternly
bids her retire ; and if a pitying swain hasten to escort
her back, he is perhaps seized by the gaunt house-dog ere
he reach her.

Æneas's route on the other side of Styx, could not have
been much worse than this, though, by his account, when
he got back to earth, it appears that he had fallen in with
"Bellua Lernæ, horrendum stridens, flammisque, armata
Chimæra."

Moreover, he had a sibyl to guide his steps ; and as
such a conductress nowadays could not be got for love
nor money, it was judged most prudent to refrain from
sauntering through this land of freedom, and wait with
patience the return of health. At last this long-looked
for, ever welcome stranger came.

SECOND JOURNEY.

CHAPTER I.

IN the year 1816, two days before the vernal equinox, I
sailed from Liverpool for Pernambuco, in the southern
hemisphere, on the coast of Brazil. There is little at this
time of the year in the European part of the Atlantic to
engage the attention of the naturalist. As you go down
the Channel you see a few divers and gannets. The
middle-sized gulls, with a black spot at the end of the
wings, attend you a little way into the Bay of Biscay.
When it blows a hard gale of wind the stormy petrel makes
its appearance. While the sea runs mountains high, and
every wave threatens destruction to the labouring vessel
this little harbinger of storms is seen enjoying itself, on
rapid pinion, up and down the roaring billows. When
the storm is over it appears no more. It is known to
every English sailor by the name of Mother Carey's
Chicken. It must have been hatched in Æolus's cave,
amongst a clutch of squalls and tempests; for whenever

they get out upon the ocean it always contrives to be of the party.

Though the calms and storms, and adverse winds in these latitudes are vexatious, still, when you reach the trade winds you are amply repaid for all disappointments and inconveniences. The trade winds prevail about thirty degrees on each side of the equator. This part of the ocean may be called the Elysian Fields of Neptune's Empire; and the torrid zone, notwithstanding Ovid's remark, " non est habitabilis æstu," is rendered healthy and pleasant by these gently-blowing breezes. The ship glides smoothly on, and you soon find yourself within the northern tropic. When you are on it, Cancer is just over your head, and betwixt him and Capricorn is the high road of the Zodiac forty-seven degrees wide, famous for Phaeton's misadventure. His father begged and entreated him not to take it into his head to drive parallel to the five zones, but to mind and keep on the turnpike which runs obliquely across the equator. " There you will distinctly see," said he, " the ruts of my chariot wheels, ' manifesta rotæ vestigia cernes.' " But," added he, " even suppose you keep on it, and avoid the by-roads, nevertheless, my dear boy, believe me, you will be most sadly put to your shifts; ' ardua prima via est,' the first part of the road is confoundedly steep! ' ultima via prona est,' and after that it is all down hill. Moreover, ' per insidias iter est, formasque ferarum,' the road is full of nooses and bull-dogs, ' Hæmoniosque arcus,' and spring guns, ' sævaque circuitu, curvantem brachia longo, Scorpio,' and steel traps of uncommon size and shape." These were nothing in the eyes of Phaeton; go he would, so off he set, full speed, four-in-hand. He had a tough drive of it; and after doing a prodigious deal of mischief, very luckily for the world, he got thrown out of the box, and tumbled into the river Po.

Some of our modern bloods have been shallow enough to try to ape this poor empty-headed coachman, on a little scale, making London their Zodiac. Well for them, if tradesmen's bills, and other trivial perplexities, have not caused them to be thrown into the King's Bench.

The productions of the torrid zone are uncommonly grand. Its plains, its swamps, its savannas, and forests abound with the largest serpents and wild beasts; and its trees are the habitation of the most beautiful of the feathered race. While the traveller in the old world is astonished at the elephant, the tiger, the lion, and rhinoceros, he who wanders through the torrid regions of the new, is lost in admiration at the cotingas, the toucans, the humming-birds, and aras.

The ocean, likewise, swarms with curiosities. Probably the Flying-fish may be considered as one of the most singular. This little scaled inhabitant of water and air seems to have been more favoured than the rest of its finny brethren. It can rise out of the waves, and on wing visit the domain of the birds.

After flying two or three hundred yards, the intense heat of the sun has dried its pellucid wings, and it is obliged to wet them in order to continue its flight. It just drops into the ocean for a moment, and then rises again and flies on; and then descends to remoisten them, and then up again into the air; thus passing its life, sometimes wet, sometimes dry, sometimes in sunshine, and sometimes in the pale moon's nightly beam, as pleasure dictates, or as need requires. The additional assistance of wings is not thrown away upon it. It has full occupation both for fins and wings, as its life is in perpetual danger.

The Bonito and Albicore chase it day and night; but the Dolphin is its worst and swiftest foe. If it escape into the air, the dolphin pushes on with proportional velocity beneath, and is ready to snap it up the moment it descends to wet its wings.

You will often see above one hundred of these little marine aerial fugitives on the wing at once. They appear to use every exertion to prolong their flight, but vain are all their efforts; for when the last drop of water on their wings is dried up, their flight is at an end, and they must drop into the ocean. Some are instantly devoured by their merciless pursuer, part escape by swimming, and others get out again as quick as possible, and trust once more to their wings.

It often happens that this unfortunate little creature, after alternate dips and flights, finding all its exertions of no avail, at last drops on board the vessel, verifying the old remark,

"Incidit in Scyllam, cupiens vitare Charybdim."

There, stunned by the fall, it beats the deck with its tail and dies. When eating it, you would take it for a fresh herring. The largest measure from fourteen to fifteen inches in length. The dolphin, after pursuing it to the ship, sometimes forfeits his own life.

In days of yore, the musician used to play in softest, sweetest strain, and then take an airing amongst the dolphins; "inter delphinas Arion." But nowadays, our tars have quite capsized the custom; and instead of riding ashore on the dolphin, they invite the dolphin aboard. While he is darting and playing around the vessel, a sailor goes out to the spritsailyard-arm, and with a long staff, leaded at one end, and armed at the other with five barbed spikes, he heaves it at him. If successful in his aim, there is a fresh mess for all hands. The dying dolphin affords a superb and brilliant sight:

"Mille trahit moriens, adverso sole colores."

All the colours of the rainbow pass and repass in rapid succession over his body, till the dark hand of death closes the scene.

From the Cape de Verd islands to the coast of Brazil, you see several different kinds of gulls, which probably are bred in the island of St. Paul. Sometimes the large bird called the Frigate Pelican soars majestically over the vessel, and the Tropic-Bird comes near enough to let you have a fair view of the long feathers in his tail. On the line, when it is calm, Sharks of a tremendous size make their appearance. They are descried from the ship by means of the dorsal fin, which is above the water.

On entering the bay of Pernambuco, the Frigate Pelican is seen watching the shoals of fish from a prodigious height. It seldom descends without a successful attack on its numerous prey below.

As you approach the shore, the view is charming. The hills are clothed with wood, gradually rising towards the interior, none of them of any considerable height. A singular reef of rocks runs parallel to the coast, and forms the harbour of Pernambuco. The vessels are moored betwixt it and the town, safe from every storm. You enter the harbour through a very narrow passage, close by a fort built on the reef. The hill of Olinda, studded with houses and convents, is on your right hand, and an island thickly planted with cocoa-nut trees, adds considerably to the scene on your left. There are two strong forts on the isthmus, betwixt Olinda and Pernambuco, and a pillar midway to aid the pilot.

Pernambuco probably contains upwards of fifty thousand souls. It stands on a flat, and is divided into three parts—a peninsula, an island, and the continent. Though within a few degrees of the line, its climate is remarkably salubrious, and rendered almost temperate by the refreshing sea breeze. Had art and judgment contributed their portion to its natural advantages, Pernambuco at this day, would have been a stately ornament to the coast of Brazil. On viewing it, it will strike you that every one has built his house entirely for himself, and deprived public convenience of the little claim she had a right to put in. You would wish that this city, so famous for its harbour, so happy in its climate, and so well situated for commerce, could have risen under the flag of Dido, in lieu of that of Braganza.

As you walk down the streets, the appearance of the houses is not much in their favour. Some of them are very high, and some very low; some newly whitewashed, and others stained, and mouldy, and neglected, as though they had no owner.

The balconies, too, are of a dark and gloomy appearance. They are not, in general, open, as in most tropical cities, but grated like a farmer's dairy window, though somewhat closer.

There is a lamentable want of cleanliness in the streets. The impurities from the houses, and the accumulation of litter from the beasts of burden, are unpleasant sights to the passing stranger. He laments the want of a police as he goes along; and when the wind begins to blow, his nose and eyes are too often exposed to a cloud of very unsavoury dust.

When you view the port of Pernambuco, full of ships of all nations, when you know that the richest commodities of Europe, Africa, and Asia, are brought to it; when you see immense quantities of cotton, dye-wood, and the choicest fruits pouring into the town, you are apt to wonder at the little attention these people pay to the common comforts which one always expects to find in a large and opulent city. However, if the inhabitants are satisfied, there is

nothing more to be said. Should they ever be convinced
that inconveniences exist, and that nuisances are too frequent, the remedy is in their own hands. At present, certainly, they seem perfectly regardless of them ; and the Captain-General of Pernambuco walks through the streets with
as apparent content and composure as an English statesman
would proceed down Charing-cross. Custom reconciles
everything. In a week or two the stranger himself begins
to feel less the things which annoyed him so much upon
his first arrival, and after a few months' residence, he thinks
no more about them, while he is partaking of the hospitality, and enjoying the elegance and splendour within
doors in this great city.

Close by the river-side stands what is called the palace
of the Captain-General of Pernambuco. Its form and appearance altogether strike the traveller that it was never
intended for the use it is at present put to.

Reader, throw a veil over thy recollection for a little
while, and forget the cruel, unjust, and unmerited censures
thou hast heard against an unoffending order. This palace
was once the Jesuits' college, and originally built by those
charitable fathers. Ask the aged and respectable inhabitants of Pernambuco, and they will tell thee that the destruction of the Society of Jesus was a terrible disaster
to the public, and its consequences severely felt to the
present day.

When Pombal took the reins of power into his own
hands, virtue and learning beamed bright within the college walls. Public catechism to the children, and religious
instruction to all, flowed daily from the mouths of its
venerable priests.

They were loved, revered, and respected throughout the
whole town. The illuminating philosophers of the day had
sworn to exterminate Christian knowledge, and the college

of Pernambuco was doomed to founder in the general storm. To the long-lasting sorrow and disgrace of Portugal, the philosophers blinded her king and flattered her prime minister. Pombal was exactly the tool these sappers of every public and private virtue wanted. He had the naked sword of power in his own hand, and his heart was as hard as flint. He struck a mortal blow, and the Society of Jesus, throughout the Portuguese dominions, was no more.

One morning all the fathers of the college in Pernambuco, some of them very old and feeble, were suddenly ordered into the refectory. They had notice beforehand of the fatal storm, in pity from the governor, but not one of them abandoned his charge. They had done their duty, and had nothing to fear. They bowed with resignation to the will of Heaven. As soon as they had all reached the refectory, they were there locked up, and never more did they see their rooms, their friends, their scholars, or acquaintance. In the dead of the following night, a strong guard of soldiers literally drove them through the streets to the water's edge. They were then conveyed in boats aboard a ship, and steered for Bahia. Those who survived the barbarous treatment they experienced from Pombal's creatures were at last ordered to Lisbon. The college of Pernambuco was plundered, and some time after an elephant was kept there.

Thus the arbitrary hand of power, in one night, smote and swept away the sciences ; to which succeeded the low vulgar buffoonery of a showman. Virgil and Cicero made way for a wild beast from Angola! and now a guard is on duty at the very gate where, in times long past, the poor were daily fed !!!

Trust not, kind reader, to the envious remarks which their enemies have scattered far and near ; believe not the stories of those who have had a hand in the sad tragedy.

Go to Brazil, and see with thine own eyes the effect of Pombal's short-sighted policy. There vice reigns triumphant, and learning is at its lowest ebb. Neither is this to be wondered at. Destroy the compass, and will the vessel find her far-distant port? Will the flock keep together, and escape the wolves, after the shepherds are all slain? The Brazilians were told that public education would go on just as usual. They might have asked government, who so able to instruct our youth as those whose knowledge is proverbial? who so fit, as those who enjoy our entire confidence? who so worthy, as those whose lives are irreproachable.

They soon found that those who succeeded the fathers of the Society of Jesus had neither their manners nor their abilities. They had not made the instruction of youth their particular study. Moreover, they entered on the field after a defeat, where the officers had all been slain; where the plan of the campaign was lost; where all was in sorrow and dismay. No exertions of theirs could rally the dispersed, or skill prevent the fatal consequences. At the present day, the seminary of Olinda, in comparison with the former Jesuits' college, is only as the waning moon's beam to the sun's meridian splendour.

When you visit the places where those learned fathers once flourished, and see with your own eyes the evils their dissolution has caused; when you hear the inhabitants telling you how good, how clever, how charitable they were; what will you think of our poet laureate for calling them, in his " History of Brazil," " Missioners, whose zeal the most fanatical was directed by the coolest policy " ?

Was it *fanatical* to renounce the honours and comforts of this transitory life, in order to gain eternal glory in the next, by denying themselves, and taking up the cross? Was it *fanatical* to preach salvation to innumerable wild

hordes of Americans? to clothe the naked? to encourage
the repenting sinner? to aid the dying Christian. The
fathers of the Society of Jesus did all this. And for this
their zeal is pronounced to be the most fanatical, directed
by the coolest policy. It will puzzle many a clear brain to
comprehend how it is possible, in the nature of things,
that zeal the most *fanatical* should be directed by the
coolest policy. Ah, Mr. Laureate, Mr. Laureate, that
" quidlibet audendi " of yours, may now and then gild the
poet, at the same time that it makes the historian cut a
sorry figure !

Could Father Nobrega rise from the tomb, he would
thus address you :—" Ungrateful Englishman, you have
drawn a great part of your information from the writings
of the Society of Jesus, and in return you attempt to
stain its character by telling your countrymen that ' we
taught the idolatry we believed !' In speaking of me, you
say, it was my happy fortune to be stationed in a country
where *none* but the good principles of my order were called
into action. Ungenerous laureate, the narrow policy of the
times has kept your countrymen in the dark with regard to
the true character of the Society of Jesus; and you draw
the bandage still tighter over their eyes by a malicious in-
sinuation. I lived, and taught, and died in Brazil, where
you state that *none* but the good principles of my order
were called into action, and still, in most absolute contra-
diction to this, you remark we believed the *idolatry* we
taught in Brazil. Thus we brought none but good principles into action, and still taught idolatry !

" Again, you state there is no individual to whose talents
Brazil is so greatly and permanently indebted as mine, and
that I must be regarded as the founder of that system so
successfully pursued by the Jesuits in Paraguay ; a system
productive of as much good as is compatible with pious

fraud. Thus you make me, at one and the same time, a teacher of none but good principles, and a teacher of idolatry, and a believer in idolatry, and still the founder of a system for which Brazil is greatly and permanently indebted to me, though, by the by, the system was only productive of as much good as is compatible with pious fraud!

"What means all this? After reading such incomparable nonsense, should your countrymen wish to be properly informed concerning the Society of Jesus, there are in England documents enough to show that the system of the Jesuits was a system of Christian charity towards their fellow-creatures, administered in a manner which human prudence judged best calculated to ensure success; and that the idolatry which you uncharitably affirm they taught, was really and truly the very same faith which the Catholic Church taught for centuries in England, which she still teaches to those who wish to hear her, and which she will continue to teach, pure and unspotted, till time shall be no more."

The environs of Pernambuco are very pretty. You see country houses in all directions, and the appearance of here and there a sugar plantation enriches the scenery. Palm-trees, Cocoa-nut-trees, Orange and Lemon groves, and all the different fruits peculiar to Brazil, are here in the greatest abundance.

At Olinda there is a national botanical garden; it wants space, produce, and improvement. The forests, which are several leagues off, abound with birds, beasts, insects, and serpents. Besides a brilliant plumage, many of the birds have a very fine song. The Troupiale, noted for its rich colours, sings delightfully in the environs of Pernambuco. The Red-headed Finch, larger than the European sparrow, pours forth a sweet and varied strain, in company with two species of wrens, a little before daylight. There are also several species of the thrush, which have a song somewhat different from that of the European thrush; and two species of the linnet, whose strain is so soft and sweet that it dooms them to captivity in the houses. A bird called here Sangre do Buey, blood of the ox, cannot fail to engage your attention: he is of the passerine tribe, and very common about the houses; the wings and tail are black, and every other part of the body a flaming red. In Guiana, there is a species exactly the same as this in shape, note, and economy, but different in colour, its whole body being like black velvet; on its breast a tinge of red appears through the black. Thus nature has ordered this little Tangara to put on mourning to the north of the line, and wear scarlet to the south of it.

For three months in the year the environs of Pernambuco are animated beyond description. From November to March the weather is particularly fine; then it is that rich and poor, young and old, foreigners and natives, all issue from the city to enjoy the country, till Lent approaches, when back they hie them. Villages and hamlets, where nothing before but rags was seen, now shine in all the elegance of dress; every house, every room, every shed become eligible places for those whom nothing but extreme necessity could have forced to live there a few weeks ago: some join in the merry dance, others saunter up and down the orange-groves; and towards evening the roads become a moving scene of silk and jewels. The gaming-tables have constant visitors; there, thousands are daily and nightly lost and won; parties even sit down to try their luck round the outside of the door as well as in the room:—

"Vestibulum ante ipsum primisque in faucibus aulæ
Luctus et ultrices, posuere sedilia curæ."

About six or seven miles from Pernambuco stands a pretty little village called Monteiro; the river runs close by it, and its rural beauties seem to surpass all others in the neighbourhood; there the Captain-General of Pernambuco resides during this time of merriment and joy.

The traveller who allots a portion of his time to peep at his fellow-creatures in their relaxations, and accustoms himself to read their several little histories in their looks and gestures as he goes musing on, may have full occupation for an hour or two every day at this season amid the variegated scenes around the pretty village of Monteiro. In the evening groups sitting at the door, he may sometimes see with a sigh how wealth and the prince's favour cause a booby to pass for a Solon, and be reverenced as such, while perhaps a poor neglected Camoens stands silent at a distance, awed by the dazzling glare of wealth and power. Retired from the public road he may see poor Maria sitting under a palm-tree, with her elbow in her lap, and her head leaning on one side within her hand, weeping over her forbidden bans. And as he moves on " with wandering step and slow," he may hear a broken-hearted nymph ask her faithless swain,—

> " How could you say my face was fair,
>   And yet that face forsake ?
> How could you win my virgin heart,
>   Yet leave that heart to break ?"

One afternoon, in an unfrequented part not far from Monteiro, these adventures were near being brought to a speedy and a final close: six or seven blackbirds, with a white spot betwixt the shoulders, were making a noise, and passing to and fro on the lower branches of a tree in an abandoned, weed-grown, orange orchard. In the long grass underneath the tree, apparently a pale green grasshopper was fluttering, as though it had got entangled in it. When you once fancy that the thing you are looking at is really what you take it for, the more you look at it the more you are convinced it is so. In the present case, this was a grasshopper beyond all doubt, and nothing more remained to be done but to wait in patience till it had settled, in order that you might run no risk of breaking its legs in attempting to lay hold of it while it was fluttering—it still kept fluttering; and having quietly approached it, intending to make sure of it—behold, the head of a large rattlesnake appeared in the grass close by : an instantaneous spring backwards prevented fatal consequences. What had been taken for a grasshopper was, in fact, the elevated rattle of the snake in the act of announcing that he was quite prepared, though unwilling, to make a sure and deadly spring. He shortly after passed slowly from under the orange-tree to the neighbouring wood on the side of a hill : as he moved over a place bare of grass and weeds, he appeared to be about eight feet long ; it was he who had engaged the attention of the birds, and made them heedless of danger from another quarter : they flew away on his retiring ; one alone left his little life in the air, destined to become a specimen, mute and motionless, for the inspection of the curious in a far distant clime.

It was now the rainy season ; the birds were moulting ; fifty-eight specimens of the handsomest of them in the neighbourhood of Pernambuco had been collected ; and it was time to proceed elsewhere. The conveyance to the interior was by horses ; and this mode, together with the heavy rains, would expose preserved specimens to almost certain damage. The journey to Maranham by land would take at least forty days. The route was not wild enough to engage the attention of an explorer, or civilized enough to afford common comforts to a traveller. By sea there

were no opportunities, except slave ships.   As the trans-
porting poor negroes from port to port for sale pays well in
Brazil, the ships' decks are crowded with them.   This
would not do.

Excuse here, benevolent reader, a small tribute of gratitude to an Irish family, whose urbanity and goodness have
long gained it the esteem and respect of all ranks in
Pernambuco.   The kindness and attention I received
from Dennis Kearney, Esq., and his amiable lady, will
be remembered with gratitude to my dying day.

After wishing farewell to this hospitable family, I embarked on board a Portuguese brig, with poor accommodation, for Cayenne in Guiana.   The most eligible bed-
room was the top of a hen-coop on deck.   Even here, an
unsavoury little beast, called bug, was neither shy nor
deficient in appetite.

The Portuguese seamen are famed for catching fish.   One
evening, under the line, four sharks made their appearance
in the wake of the vessel.   The sailors caught them all.

CHAPTER II.

On the fourteenth day after leaving Pernambuco, the
brig cast anchor off the island of Cayenne. The entrance
is beautiful. To windward, not far off, there are two bold
wooded islands, called the Father and Mother; and near
them are others, their children, smaller, though as beautiful
as their parents. Another is seen a long way to leeward of
the family, and seems as if it had strayed from home, and
cannot find its way back. The French call it " l'enfant
perdu." As you pass the islands, the stately hills on the
main, ornamented with ever-verdant foliage, show you that
this is by far the sublimest scenery on the sea-coast, from
the Amazons to the Oroonoque. On casting your eye towards Dutch Guiana, you will see that the mountains
become unconnected, and few in number, and long before
you reach Surinam the Atlantic wave washes a flat and
muddy shore.

Considerably to windward of Cayenne, and about twelve
leagues from land, stands a stately and towering rock, called

the Constable.   As nothing grows on it to tempt greedy and
aspiring man to claim it as his own, the sea-fowl rest and
raise their offspring there.   The bird called the Frigate is
ever soaring round its rugged summit.   Hither the Phaeton
bends his rapid flight, and flocks of rosy Flamingos here
defy the fowler's cunning.   All along the coast, opposite
the Constable, and indeed on every uncultivated part of it
to windward and leeward, are seen innumerable quantities
of Snow-white Egrets, Scarlet Curlews, Spoonbills, and
Flamingos.

Cayenne is capable of being a noble and productive
colony.   At present it is thought to be the poorest on the
coast of Guiana.   Its estates are too much separated one
from the other by immense tracts of forest; and the revo_
lutionary war, like a cold eastern wind, has chilled their
zeal and blasted their best expectations.

The Clove-tree, the Cinnamon, Pepper and Nutmeg, and
many other choice spices and fruits of the eastern and
Asiatic regions, produce abundantly in Cayenne.

The town itself is prettily laid out, and was once well
fortified.   They tell you it might easily have been defended
against the invading force of the two united nations; but
Victor Hugues, its governor, ordered the tri-coloured flag to
be struck; and ever since that day the standard of Braganza
has waved on the ramparts of Cayenne.

He who has received humiliations from the hand of this
haughty, iron-hearted governor, may see him now in Cayenne, stripped of all his revolutionary honours, broken
down and ruined, and under arrest in his own house.   He
has four accomplished daughters, respected by the whole
town.   Towards the close of day, when the sun's rays are
no longer oppressive, these much-pitied ladies are seen
walking up and down the balcony with their aged parent,
trying, by their kind and filial attention, to remove the
settled gloom from his too guilty brow.

This was not the time for a traveller to enjoy Cayenne. The hospitality of the inhabitants was the same as ever, but they had lost their wonted gaiety in public, and the stranger might read in their countenances, as the recollection of recent humiliations and misfortunes every now and then kept breaking in upon them, that they were still in sorrow for their fallen country: the victorious hostile cannon of Waterloo still sounded in their ears: their Emperor was a prisoner amongst the hideous rocks of St. Helena; and many a Frenchman who had fought and bled for France was now amongst them, begging for a little support to prolong a life which would be forfeited on the parent soil. To add another handful to the cypress and wormwood already scattered amongst these polite colonists, they had just received orders from the court of Janeiro to put on deep mourning for six months, and half-mourning for as many more, on account of the death of the Queen of Portugal.

About a day's journey in the interior is the celebrated national plantation. This spot was judiciously chosen, for it is out of the reach of enemies' cruisers. It is called La Gabrielle. No plantation in the western world can vie with La Gabrielle. Its spices are of the choicest kind; its soil particularly favourable to them; its arrangements beautiful; and its directeur, Monsieur Martin, a botanist of first-rate abilities. This indefatigable naturalist ranged through the East, under a royal commission, in quest of botanical knowledge; and during his stay in the western regions has sent over to Europe from twenty to twenty-five thousand specimens, in botany and zoology. La Gabrielle is on a far-extending range of woody hills. Figure to yourself a hill in the shape of a bowl reversed, with the buildings on the top of it, and you will have an idea of the appearance of La Gabrielle. You approach the house through a noble avenue, five hundred toises long, of the choicest tropical fruit-trees, planted with the greatest care and judgment; and should you chance to stray through it, after sunset, when the clove-trees are in blossom, you would fancy yourself in the Idalian groves, or near the banks of the Nile, where they were burning the finest incense as the Queen of Egypt passed.

On La Gabrielle there are twenty-two thousand clove-trees in full bearing. They are planted thirty feet asunder. Their lower branches touch the ground. In general the trees are topped at five-and-twenty feet high; though you will see some here towering up above sixty. The black pepper, the cinnamon, and nutmeg are also in great abundance here, and very productive.

While the stranger views the spicy groves of La Gabrielle, and tastes the most delicious fruits which have been originally imported hither from all parts of the tropical world, he will thank the government which has supported, and admire the talents of the gentleman who has raised to its present grandeur, this noble collection of useful fruits. There is a large nursery attached to La Gabrielle, where plants of all the different species are raised and distributed gratis to those colonists who wish to cultivate them.

Not far from the banks of the river Oyapoc, to windward of Cayenne, is a mountain which contains an immense cavern. Here the Cock of the Rock is plentiful. He is about the size of a fantail pigeon, his colour a bright orange, and his wings and tail appear as though fringed; his head is ornamented with a superb double-feathery crest, edged with purple. He passes the day amid gloomy damps and silence, and only issues out for food a short time at sunrise and sunset. He is of the gallinaceous tribe. The South-American Spaniards call him " Gallo del Rio Negro," (Cock of the Black River,) and suppose that he is only to be met with in the vicinity of that far-inland stream ; but he is common in the interior of Demerara, amongst the huge rocks in the forests of Macoushia ; and he has been shot south of the line, in the captainship of Para.

The bird called by Buffon Grand Gobe-mouche has never been found in Demerara, although very common in Cayenne. He is not quite so large as the jackdaw, and is entirely black, except a large spot under the throat, which is a glossy purple.

You may easily sail from Cayenne to the river Surinam in two days.   Its capital, Paramaribo, is handsome, rich and populous : hitherto it has been considered by far the finest town in Guiana ; but probably the time is not far off when the capital of Demerara may claim the prize of superiority.   You may enter a creek above Paramaribo, and travel through the interior of Surinam, till you come to the Nicari, which is close to the large river Coryntin. When you have passed this river, there is a good public road to New Amsterdam, the capital of Berbice.

On viewing New Amsterdam, it will immediately strike you that something or other has intervened to prevent its arriving at that state of wealth and consequence for which its original plan shows it was once intended.   What has caused this stop in its progress to the rank of a fine and populous city remains for those to find out who are interested in it ; certain it is, that New Amsterdam has been languid for some years, and now the tide of commerce seems ebbing fast from the shores of Berbice.

Gay and blooming is the sister colony of Demerara. Perhaps, kind reader, thou hast not forgot that it was from Stabroek, the capital of Demerara, that the adventurer set out, some years ago, to reach the Portuguese frontier fort, and collect the wourali-poison.   It was not intended, when this second sally was planned in England, to have visited

Stabroek again by the route here described. The plan was to have ascended the Amazons from Para and got into the Rio Negro, and from thence to have returned towards the source of the Essequibo, in order to examine the crystal mountains, and look once more for Lake Parima, or the White Sea; but on arriving at Cayenne, the current was running with such amazing rapidity to leeward, that a Portuguese sloop, which had been beating up towards Para for four weeks, was then only half way. Finding, therefore, that a beat to the Amazons would be long, tedious, and even uncertain, and aware that the season for procuring birds in fine plumage had already set in, I left Cayenne in an American ship for Paramaribo, went through the interior to the Coryntin, stopped a few days in New Amsterdam, and proceeded to Demerara. If, gentle reader, thy patience be not already worn out, and thy eyes half closed in slumber, by perusing the dull adventures of this second sally, perhaps thou wilt pardon a line or two on Demerara; and then we will retire to its forests, to collect and examine the economy of its most rare and beautiful birds, and give the world a new mode of preserving them.

Stabroek, the capital of Demerara, has been rapidly increasing for some years back; and if prosperity go hand in hand with the present enterprising spirit, Stabroek, ere long, will be of the first colonial consideration. It stands on the eastern bank at the mouth of the Demerara, and enjoys all the advantages of the refreshing sea-breeze; the streets are spacious, well bricked, and elevated, the trenches clean, the bridges excellent, and the houses handsome. Almost every commodity and luxury of London may be bought in the shops at Stabroek: its market wants better regulations. The hotels are commodious, clean, and well attended. Demerara boasts as fine and well-disciplined militia as any colony in the western world.

The court of justice, where, in times of old, the bandage was easily removed from the eyes of the goddess, and her scales thrown out of equilibrium, now rises in dignity under the firmness, talents, and urbanity of Mr. President Rough.

The plantations have an appearance of high cultivation; a tolerable idea may be formed of their value when you know that last year Demerara numbered seventy-two thousand nine hundred and ninety-nine slaves. They made above forty-four million pounds of sugar, near two million gallons of rum, above eleven million pounds of coffee, and three million eight hundred and nineteen thousand five hundred and twelve pounds of cotton; the receipt into the public chest was five hundred and fifty-three thousand nine hundred and fifty-six guilders; the public expenditure, four hundred and fifty-one thousand six hundred and three guilders.

Slavery can never be defended; he whose heart is not of iron can never wish to be able to defend it: while he heaves a sigh for the poor negro in captivity, he wishes from his soul that the traffic had been stifled in its birth; but, unfortunately, the governments of Europe nourished it, and now that they are exerting themselves to do away the evil, and ensure liberty to the sons of Africa, the situation of the plantation slaves is depicted as truly deplorable, and their condition wretched. It is not so. A Briton's heart, proverbially kind and generous, is not changed by climate, or its streams of compassion dried up by the scorching heat of a Demerara sun; he cheers his negroes in labour, comforts them in sickness, is kind to them in old age, and never forgets that they are his fellow-creatures.

Instances of cruelty and depravity certainly occur here as well as all the world over; but the edicts of the colonial government are well calculated to prevent them; and the British planter, except here and there one, feels for the wrongs done to a poor ill-treated slave, and shows that his heart grieves for him by causing immediate redress, and preventing a repetition.

Long may ye flourish, peaceful and liberal inhabitants of Demerara ! Your doors are ever open to harbour the harbourless ; your purses never shut to the wants of the distressed : many a ruined fugitive from the Oroonoque will bless your kindness to him in the hour of need, when flying from the woes of civil discord, without food or raiment, he begged for shelter underneath your roof. The poor sufferer in Trinidad, who lost his all in the devouring flames, will remember your charity to his latest moments. The traveller, as he leaves your port, casts a longing, lingering look behind ; your attentions, your hospitality, your pleasantry and mirth, are uppermost in his thoughts : your prosperity is close to his heart. Let us now, gentle reader, retire from the busy scenes of man, and journey on towards the wilds in quest of the feathered tribe.

Leave behind you your high-seasoned dishes, your wines and your delicacies ; carry nothing but what is necessary for your own comfort and the object in view, and depend upon the skill of an Indian, or your own, for fish and game. A sheet, about twelve feet long, ten wide, painted, and with loop-holes on each side, will be of great service ; in a few minutes you can suspend it betwixt two trees in the shape of a roof. Under this, in your hammock, you -may defy the pelting shower, and sleep heedless of the dews of night. A hat, a shirt, and a light pair of trousers, will be all the raiment you require. Custom will soon teach you to tread lightly and barefoot on the little inequalities of the ground, and show you how to pass on, unwounded, amid the mantling briers.

Snakes in these wilds are certainly an annoyance, though perhaps more in imagination than reality ; for you must recollect that the serpent is never the first to offend; his poisonous fang was not given him for conquest: he never inflicts a wound with it but to defend existence. Provided you walk cautiously, and do not absolutely touch him, you may pass in safety close by him.   As he is often coiled up on the ground, and amongst the branches of the trees above you, a degree of circumspection is necessary, lest you unwarily disturb him.

Tigers are too few, and too apt to fly before the noble face of man, to require a moment of your attention.

The bite of the most noxious of the insects, at the very worst, only causes a transient fever, with a degree of pain more or less.

Birds in general, with few exceptions, are not common in the very remote parts of the forest.   The sides of rivers, lakes, and creeks, the borders of savannas, the old abandoned habitations of Indians and woodcutters, seem to be their favourite haunts.

Though least in size, the glittering mantle of the Humming-bird entitles it to the first place in the list of the birds of the new world.   It may truly be called the Bird of Paradise; and had it existed in the old world, it would have claimed the title instead of the bird which has now the honour to bear it :—see it darting through the air almost as quick as thought!—now it is within a yard of your face !—in an instant gone !—now it flutters from flower to flower to sip the silver dew—it is now a ruby—now a topaz—now an emerald—now all burnished gold !   It would be arrogant to pretend to describe this winged gem of nature after Buffon's elegant description of it.

Cayenne and Demerara produce the same humming-birds. Perhaps you would wish to know something of their haunts.   Chiefly in the months of July and August the tree called Bois Immortel, very common in Demerara, bears abundance of red blossom, which stays on the tree some weeks; then it is that most of the different species of humming-birds are very plentiful. The wild red sage is also their favourite shrub, and they buzz like bees round the blossom of the wallaba-tree. Indeed, there is scarce a flower in the interior, or on the sea-coast, but what receives frequent visits from one or other of the species.

On entering the forests, on the rising land in the interior, the blue and green, the smallest brown, no bigger than the humblebee, with two long feathers in the tail, and the little forked-tail purple-throated humming-birds, glitter before you in ever-changing attitudes. One species alone never shows his beauty to the sun; and were it not for his lovely shining colours, you might almost be tempted to class him with the goatsuckers on account of his habits. He is the largest of all the humming-birds, and is all red and changing gold green, except the head, which is black. He has two long feathers in the tail, which cross each other, and these have gained him the name of Karabimiti, or Ara humming-bird, from the Indians. You never find him on the sea-coast, or where the river is salt, or in the heart of the forest, unless fresh water be there. He keeps close by the side of woody fresh-water rivers and dark and lonely creeks. He leaves his retreat before sunrise to feed on the insects over the water; he returns to it as soon as the sun's rays cause a glare of light, is sedentary all day long, and comes out again for a short time after sunset. He builds his nest on a twig over the water in the unfrequented creeks; it looks like tanned cow-leather.

As you advance towards the mountains of Demerara, other species of humming-birds present themselves before you. It seems to be an erroneous opinion that the humming-bird lives entirely on honey-dew. Almost every flower of the tropical climate contains insects of one kind

or other; now, the humming-bird is most busy about the
flowers an hour or two after sunrise and after a shower of
rain, and it is just at this time that the insects come out to
the edge of the flower in order that the sun's rays may
dry the nocturnal dew and rain which they have received.
On opening the stomach of the humming-bird, dead insects
are almost always found there.

Next to the humming-birds, the Cotingas display the
gayest plumage. They are of the order of Passeres, and
you number five species betwixt the sea-coast and the rock
Saba. Perhaps the Scarlet Cotinga is the richest of the five,
and is one of those birds which are found in the deepest
recesses of the forest. His crown is flaming red; to this
abruptly succeeds a dark shining brown, reaching half way
down the back : the remainder of the back, the rump, and
tail, the extremity of which is edged with black, are a
lively red; the belly is a somewhat lighter red; the breast
reddish black; the wings brown. He has no song, is solitary, and utters a monotonous whistle which sounds like
" quet." He is fond of the seeds of the hitia-tree, and
those of the siloabali and bastard-siloabali trees, which
ripen in December, and continue on the trees for above two
months. He is found throughout the year in Demerara ;
still nothing is known of his incubation. The Indians all
agree in telling you that they have never seen his nest.

The Purple-breasted Cotinga has the throat and breast of
a deep purple, the wings and tail black, and all the rest of
the body a most lovely shining blue.

The Purple-throated Cotinga has black wings and tail,
and every other part a light and glossy blue, save the
throat, which is purple.

The Pompadour Cotinga is entirely purple, except his
wings, which are white, their four first feathers tipped with
brown. The great coverts of the wings are stiff, narrow,

and pointed, being shaped quite different from those of any other bird. When you are betwixt this bird and the sun in his flight, he appears uncommonly brilliant. He makes a hoarse noise, which sounds like "Wallababa." Hence his name amongst the Indians.

None of these three cotingas have a song. They feed on the hitia, siloabali, and bastard-siloabali seeds, the wild guava, the fig, and other fruit trees of the forest. They are easily shot in these trees during the months of December, January, and part of February. The greater part of them disappear after this, and probably retire far away to breed. Their nests have never been found in Demerara.

The fifth species is the celebrated Campanero of the Spaniards, called Dara by the Indians, and Bell-bird by the English. He is about the size of the jay. His plumage is white as snow. On his forehead rises a spiral tube nearly three inches long. It is jet black, dotted all over with small white feathers. It has a communication with the palate, and when filled with air, looks like a spire; when empty, it becomes pendulous. His note is loud and clear, like the sound of a bell, and may be heard at the distance of three miles. In the midst of these extensive wilds, generally on the dried top of an aged mora, almost out of gun reach, you will see the campanero. No sound or song from any of the winged inhabitants of the forest, not even the clearly pronounced "Whip-poor-Will," from the goatsucker, cause such astonishment as the toll of the campanero.

With many of the feathered race, he pays the common tribute of a morning and an evening song; and even when the meridian sun has shut in silence the mouths of almost the whole of animated nature, the campanero still cheers the forest. You hear his toll, and then a pause for a minute, then another toll, and then a pause again, and then a toll, and again a pause. Then he is silent for six or eight minutes, and then another toll, and so on. Acteon would stop in mid chace, Maria would defer her evening song, and Orpheus himself would drop his lute to listen to him, so sweet, so novel, and romantic is the toll of the pretty snow-white campanero. He is never seen to feed with the other cotingas, nor is it known in what part of Guiana he makes his nest.

While the cotingas attract your attention by their superior plumage, the singular form of the Toucan makes a lasting impression on your memory. There are three species of toucans in Demerara, and three diminutives, which may be called Toucanets. The largest of the first species frequents the mangrove-trees on the sea-coast. He is never seen in the interior till you reach Macoushia, where he is found in the neighbourhood of the river Tacatou. The other two species are very common. They feed entirely on the fruits of the forest, and though of the pie kind, never kill the young of other birds or touch carrion. The larger is called Bouradi by the Indians, (which means Nose,) the other, Scirou. They seem partial to each other's company, and often resort to the same feeding tree, and retire together to the same shady noon-day retreat. They are very noisy in rainy weather at all hours of the day, and in fair weather, at morn and eve. The sound which the bouradi makes is like the clear yelping of a puppy dog, and you fancy he says " Pia-po-o-co," and thus the South American Spaniards call him Piapoco.

All the toucanets feed on the same trees on which the toucan feeds, and every species of this family of enormous bill, lays its eggs in the hollow trees. They are social, but not gregarious. You may sometimes see eight or ten in company, and from this you would suppose they are gregarious ; but, upon a closer examination, you will find it

has only been a dinner party, which breaks up and dis-
perses towards roosting-time.

You will be at a loss to conjecture for what ends nature
has overloaded the head of this bird with such an enormous bill. It cannot be for the offensive, as it has no need
to wage war with any of the tribes of animated nature;
for its food is fruit and seeds, and those are in superabundance throughout the whole year in the regions where the
toucan is found. It can hardly be for the defensive, as the
toucan is preyed upon by no bird in South America, and
were it obliged to be at war, the texture of the bill is ill
adapted to give or receive blows, as you will see in dissecting it. It cannot be for any particular protection to the
tongue, as the tongue is a perfect feather.

The flight of the toucan is by jerks; in the action of
flying it seems incommoded by this huge disproportioned
feature, and the head seems as if bowed down to the earth
by it against its will; if the extraordinary form and size of
the bill expose the toucan to ridicule, its colours make it
amends. Were a specimen of each species of the toucan
presented to you, you would pronounce the bill of the
bouradi the most rich and beautiful; on the ridge of the
upper mandible a broad stripe of most lovely yellow extends from the head to the point; a stripe of the same
breadth, though somewhat deeper yellow, falls from it at
right angles next the head down to the edge of the mandible; then follows a black stripe, half as broad, falling at
right angles from the ridge, and running narrower along the
edge to within half an inch of the point. The rest of the
mandible is a deep bright red. The lower mandible has no
yellow: its black and red are distributed in the same
manner as on the upper one, with this difference, that
there is black about an inch from the point. The stripe
corresponding to the deep yellow stripe on the upper

mandible is sky blue. It is worthy of remark that all these brilliant colours of the bill are to be found in the plumage of the body, and the bare skin round the eye.

All these colours, except the blue, are inherent in the horn ; that part which appears blue is in reality transparent white, and receives its colour from a thin piece of blue skin inside. This superb bill fades in death, and in three or four days' time has quite lost its original colours.

Till within these few years, no idea of the true colours of the bill could be formed from the stuffed toucans brought to Europe. About eight years ago, while eating a boiled toucan, the thought struck me that the colours in the bill of a preserved specimen might be kept as bright as those in life. A series of experiments proved this beyond a doubt. If you take your penknife and cut away the roof of the upper mandible, you will find that the space betwixt it and the outer shell contains a large collection of veins, and small osseous fibres running in all directions through the whole extent of the bill. Clear away all these with your knife, and you will come to a substance more firm than skin, but of not so strong a texture as the horn itself ; cut this away also, and behind it is discovered a thin and tender membrane; yellow, where it has touched the yellow part of the horn; blue, where it has touched the red part, and black towards the edge and point; when dried, this thin and tender membrane becomes nearly black ; as soon as it is cut away, nothing remains but the outer horn, red and yellow, and now become transparent ; the under mandible must undergo the same operation. Great care must be taken, and the knife used very cautiously when you are cutting through the different parts close to where the bill joins on to the head; if you cut away too much, the bill drops off; if you press too hard, the knife comes through the horn ; if you leave too great a portion of the membrane, it appears through the horn, and by becoming black when dried, makes the horn appear black also, and has a bad effect; judgment, caution, skill, and practice, will ensure success.

You have now cleared the bill of all those bodies which are the cause of its apparent fading; for, as has been said before, these bodies dry in death, and become quite discoloured, and appear so through the horn; and reviewing the bill in this state, you conclude that its former bright colours are lost.

Something still remains to be done. You have rendered the bill transparent by the operation, and that transparency must be done away to make it appear perfectly natural. Pound some clean chalk, and give it enough water till it be of the consistency of tar; add a proportion of gum-arabic to make it adhesive; then take a camel-hair brush, and give the inside of both mandibles a coat; apply a second when the first is dry, then another, and a fourth to finish all. The gum-arabic will prevent the chalk from cracking and falling off. If you remember, there is a little space of transparent white in the lower mandible, which originally appeared blue, but which became transparent white as soon as the thin piece of blue skin was cut away; this must be painted blue inside. When all this is completed, the bill will please you; it will appear in its original colours. Probably your own abilities will suggest a cleverer mode of operating than the one here described. A small gouge would assist the penknife, and render the operation less difficult.

CHAPTER III.

The Houtou.—Curious habit of trimming the tail and feathers—its habits.
—The Guianan Jay.—The Boclora.—Slight attachment of the feathers.
—The Cuia. — Rice-birds.— Cassiques—their habit of mockery.—
Pendulous nests.—Gregarious nesting of different species.—Wood-
peckers of America and England.—Kingfishers.—Jacamars and their
fly-catching habits.—Troupiales and their songs.—Tangaras.—Mani-
kins.—Tiger-birds.—Yawaraciri.—Ant Thrushes.—Parrot of the Sun.
—Aras, or Macaws.—Bitterns.—Egret, Herons, etc.—Goatsuckers. —
Whip-poor-Will.—Superstitions.—Tinamous.—Powis and Maroudi.—
Horned Screamer.—Trumpeter.—King Vulture.—Anhinga.—Dangers
of travel.—Quartan ague.

THE Houtou ranks high in beauty amongst the birds of
Demerara—his whole body is green, with a bluish cast in
the wings and tail ; his crown, which he erects at pleasure,
consists of black in the centre, surrounded with lovely blue
of two different shades : he has a triangular black spot,
edged with blue, behind the eye extending to the ear; and
on his breast a sable tuft, consisting of nine feathers edged
also with blue. This bird seems to suppose that its beauty
can be increased by trimming the tail, which undergoes the
same operation as our hair in a barber's shop, only with
this difference, that it uses its own beak, which is serrated,
in lieu of a pair of scissors ; as soon as his tail is full
grown, he begins about an inch from the extremity of the
two longest feathers in it, and cuts away the web on both
sides of the shaft, making a gap about an inch long : both

male and female Adonise their tails in this manner, which gives them a remarkable appearance amongst all other birds. While we consider the tail of the houtou blemished and defective, were he to come amongst us, he would probably consider our heads, cropped and bald, in no better light. He who wishes to observe this handsome bird in his native haunts, must be in the forest at the morning's dawn. The houtou shuns the society of man: the plantations and cultivated parts are too much disturbed to engage it to settle there; the thick and gloomy forests are the places preferred by the solitary houtou. In those far-extending wilds, about daybreak, you hear him articulate, in a distinct and mournful tone, "Houtou, houtou." Move cautious on to where the sound proceeds from, and you will see him sitting in the underwood, about a couple of yards from the ground, his tail moving up and down every time he articulates "houtou." He lives on insects and the berries amongst the underwood, and very rarely is seen in the lofty trees, except the bastard-siloabali tree, the fruit of which is grateful to him. He makes no nest, but rears his young in a hole in the sand, generally on the side of a hill.

While in quest of the houtou, you will now and then fall in with the Jay of Guiana, called by the Indians Ibibirou. Its forehead is black, the rest of the head white; the throat and breast like the English magpie: about an inch of the extremity of the tail is white, the other part of it, together with the back and wings, a greyish changing purple; the belly is white: there are generally six or eight of them in company; they are shy and garrulous, and tarry a very short time in one place; they are never seen in the cultivated parts.

Through the whole extent of the forest, chiefly from sunrise till nine o'clock in the morning, you hear a sound of "Wow, wow, wow, wow." This is the bird called Boclora by the Indians.   It is smaller than the common pigeon, and seems, in some measure, to partake of its nature : its head and breast are blue ; the back and rump somewhat resemble the colour on the peacock's neck ; its belly is a bright yellow ; the legs are so very short that it always appears as if sitting on the branch ; it is as ill-adapted for walking as the swallow ; its neck, for above an inch all round, is quite bare of feathers, but this deficiency is not seen, for it always sits with its head drawn in upon its shoulders : it sometimes feeds with the cotingas on the guava and hitia trees; but its chief nutriment seems to be insects, and, like most birds which follow this prey, its chaps are well armed with bristles : it is found in Demerara at all times of the year, and makes a nest resembling that of the stock-dove.   This bird never takes long flights, and when it crosses a river or creek it goes by long jerks.

The boclora is very unsuspicious, appearing quite heedless of danger : the report of a gun within twenty yards will not cause it to leave the branch on which it is sitting, and you may often approach it so near as almost to touch it with the end of your bow.   Perhaps there is no bird known whose feathers are so slightly fixed to the skin as those of the boclora.   After shooting it, if it touch a branch in its descent, or if it drop on hard ground, whole heaps of feathers fall off ; on this account it is extremely hard to procure a specimen for preservation.   As soon as the skin is dry in the preserved specimen, the feathers become as well fixed as those in any other bird.

Another species, larger than the boclora, attracts much of your notice in these wilds ; it is called Cuia by the Indians, from the sound of its voice ; its habits are the same as those of the boclora, but its colours different ; its head, breast, back, and rump, are a shining, changing green ; its tail not quite so bright ; a black bar runs across the tail towards the extremity, and the outside feathers are partly white, as in the boclora; its belly is entirely vermilion, a bar of white separating it from the green on the breast.

There are diminutives of both these birds; they have the same habits, with a somewhat different plumage, and about half the size. Arrayed from head to tail in a robe of richest sable hue, the bird called Rice-bird loves spots cultivated by the hand of man. The woodcutter's house on the hills in the interior, and the planter's habitation on the sea-coast, equally attract this songless species of the order of pie, provided the Indian corn be ripe there. He is nearly of the jackdaw's size, and makes his nest far away from the haunts of man; he may truly be called a blackbird: independent of his plumage, his beak, inside and out, his legs, his toes, and claws are jet black.

Mankind, by clearing the ground, and sowing a variety of seeds, induces many kinds of birds to leave their native haunts and come and settle near him; their little depredations on his seeds and fruits prove that it is the property, and not the proprietor, which has the attractions.

One bird, however, in Demerara is not actuated by selfish motives: this is the Cassique; in size, he is larger than the starling; he courts the society of man, but disdains to live by his labours. When nature calls for support, he repairs to the neighbouring forest, and there partakes of the store of fruits and seeds which she has produced in abundance for her aërial tribes. When his repast is over, he returns to man, and pays the little tribute which he owes him for his protection; he takes his station on a tree close to his house; and there, for hours together, pours forth a succession of imitative notes. His own song is sweet, but very short. If a toucan be yelping in the neighbourhood, he drops it, and imitates him. Then he will amuse his protector with the cries of the different species of the woodpecker; and when the sheep bleat, he will distinctly answer them. Then comes his own song again; and if a puppy-dog, or a Guinea-fowl interrupt him, he takes them off admirably, and by his different gestures during the time, you would conclude that he enjoys the sport.

The cassique is gregarious, and imitates any sound he hears with such exactness, that he goes by no other name than that of Mocking-bird amongst the colonists.

At breeding time, a number of these pretty choristers resort to a tree near the planter's house, and from its outside branches weave their pendulous nests. So conscious do they seem that they never give offence, and so little suspicious are they of receiving any injury from man, that they will choose a tree within forty yards from his house, and occupy the branches so low down, that he may peep into the nests. A tree in Waratilla creek affords a proof of this.

The proportions of the cassique are so fine, that he may be said to be a model of symmetry in ornithology. On each wing he has a bright yellow spot, and his rump, belly, and half the tail, are of the same colour. All the rest of the body is black. His beak is the colour of sulphur, but it fades in death, and requires the same operation as the bill of the toucan to make it keep its colours. Up the rivers, in the interior, there is another cassique, nearly the same size, and of the same habits, though not gifted with its powers of imitation. Except in breeding time you will see hundreds of them retiring to roost, amongst the moca-moca-trees and low shrubs on the banks of the Demerara, after you pass the first island. They are not common on the sea-coast. The rump of this cassique is a flaming scarlet. All the rest of the body is a rich glossy black. His bill is sulphur colour. You may often see numbers of this species weaving their pendulous nests on one side of a tree, while numbers of the other species are busy in forming theirs on the opposite side of the same tree. Though such near neighbours, the females are never observed to kick up a row, or come to blows !

Another species of cassique, as large as a crow, is very common in the plantations. In the morning, he generally repairs to a large tree, and there, with his tail spread over his back, and shaking his lowered wings, he produces notes, which though they cannot be said to amount to a song, still have something very sweet and pleasing in them. He makes his nest in the same form as the other cassiques. It is above four feet long; and when you pass under the tree, which often contains fifty or sixty of them, you cannot help stopping to admire them as they wave to and fro, the sport of every storm and breeze. The rump is chestnut; ten feathers of the tail are a fine yellow, the remaining two, which are the middle ones, are black, and an inch shorter than the others. His bill is sulphur colour; all the rest of the body black, with here and there shades of brown. He has five or six long narrow black feathers on the back of his head, which he erects at pleasure.

There is one more species of cassique in Demerara, which always prefers the forests to the cultivated parts. His economy is the same as that of the other cassiques. He is rather smaller than the last described bird. His body is greenish, and his tail and rump paler than those of the former. Half of his beak is red.

You would not be long in the forests of Demerara without noticing the Woodpeckers. You meet with them feeding at all hours of the day. Well may they do so. Were they to follow the example of most of the other birds, and only feed in the morning and evening, they would be often on short allowance, for they sometimes have to labour three or four hours at the tree before they get to their food. The sound which the largest kind makes in hammering against the bark of the tree, is so loud, that you would never suppose it to proceed from the efforts of a bird. You would take it to be the woodman, with his axe, trying by a sturdy blow, often repeated, whether the tree were sound or not. There are fourteen species here; the largest the size of a magpie, the smallest no bigger than the wren. They are all beautiful; and the greater part of them have their heads ornamented with a fine crest, movable at pleasure.

It is said, if you once give a dog a bad name, whether innocent or guilty, he never loses it. It sticks close to him wherever he goes. He has many a kick and many a blow to bear on account of it; and there is nobody to stand up for him. The woodpecker is little better off. The proprietors of woods, in Europe, have long accused him of injuring their timber, by boring holes in it, and letting in the water, which soon rots it. The colonists in America have the same complaint against him. ˙Had he the power of speech, which Ovid's birds possessed in days of yore, he could soon make a defence. "Mighty lord of the woods," he would say to man, "why do you wrongfully accuse me? why do you hunt me up and down to death for an imaginary offence? I have never spoiled a leaf of your property, much less your wood. Your merciless shot strikes me, at the very time I am doing you a service. But your shortsightedness will not let you see it, or your pride is above examining closely the actions of so insignificant a little bird as I am. If there be that spark of feeling in your breast which they say man possesses, or ought to possess, above all other animals, do a poor injured creature a little kindness, and watch me in your woods only for one day. I never wound your healthy trees. I should perish for want in the attempt. The sound bark would easily

resist the force of my bill : and were I even to pierce
through it, there would be nothing inside that I could
fancy, or my stomach digest. I often visit them, it is
true, but a knock or two convinces me that I must go elsewhere for support; and were you to listen attentively to
the sound which my bill causes, you would know whether
I am upon a healthy or an unhealthy tree. Wood and
bark are not my food. I live entirely upon the insects
which have already formed a lodgement in the distempered
tree. When the sound informs me that my prey is there,
I labour for hours together till I get at it ; and by consuming it, for my own support, I prevent its further depredations in that part. Thus I discover for you your hidden
and unsuspected foe, which has been devouring your wood
in such secrecy, that you had not the least suspicion it was
there. The hole which I make in order to get at the pernicious vermin will be seen by you as you pass under the
tree. I leave it as a signal to tell you that your tree has
already stood too long. It is past its prime. Millions of
insects, engendered by disease, are preying upon its vitals.
Ere long it will fall a log in useless ruins. Warned by
this loss, cut down the rest in time, and spare, O spare the
unoffending woodpecker !"

In the rivers, and different creeks, you number six
species of the Kingfisher. They make their nest in a hole
in the sand on the side of the bank. As there is always
plenty of foliage to protect them from the heat of the sun,
they feed at all hours of the day. Though their plumage
is prettily varied, still it falls far short of the brilliancy displayed by the English kingfisher. This little native of
Britain would outweigh them altogether in the scale of
beauty.

A bird called Jacamar is often taken for a king-fisher,
but it has no relationship to that tribe ; it frequently sits in

the trees over the water, and as its beak bears some resemblance to that of the kingfisher, this may probably account for its being taken for one; it feeds entirely upon insects; it sits on a branch in motionless expectation, and as soon as a fly, butterfly, or moth passes by, it darts at it, and returns to the branch it had just left. It seems an indolent, sedentary bird, shunning the society of all others in the forest. It never visits the plantations, but is found at all times of the year in the woods. There are four species of jacamar in Demerara; they are all beautiful; the largest, rich and superb in the extreme. Its plumage is of so fine a changing blue and golden green, that it may be ranked with the choicest of the humming-birds. Nature has denied it a song, but given a costly garment in lieu of it. The smallest species of jacamar is very common in the dry savannas. The second size, all golden green on the back, must be looked for in the wallaba forest. The third is found throughout the whole extent of these wilds; and the fourth, which is the largest, frequents the interior, where you begin to perceive stones in the ground.

When you have penetrated far into Macoushia, you hear the pretty songster called Troupiale pour forth a variety of sweet and plaintive notes. This is the bird which the Portuguese call the Nightingale of Guiana; its predominant colours are rich orange and shining black, arrayed to great advantage; his delicate and well-shaped frame seems unable to bear captivity. The Indians sometimes bring down troupiales to Stabroek, but in a few months they languish and die in a cage. They soon become very familiar; and if you allow them the liberty of the house, they live longer than in a cage, and appear in better spirits; but, when you least expect it, they drop down and die in epilepsy.

Smaller in size, and of colour not so rich and somewhat differently arranged, another species of troupiale sings melodiously in Demerara. The woodcutter is particularly favoured by him ; for while the hen is sitting on her nest, built in the roof of the woodcutter's house, he sings for hours together close by : he prefers the forests to the cultivated parts.

You would not grudge to stop for a few minutes, as you are walking in the plantations, to observe a third species of troupiale : his wings, tail, and throat are black, all the rest of the body is a bright yellow. There is something very sweet and plaintive in his song, though much shorter than that of the troupiale in the interior.

A fourth species goes in flocks from place to place in the cultivated parts at the time the Indian corn is ripe ; he is all black, except the head and throat, which are yellow ; his attempt at song is not worth attending to.

Wherever there is a wild fig-tree ripe, a numerous species of birds, called Tangara, is sure to be on it. There are eighteen beautiful species here. Their plumage is very rich and diversified ; some of them boast six separate colours ; others have the blue, purple, green, and black so kindly blended into each other, that it would be impossible to mark their boundaries ; while others again exhibit them strong, distinct, and abrupt : many of these tangaras have a fine song. They seem to partake much of the nature of our linnets, sparrows, and finches. Some of them are fond of the plantations ; others are never seen there, pre-ferring the wild seeds of the forest to the choicest fruits planted by the hand of man.

On the same fig-trees to which they repair, and often accidentally up and down the forest, you fall in with four species of Manikin. The largest is white and black, with the feathers on the throat remarkably long : the next in size is half red and half black : the third, black, with a white crown : the fourth, black, with a golden crown, and red feathers at the knee. The half red and half black species is the scarcest. There is a creek in the Demerara called Camouni. About ten minutes from the mouth, you see a common-sized fig-tree on your right hand, as you ascend, hanging over water; it bears a very small fig twice a year. When its fruit is ripe, this manikin is on the tree from morn till eve.

On all the ripe fig-trees in the forest you see the bird called the small Tiger-bird. Like some of our belles and dandies, it has a gaudy vest to veil an ill-shaped body : the throat, and part of the head, are a bright red ; the breast and belly have black spots on a yellow ground; the wings are a dark green, black, and white ; and the rump and tail black and green. Like the manikin, it has no song : it depends solely upon a showy garment for admiration.

Devoid, too, of song, and in a still superber garb, the Yawaraciri comes to feed on the same tree. It has a bar like black velvet from the eyes to the beak ; its legs are yellow; its throat, wings, and tail black ; all the rest of the body a charming blue. Chiefly in the dry savannas, and here and there accidentally in the forest, you see a songless yawaraciri still lovelier than the last: his crown is whitish blue, arrayed like a coat of mail : his tail is black, his wings black and yellow ; legs red ; and the whole body a glossy blue. Whilst roving through the forest, ever and anon you see individuals of the wren species, busy amongst the fallen leaves, or seeking insects at the roots of the trees.

Here, too, you find six or seven species of small birds, whose backs appear to be overloaded with silky plumage, One of these, with a chestnut breast, smoke-coloured backs red tail, white feathers like horns on his head, and white narrow-pointed feather under the jaw, feeds entirely upon ants. When a nest of large, light, brown ants emigrates, one following the other in meandering lines above a mile long, you see this bird watching them, and every now and then picking them up. When they disappear he is seen no more: perhaps this is the only kind of ant he is fond of; when these ants are stirring, you are sure to find him near them. You cannot well mistake the ant after you have once been in its company, for its sting is very severe, and you can hardly shoot the bird and pick it up, without having five or six upon you.

Parrots and Paroquets are very numerous here, and of many different kinds. You will know when they are near you in the forest, not only by the noise they make, but also by the fruits and seeds which they let fall while they are feeding.

The Hia-hia Parrot, called in England the Parrot of the Sun, is very remarkable : he can erect at pleasure a fine radiated circle of tartan feathers quite round the back of his head from jaw to jaw. The fore-part of his head is white; his back, tail, and wings, green; and his breast and belly tartan.

Superior in size and beauty to every parrot of South America, the Ara will force you to take your eyes from the rest of animated nature, and gaze at him : his commanding strength, the flaming scarlet of his body, the lovely variety of red, yellow, blue, and green in his wings, the extraordinary length of his scarlet and blue tail, seem all to join and demand for him the title of "emperor of all the parrots." He is scarce in Demerara till you reach the confines of the Macoushi country; there he is in vast abundance; he mostly feeds on trees of the palm species. When the coucourite-trees have ripe fruit on them, they are covered with this magnificent parrot : he is not shy or wary ; you may take your blow-pipe and quiver of poisoned arrows, and kill more than you are able to carry back to your hut. They are very vociferous, and, like the common parrots, rise up

in bodies towards sunset, and fly two and two to their
place of rest. It is a grand sight in ornithology to see
thousands of aras flying over your head, low enough to let
you have a full view of their flaming mantle. The Indians
find their flesh very good, and the feathers serve for
ornaments in their head-dresses. They breed in the holes
of trees, are easily reared and tamed, and learn to speak
pretty distinctly.

Another species frequents the low lands of Demerara.
He is nearly the size of the scarlet ara, but much inferior
in plumage. Blue and yellow are his predominant colours.

Along the creeks and river sides, and in the wet savannas,
six species of the Bittern will engage your attention. They
are all handsome. The smallest not so large as the English
water-hen.

In the savannas, too, you will sometimes surprise the
snow-white Egrette, whose back is adorned with the plumes
from which it takes its name. Here too the spur-winged
Water-hen, the blue and green Water-hen, and two other
species of ordinary plumage, are found. While in quest
of these, the Blue Heron, the large and small Brown
Heron, the Boat-bill, and Muscovy Duck, now and then
rise up before you.

When the sun has sunk in the western woods, no longer
agitated by the breeze ; when you can only see a straggler
or two of the feathered tribe hastening to join its mate,
already at its roosting-place, then it is that the Goatsucker
comes out of the forest, where it has sat all day long in
slumbering ease, unmindful of the gay and busy scenes
around it. Its eyes are too delicately formed to bear the
light, and thus it is forced to shun the flaming face of day,
and wait in patience till night invites him to partake of the
pleasures her dusky presence brings.

The harmless, unoffending goatsucker, from the time of

Aristotle down to the present day, has been in disgrace with man. Father has handed down to son, and author to author that this nocturnal thief subsists by milking the flocks. Poor injured little bird of night, how sadly hast thou suffered, and how foul a stain has inattention to facts put upon thy character ! Thou hast never robbed man of any part of his property, nor deprived the kid of a drop of milk.

When the moon shines bright, you may have a fair opportunity of examining the goatsucker. You will see it close by the cows, goats, and sheep, jumping up every now and then, under their bellies. Approach a little nearer,— he is not shy, " he fears no danger, for he knows no sin." See how the nocturnal flies are tormenting the herd, and with what dexterity he springs up and catches them, as fast as they alight on the belly, legs, and udder of the animals. Observe how quiet they stand, and how sensible they seem of his good offices, for they neither strike at him, nor hit him with their tail, nor tread on him, nor try to drive him away as an uncivil intruder. Were you to dissect him, and inspect his stomach, you would find no milk there. It is full of the flies which have been annoying the herd.

The prettily mottled plumage of the goatsucker, like that of the owl, wants the lustre which is observed in the feathers of the birds of day. This at once marks him as a lover of the pale moon's nightly beams. There are nine species here. The largest appears nearly the size of the English wood-owl. Its cry is so remarkable, that having once heard it you will never forget it. When night reigns over these immeasurable wilds, whilst lying in your hammock, you will hear this goatsucker lamenting like one in deep distress. A stranger would never conceive it to be the cry of a bird. He would say it was the departing voice of a midnight-murdered victim, or the last wailing of

Niobe for her poor children, before she was turned into
stone. Suppose yourself in hopeless sorrow, begin with a
high loud note, and pronounce, "ha, ha, ha, ha, ha, ha, ha,"
each note lower and lower, till the last is scarcely heard,
pausing a moment or two betwixt every note, and you will
have some idea of the moaning of the largest goatsucker in
Demerara.

Four other species of the goatsucker articulate some
words so distinctly, that they have received their names
from the sentences they utter, and absolutely bewilder the
stranger on his arrival in these parts. The most common
one sits down close by your door, and flies and alights three
or four yards before you, as you walk along the road, cry-
ing, "Who-are-you, who-who-who-are-you?" Another bids
you, "Work-away, work-work-work-away." A third cries,
mournfully, "Willy-come-go. Willy-Willy-Willy-come
go." And high up in the country, a fourth tells you to
"Whip-poor-Will. Whip-whip-whip-poor-Will."

You will never persuade the negro to destroy these birds
or get the Indian to let fly his arrow at them. They are
birds of omen and reverential dread. Jumbo, the demon
of Africa, has them under his command; and they equally
obey the Yabahou, or Demerara Indian devil. They are
the receptacles for departed souls, who come back again to
earth, unable to rest for crimes done in their days of nature;
or they are expressly sent by Jumbo, or Yabahou, to haunt
cruel and hard-hearted masters, and retaliate injuries received from them. If the largest goatsucker chance to
cry near the white man's door, sorrow and grief will soon
be inside; and they expect to see the master waste away
with a slow consuming sickness. If it be heard close to
the negro's or Indian's hut, from that night misfortune sits
brooding over it; and they await the event in terrible
suspense.

You will forgive the poor Indian of Guiana for this. He knows no better; he has nobody to teach him. But shame it is, that in our own civilized country, the black cat and broomstaff should be considered as conductors to and from the regions of departed spirits.

Many years ago I knew poor harmless Mary; old age had marked her strongly, just as he will mark you and me, should we arrive at her years and carry the weight of grief which bent her double. The old men of the village said she had been very pretty in her youth; and nothing could be seen more comely than Mary when she danced on the green. He who had gained her heart, left her for another, less fair, though richer than Mary. From that time she became sad and pensive; the rose left her cheek, and she was never more seen to dance round the May-pole on the green : her expectations were blighted ; she became quite indifferent to everything around her, and seemed to think of nothing but how she could best attend her mother, who was lame, and not long for this life. Her mother had begged a black kitten from some boys who were going to drown it, and in her last illness she told Mary to be kind to it for her sake.

When age and want had destroyed the symmetry of Mary's fine form, the village began to consider her as one who had dealings with spirits ; her cat confirmed the suspicion. If a cow died, or a villager wasted away with an unknown complaint, Mary and her cat had it to answer for. Her broom sometimes served her for a walking-stick ; and if ever she supported her tottering frame with it as far as the May-pole, where once, in youthful bloom and beauty, she had attracted the eyes of all, the boys would surround her, and make sport of her, while her cat had neither friend nor safety beyond the cottage wall. Nobody considered it cruel or uncharitable to torment a witch ; and it is probable, long before this, that cruelty, old age, and want, have worn her out, and that both poor Mary and her cat have ceased to be.

Would you wish to pursue the different species of game, well stored and boundless is your range in Demerara. Here no one dogs you, and afterwards clandestinely inquires if you have a hundred a year in land to entitle you to enjoy such patrician sport. Here no saucy intruder asks if you have taken out a licence, by virtue of which you are allowed to kill the birds which have bred upon your own property. Here

> " You are as free as when God first made man,
> Ere the vile laws of servitude began,
> And wild in woods the noble savage ran."

Before the morning's dawn you hear a noise in the forest, which sounds like " duraquaura " often repeated. This is the Partridge, a little smaller, and differing somewhat in colour from the English partridge ; it lives entirely in the forest, and probably the young brood very soon leave their parents, as you never flush more than two birds in the same place, and in general only one.

About the same hour, and sometimes even at midnight, you hear two species of Maam, or Tinamou, send forth their long and plaintive whistle from the depth of the forest. The flesh of both is delicious. The largest is plumper, and almost equals in size the black cock of Northumberland. The quail is said to be here, though rare.

The Hannaquoi, which some have compared to the pheasant, though with little reason, is very common.

Here are also two species of the Powise, or Hocco, and two of the small wild turkeys called Maroudi ; they feed on the ripe fruits of the forest, and are found in all directions

in these extensive wilds. You will admire the Horned
Screamer as a stately and majestic bird : he is almost the
size of the turkey cock ; on his head is a long slender horn,
and each wing is armed with a strong, sharp, triangular
spur, an inch long.

Sometimes you will fall in with flocks of two or three
hundred Waracabas, or Trumpeters, called so from the
singular noise they produce. Their breast is adorned with
beautiful changing blue and purple feathers ; their head
and neck like velvet ; their wings and back grey, and belly
black. They run with great swiftness, and when domesticated, attend their master in his walks with as much apparent affection as his dog. They have no spurs, but still,
such is their high spirit and activity, that they browbeat
every dunghill fowl in the yard, and force the Guinea birds.
dogs, and turkeys to own their superiority.

If, kind and gentle reader, thou shouldst ever visit these
regions with an intention to examine their productions,
perhaps the few observations contained in these Wanderings may be of service to thee ; excuse their brevity :
more could have been written, and each bird more particularly described, but it would have been pressing too
hard upon thy time and patience.

Soon after arriving in these parts, thou wilt find that the
species here enumerated are only as a handful from a well-
stored granary. Nothing has been said of the Eagles, the
Falcons, the Hawks, and Shrikes ; nothing of the different
species of Vultures, the king of which is very handsome,
and seems to be the only bird which claims regal honours
from a surrounding tribe. It is a fact beyond all dispute,
that when the scent of carrion has drawn together hundreds
of the common vultures, they all retire from the carcass as
soon as the King of the Vultures makes his appearance.
When his majesty has satisfied the cravings of his royal

stomach with the choicest bits from the most stinking and
corrupted parts, he generally retires to a neighbouring tree,
and then the common vultures return in crowds to gobble
down his leavings. The Indians, as well as the whites.
have observed this; for when one of them, who has learned
a little English, sees the king, and wishes you to have a
proper notion of the bird, he says, "There is the governor
of the carrion crows."

Now, the Indians have never heard of a personage in
Demerara higher than that of governor; and the colonists,
through a common mistake, call the vultures carrion crows.
Hence the Indian, in order to express the dominion of this
bird over the common vultures, tells you he is governor of
the carrion crows. The Spaniards have also observed it;
for, through all the Spanish Main, he is called Rey de
Zamuros, King of the Vultures. The many species of Owls,
too, have not been noticed; and no mention made of the
Columbine tribe. The prodigious variety of Water Fowl
on the sea-shore has been but barely hinted at.

There, and on the borders and surface of the inland
waters, in the marshes and creeks, besides the flamingos,
scarlet curlews, and spoonbills, already mentioned, will be
found Greenish-Brown Curlews, Sandpipers, Rails, Coots,
Gulls, Pelicans, Jabirus, Nandapoas, Crabiers, Snipes,
Plovers, Ducks, Geese, Cranes, and Anhingas; most of
them in vast abundance; some frequenting only the sea-
coast, others only the interior, according to their different
natures; all worthy the attention of the naturalist, all
worthy of a place in the cabinet of the curious.

Should thy comprehensive genius not confine itself to
birds alone, grand is the appearance of other objects all
around. Thou art in a land rich in botany and mineralogy,
rich in zoology and entomology. Animation will glow in
thy looks, and exercise will brace thy frame in vigour

The very time of thy absence from the tables of heterogeneous luxury will be profitable to thy stomach, perhaps
already sorely drenched with Londo-Parisian sauces, and a
new stock of health will bring thee an appetite to relish
the wholesome food of the chase; never-failing sleep will
wait on thee at the time she comes to soothe the rest of
animated nature; and, ere the sun's rays appear in the
horizon, thou wilt spring from thy hammock fresh as the
April lark.   Be convinced also, that the dangers and difficulties which are generally supposed to accompany the
traveller in his journey through distant regions, are not
half so numerous or dreadful as they are commonly
thought to be.

The youth who incautiously reels into the lobby of
Drury-lane, after leaving the table sacred to the god of
wine, is exposed to more certain ruin, sickness, and decay,
than he who wanders a whole year in the wilds of Demerara. But this will never be believed; because the disasters
arising from dissipation are so common and frequent in
civilized life, that man becomes quite habituated to them;
and sees daily victims sink into the tomb long before their
time, without ever once taking alarm at the causes which
precipitated them headlong into it.

But the dangers which a traveller exposes himself to in
foreign parts are novel, out of the way things to a man at
home.   The remotest apprehension of meeting a tremendous tiger, of being carried off by a flying dragon, or having his bones picked by a famished cannibal; oh, that
makes him shudder.   It sounds in his ears like the bursting of a bomb-shell. Thank Heaven, he is safe by his own
fire-side!

Prudence and resolution ought to be the traveller's constant companions.   The first will cause him to avoid a
number of snares which he will find in the path as he

journeys on; and the second will always lend a hand to assist him, if he has unavoidably got entangled in them. The little distinctions which have been shown him at his own home ought to be forgotten when he travels over the world at large; for strangers know nothing of his former merits, and it is necessary that they should witness them before they pay him the tribute which he was wont to receive within his own doors. Thus, to be kind and affable to those we meet, to mix in their amusements, to pay a compliment or two to their manners and customs, to respect their elders, to give a little to their distressed and needy, and to feel, as it were, at home amongst them, is the sure way to enable you to pass merrily on, and to find other comforts as sweet and palatable as those which you were accustomed to partake of amongst your friends and acquaintance in your own native land.

We will now ascend in fancy on Icarian wing, and take a view of Guiana in general. See an immense plain! betwixt two of the largest rivers in the world, level as a bowling-green, save at Cayenne, and covered with trees along the coast quite to the Atlantic wave, except where the plantations make a little vacancy amongst the foliage.

Though nearly in the centre of the torrid zone, the sun's rays are not so intolerable as might be imagined, on account of the perpetual verdure and refreshing north-east breeze. See what numbers of broad and rapid rivers intersect it in their journey to the ocean, and that not a stone or a pebble is to be found on their banks, or in any part of the country, till your eye catches the hills in the interior. How beautiful and magnificent are the lakes in the heart of the forests, and how charming the forests themselves, for miles after miles on each side of the rivers! How extensive appear the savannas or natural meadows, teeming with innumerable herds of cattle, where the Portuguese and Spaniards are settled, but desert as Saara, where the English and Dutch claim dominion! How gradually the face of the country rises! See the sand-hills all clothed in wood first emerging from the level, then hills a little higher, rugged with bold and craggy rocks, peeping out from amongst the most luxuriant timber. Then come plains, and dells, and far-extending valleys, arrayed in richest foliage; and beyond them, mountains piled on mountains, some bearing prodigious forests, others of bleak and barren aspect. Thus your eye wanders on, over scenes of varied loveliness and grandeur, till it rests on the stupendous pinnacles of the long-continued Cordilleras de los Andes, which rise in towering majesty, and command all America.

How fertile must the low-lands be, from the accumulation of fallen leaves and trees for centuries! How propitious the swamps and slimy beds of the rivers, heated by a downward sun, to the amazing growth of alligators, serpents, and innumerable insects! How inviting the forests to the feathered tribes, where you see buds, blossoms, green and ripe fruit, full grown and fading leaves, all on the same tree! How secure the wild beasts may rove in endless mazes! Perhaps those mountains too, which appear so bleak and naked, as if quite neglected, are, like Potosi, full of precious metals.

Let us now return the pinions we borrowed from Icarus, and prepare to bid farewell to the wilds. The time allotted to these Wanderings is drawing fast to a close. Every day for the last six months has been employed in paying close attention to natural history in the forests of Demerara. Above two hundred specimens of the finest birds have been collected, and a pretty just knowledge formed of their haunts and economy. From the time of leaving England, in March, 1816, to the present day, nothing has intervened to arrest a fine flow of health, saving a quartan ague, which did not tarry, but fled as suddenly as it appeared.

And now I take leave of thee, kind and gentle reader. The new mode of preserving birds, heretofore promised thee, shall not be forgotten. The plan is already formed in imagination, and can be penned down during the passage across the Atlantic. If the few remarks in these Wanderings shall have any weight in inciting thee to sally forth and explore the vast and well-stored regions of Demerara, I have gained my end. Adieu.

CHARLES WATERTON.

April 6, 1817.

THIRD JOURNEY.

CHAPTER I.

" Desertosque videre locos, littusque relictum."

GENTLE reader, after staying a few months in England, I
strayed across the Alps and the Apennines, and returned
home, but could not tarry. Guiana still whispered in my
ear, and seemed to invite me once more to wander through
her distant forests.

Shouldst thou have a leisure hour to read what follows,
I pray thee pardon the frequent use of that unwelcome
monosyllable *I.* It could not well be avoided, as will be
seen in the sequel. In February, 1820, I sailed from the
Clyde, on board the *Glenbervie,* a fine West-Indiaman.
She was driven to the north-west of Ireland, and had to
contend with a foul and wintry wind for above a fortnight

At last it changed, and we had a pleasant passage across the Atlantic.

Sad and mournful was the story we heard on entering the river Demerara. The yellow fever had swept off numbers of the old inhabitants, and the mortal remains of many a new comer were daily passing down the streets, in slow and mute procession to their last resting-place.

After staying a few days in the town, I went up the Demerara to the former habitation of my worthy friend, Mr. Edmonstone, in Mibiri creek.

The house had been abandoned for some years. On arriving at the hill, the remembrance of scenes long past and gone naturally broke in upon the mind. All was changed; the house was in ruins, and gradually sinking under the influence of the sun and rain; the roof had nearly fallen in; and the room where once governors and generals had caroused, was now dismantled, and tenanted by the vampire. You would have said,

> " 'Tis now the vampire's bleak abode,
> 'Tis now the apartment of the toad;
> 'Tis here the painful Chegoe feeds,
> 'Tis here the dire Labarri breeds,
> Conceal'd in ruins, moss, and weeds."

On the outside of the house, nature had nearly re-assumed her ancient right: a few straggling fruit-trees were still discernible amid the varied hue of the near approaching forest; they seemed like strangers lost, and bewildered, and unpitied, in a foreign land, destined to linger a little longer, and then sink down for ever.

I hired some negroes from a woodcutter in another creek to repair the roof; and then the house, or at least what remained of it, became head-quarters for natural history. The frogs, and here and there a snake, received that attention which the weak in this world generally experience from the strong, and which the law commonly denominates an ejectment. But here, neither the frogs nor serpents were ill-treated ; they sallied forth, without buffet or rebuke, to choose their place of residence ; the world was all before them. The owls went away of their own accord, preferring to retire to a hollow tree rather than to associate with their new landlord. The bats and vampires stayed with me, and went in and out as usual.

It was upon this hill in former days that I first tried to teach John, the black slave of my friend Mr. Edmonstone, the proper way to do birds. But John had poor abilities, and it required much time and patience to drive anything into him. Some years after this his master took him to Scotland, where, becoming free, John left him, and got employed in the Glasgow, and then the Edinburgh museum Mr. Robert Edmonstone, nephew to the above gentleman, had a fine mulatto capable of learning anything. He requested me to teach him the art. I did so. He was docile and active, and was with me all the time in the forest ; I left him there to keep up this new art of preserving birds, and to communicate it to others. Here then I fixed my head-quarters, in the ruins of this once gay and hospitable house. Close by, in a little hut, which in times long past had served for a store to keep provisions in, there lived a coloured man and his wife, by name Backer. Many a kind turn they did to me ; and I was more than once of service to them and their children, by bringing to their relief in time of sickness what little knowledge I had acquired of medicine.

I would here, gentle reader, wish to draw thy attention, for a few minutes, to physic, raiment, and diet. Shouldst thou ever wander through these remote and dreary wilds, forget not to carry with thee bark, laudanum, calomel, and jalap, and the lancet. There are no druggist shops here, nor sons of Galen to apply to in time of need. I never go encumbered with many clothes. A thin flannel waistcoat under a check shirt, a pair of trousers, and a hat, were all my wardrobe; shoes and stockings I seldom had on. In dry weather they would have irritated the feet, and retarded me in the chase of wild beasts; and in the rainy season they would have kept me in a perpetual state of damp and moisture. I eat moderately, and never drink wine, spirits, or fermented liquors in any climate. This abstemiousness has ever proved a faithful friend; it carried me triumphant through the epidemia at Malaga, where death made such havoc about the beginning of the present century; and it has since befriended me in many a fit of sickness, brought on by exposure to the noon-day sun, to the dews of night, to the pelting shower and unwholesome food.

Perhaps it will be as well, here, to mention a fever which came on, and the treatment of it; it may possibly be of use to thee, shouldst thou turn wanderer in the tropics: a word or two also of a wound I got in the forest, and then we will say no more of the little accidents which sometimes occur, and attend solely to natural history. We shall have an opportunity of seeing the wild animals in their native haunts, undisturbed and unbroken in upon by man. We shall have time and leisure to look more closely at them, and probably rectify some errors which, for want of proper information or a near observance, have crept into their several histories.

It was in the month of June, when the sun was within a few days of Cancer, that I had a severe attack of fever. There had been a deluge of rain, accompanied with tremendous thunder and lightning, and very little sun. Nothing could exceed the dampness of the atmosphere. For two or three days I had been in a kind of twilight state of health, neither ill nor what you may call well; I yawned and felt weary without exercise, and my sleep was merely slumber. This was the time to have taken medicine; but I neglected to do so, though I had just been reading, " O navis referent in mare te novi fluctus, O quid agis? fortiter occupa portum." I awoke at midnight; a cruel headache, thirst, and pain in the small of the back, informed me what the case was. Had Chiron himself been present, he could not have told me more distinctly that I was going to have a tight brush of it, and that I ought to meet it with becoming fortitude. I dozed, and woke, and startled, and then dozed again, and suddenly awoke, thinking I was falling down a precipice.

The return of the bats to their diurnal retreat, which was in the thatch above my hammock, informed me that the sun was now fast approaching to the eastern horizon. I arose, in languor and in pain, the pulse at one hundred and twenty. I took ten grains of calomel and a scruple of jalap, and drank during the day large draughts of tea, weak and warm. The physic did its duty; but there was no remission of fever or headache, though the pain of the back was less acute. I was saved the trouble of keeping the room cool, as the wind beat in at every quarter.

At five in the evening the pulse had risen to one hundred and thirty, and the headache almost insupportable, especially on looking to the right or left. I now opened a vein, and made a large orifice, to allow the blood to rush out rapidly; I closed it after losing sixteen ounces. I then steeped my feet in warm water, and got into the hammock. After bleeding, the pulse fell to ninety, and the head was much relieved; but during the night, which was very restless, the pulse rose again to one hundred and twenty, and at times the headache was distressing. I relieved the headache from time to time by applying cold water to the temples, and holding a wet handkerchief there. The next morning the fever ran very high, and I took five more grains of calomel and ten of jalap, determined, whatever might be the case, this should be the last dose of calomel. About two o'clock in the afternoon the fever remitted, and a copious perspiration came on; there was no more headache, nor thirst, nor pain in the back, and the following night was comparatively a good one. The next morning I swallowed a large dose of castor-oil: it was genuine, for Louisa Backer had made it from the seeds of the trees which grew near the door. I was now entirely free from all symptoms of fever, or apprehensions of a return; and the morning after I began to take bark, and continued it for a fortnight. This put all to rights.

The story of the wound I got in the forest, and the mode of cure, are very short.—I had pursued a red-headed woodpecker for above a mile in the forest, without being able to get a shot at it. Thinking more of the woodpecker, as I ran along, than of the way before me, I trod upon a little hardwood stump, which was just about an inch or so above the ground; it entered the hollow part of my foot, making a deep and lacerated wound there. It had brought me to the ground, and there I lay till a transitory fit of sickness went off. I allowed it to bleed freely, and on reaching headquarters, washed it well and probed it, to feel if any foreign body was left within it. Being satisfied that there was none, I brought the edges of the wound together, and then put a piece of lint on it, and over that a very large poultice, which was changed morning, noon, and night. Luckily, Backer had a cow or two upon the hill: now as heat and moisture are the two principal virtues of a poultice, nothing could produce those two qualities better than fresh cow-dung boiled: had there been no cows there, I could have made it with boiled grass and leaves. I now took entirely to the hammock, placing the foot higher than the knee; this prevented it from throbbing, and was, indeed, the only position in which I could be at ease. When the inflammation was completely subdued, I applied a wet cloth to the wound, and every now and then steeped the foot in cold water during the day, and at night again applied a poultice. The wound was now healing fast, and in three weeks from the time of the accident, nothing but a scar remained; so that I again sallied forth sound and joyful, and said to myself—

> " I, pedes quo te rapiunt et auræ
> Dum favet sol, et locus, i secundo
> Omine, et conto latebras, ut olim,
>   Rumpe ferarum."

Now, this contus was a tough light pole, eight feet long, on the end of which was fixed an old bayonet. I never went into the canoe without it; it was of great use in starting the beasts and snakes out of the hollow trees, and, in case of need, was an excellent defence.

In 1819, I had the last conversation with Sir Joseph Banks. I saw with sorrow that death was going to rob us of him. We talked much of the present mode adopted by all museums in stuffing quadrupeds, and condemned it as being very imperfect: still we could not find out a better way; and at last concluded, that the lips and nose ought to be cut off, and replaced with wax; it being impossible to make those parts appear like life, as they shrink to nothing, and render the stuffed specimens in the different museums horrible to look at. The defects in the legs and feet would not be quite so glaring, being covered with hair.

I had paid great attention to this subject for above fourteen years; still it would not do; however, one night

while I was lying in the hammock, and harping on the
string on which hung all my solicitude, I hit upon the
proper mode by inference; it appeared clear to me that it
was the only true way of going to work, and ere I closed
my eyes in sleep, I was able to prove to myself that there
could not be any other way that would answer.   I tried it
the next day, and succeeded according to expectation.

By means of this process, which is very simple, we can
now give every feature back again to the animal's face,
after it has been skinned; and when necessary, stamp
grief, or pain, or pleasure, or rage, or mildness upon it.
But more of this hereafter.

Let us now turn our attention to the Sloth, whose native
haunts have hitherto been so little known, and probably
little looked into.   Those who have written on this singular animal, have remarked that he is in a perpetual state of
pain, that he is proverbially slow in his movements, that he
is a prisoner in space, and that as soon as he has consumed
all the leaves of the tree upon which he had mounted, he
rolls himself up in the form of a ball, and then falls to the
ground.   This is not the case.

If the naturalists who have written the history of the
sloth had gone into the wilds, in order to examine his
haunts and economy, they would not have drawn the fore-
going conclusions; they would have learned, that though
all other quadrupeds may be described while resting upon
the ground, the sloth is an exception to this rule, and that
his history must be written while he is in the tree.

This singular animal is destined by nature to be produced, to live and to die in the trees; and to do justice to
him, naturalists must examine him in this his upper element.   He is a scarce and solitary animal, and being good
food, he is never allowed to escape.   He inhabits remote
and gloomy forests, where snakes take up their abode, and

where cruelly stinging ants and scorpions, and swamps, and innumerable thorny shrubs and bushes, obstruct the steps of civilised man. Were you to draw your own conclusions from the descriptions which have been given of the sloth, you would probably suspect, that no naturalist has actually gone into the wilds with the fixed determination to find him out and examine his haunts and see whether nature has committed any blunder in the formation of this extraordinary creature, which appears to us so forlorn and miserable, so ill put together, and so totally unfit to enjoy the blessings which have been so bountifully given to the rest of animated nature; for, as it has formerly been remarked, he has no soles to his feet, and he is evidently ill at ease when he tries to move on the ground, and it is then that he looks up in your face with a countenance that says, " Have pity on me, for I am in pain and sorrow."

It mostly happens that Indians and Negroes are the people who catch the sloth, and bring it to the white man : hence it may be conjectured that the erroneous accounts we have hitherto had of the sloth, have not been penned down with the slightest intention to mislead the reader, or give him an exaggerated history, but that these errors have naturally arisen by examining the sloth in those places where nature never intended that he should be exhibited.

However, we are now in his own domain. Man but little frequents these thick and noble forests, which extend far and wide on every side of us. This, then, is the proper place to go in quest of the sloth. We will first take a near view of him. By obtaining a knowledge of his anatomy, we shall be enabled to account for his movements hereafter, when we see him in his proper haunts. His fore-legs, or, more correctly speaking, his arms, are apparently much too long, while his hind-legs are very short, and look as if they could be bent almost to the shape of a corkscrew. Both the fore and hind legs, by their form, and by the manner in which they are joined to the body, are quite incapacitated from acting in a perpendicular direction, or in supporting it on the earth, as the bodies of other quadrupeds are supported, by their legs. Hence, when you place him on the floor, his belly touches the ground. Now, granted that he supported himself on his legs like other animals, nevertheless he would be in pain, for he has no soles to his feet, and his claws are very sharp and long, and curved; so that, were his body supported by his feet it would be by their extremities, just as your body would be, were you to throw yourself on all fours, and try to support it on the ends of your toes and fingers—a trying position. Were the floor of glass, or of a polished surface, the sloth would actually be quite stationary; but as the ground is generally rough, with little protuberances upon it, such as stones, or roots of grass, &c., this just suits the sloth, and he moves his fore-legs in all directions, in order to find something to lay hold of; and when he has succeeded, he pulls himself forward, and is thus enabled to travel onwards, but at the same time in so tardy and awkward a manner, as to acquire him the name of Sloth.

Indeed his looks and his gestures evidently betray his uncomfortable situation; and as a sigh every now and then escapes him, we may be entitled to conclude that he is actually in pain.

Some years ago I kept a sloth in my room for several months. I often took him out of the house and placed him upon the ground, in order to have an opportunity of observing his motions. If the ground were rough, he would pull himself forwards, by means of his fore-legs, at a pretty good pace ; and he invariably immediately shaped his course towards the nearest tree. But if I put him upon a smooth and well-trodden part of the road, he appeared to be in trouble and distress : his favourite abode was the back of a chair : and after getting all his legs in a line upon the topmost part of it, he would hang there for hours together, and often with a low and inward cry, would seem to invite me to take notice of him.

The sloth, in its wild state, spends its whole life in trees, and never leaves them but through force or by accident. An all-ruling Providence has ordered man to tread on the surface of the earth, the eagle to soar in the expanse of the skies, and the monkey and squirrel to inhabit the trees : still these may change their relative situations without feeling much inconvenience : but the sloth is doomed to spend his whole life in the trees ; and, what is more extraordinary, not *upon* the branches, like the squirrel and the monkey, but *under* them. He moves suspended from the branch, he rests suspended from it, and he sleeps suspended from it. To enable him to do this, he must have a very different formation from that of any other known quadruped.

Hence his seemingly bungled conformation is at once accounted for ; and in lieu of the sloth leading a painful life and entailing a melancholy and miserable existence on its progeny, it is but fair to surmise that it just enjoys life as much as any other animal, and that its extra-ordinary formation and singular habits are but further proofs to engage us to admire the wonderful works of Omnipotence.

It must be observed, that the sloth does not hang head-downwards like the vampire. When asleep, he supports himself from a branch parallel to the earth. He first seizes the branch with one arm, and then with the other ; and after that, brings up both his legs, one by one, to the same branch; so that all four are in a line: he seems perfectly at rest in this position.   Now, had he a tail, he would be at a loss to know what to do with it in this position : were he to draw it up within his legs, it would interfere with them ; and were he to let it hang down, it would become the sport of the winds.   Thus his deficiency of tail is a benefit to him; it is merely an apology for a tail, scarcely exceeding an inch and a half in length.

I observed, when he was climbing, he never used his arms both together, but first one and then the other, and so on alternately.   There is a singularity in his hair, different from that of all other animals, and, I believe, hitherto unnoticed by naturalists; his hair is thick and coarse at the extremity, and gradually tapers to the root, where it becomes fine as a spider's web.   His fur has so much the hue of the moss which grows on the branches of the trees, that it is very difficult to make him out when he is at rest.

The male of the three-toed sloth has a longitudinal bar of very fine black hair on his back, rather lower than the shoulder-blades ; on each side of this black bar there is a space of yellow hair, equally fine ; it has the appearance of being pressed into the body, and looks exactly as if it had been singed.   If we examine the anatomy of his fore-legs, we shall immediately perceive by their firm and muscular texture, how very capable they are of supporting the pendent weight of his body, both in climbing and at rest ; and, instead of pronouncing them a bungled com-position, as a celebrated naturalist has done, we shall consider them as remarkably well calculated to perform their extraordinary functions.

As the sloth is an inhabitant of forests within the tropics, where the trees touch each other in the greatest profusion, there seems to be no reason why he should confine himself to one tree alone for food, and entirely strip it of its leaves. During the many years I have ranged the forests, I have never seen a tree in such a state of nudity; indeed, I would hazard a conjecture, that, by the time the animal had finished the last of the old leaves, there would be a new crop on the part of the tree he had stripped first, ready for him to begin again, so quick is the process of vegetation in these countries.

There is a saying amongst the Indians, that when the wind blows, the sloth begins to travel. In calm weather he remains tranquil, probably not liking to cling to the brittle extremity of the branches, lest they should break with him in passing from one tree to another; but as soon as the wind rises, the branches of the neighbouring trees become interwoven, and then the sloth seizes hold of them, and pursues his journey in safety. There is seldom an entire day of calm in these forests. The trade-wind generally sets in about ten o'clock in the morning, and thus the sloth may set off after breakfast, and get a considerable way before dinner. He travels at a good round pace; and were you to see him pass from tree to tree, as I have done, you would never think of calling him a sloth.

Thus, it would appear that the different histories we have of this quadruped are erroneous on two accounts: first, that the writers of them deterred by difficulties and local annoyances, have not paid sufficient attention to him in his native haunts; and secondly, they have described him in a situation in which he was never intended by nature to cut a figure; I mean on the ground. The sloth is as much at a loss to proceed on his journey upon a smooth and level floor, as a man would be who had to walk a mile in stilts upon a line of feather beds.

One day, as we were crossing the Essequibo, I saw a

large two-toed sloth on the ground upon the bank; how he had got there nobody could tell: the Indian said he had never surprised a sloth in such a situation before: he would hardly have come there to drink, for both above and below the place, the branches of the trees touched the water, and afforded him an easy and safe access to it. Be this as it may, though the trees were not above twenty yards from him, he could not make his way through the sand time enough to escape before we landed. As soon as we got up to him he threw himself upon his back, and defended himself in gallant style with his fore-legs. "Come, poor fellow," said I to him, "if thou hast got into a hobble to-day, thou shalt not suffer for it: I'll take no advantage of thee in misfortune; the forest is large enough both for thee and me to rove in: go thy ways up above, and enjoy thyself in these endless wilds; it is more than probable thou wilt never have another interview with man. So fare thee well." On saying this, I took a long stick which was lying there, held it for him to hook on, and then conveyed him to a high and stately mora. He ascended with wonderful rapidity, and in about a minute he was almost at the top of the tree. He now went off in a side direction, and caught hold of the branch of a neighbouring tree; he then proceeded towards the heart of the forest. I stood looking on, lost in amazement at his singular mode of progress. I followed him with my eye till the intervening branches closed in betwixt us; and then I lost sight for ever of the two-toed sloth. I was going to add, that I never saw a sloth take to his heels in such earnest; but the expression will not do, for the sloth has no heels.

That which naturalists have advanced of his being so tenacious of life is perfectly true. I saw the heart of one beat for half an hour after it was taken out of the body.

The wourali-poison seems to be the only thing that will
kill it quickly. On reference to a former part of these
wanderings, it will be seen that a poisoned arrow killed the
sloth in about ten minutes.

So much for this harmless, unoffending animal. He
holds a conspicuous place in the catalogue of the animals
of the new world. Though naturalists have made no
mention of what follows, still it is not less true on that
account. The sloth is the only quadruped known, which
spends its whole life from the branch of a tree, suspended
by his feet. I have paid uncommon attention to him in
his native haunts. The monkey and squirrel will seize a
branch with their fore-feet, and pull themselves up, and
rest or run upon it; but the sloth, after seizing it, still
remains suspended, and suspended moves along under the
branch, till he can lay hold of another. Whenever I have
seen him in his native woods, whether at rest, or asleep, or
on his travels, I have always observed that he was suspended
from the branch of a tree. When his form and anatomy
are attentively considered, it will appear evident that the
sloth cannot be at ease in any situation, where his body
is higher, or above his feet. We will now take our leave
of him.

In the far-extending wilds of Guiana, the traveller will
be astonished at the immense quantity of Ants which he
perceives on the ground and in the trees. They have nests
in the branches, four or five times as large as that of the
rook; and they have a covered way from them to the ground.
In this covered way thousands are perpetually passing and
repassing; and if you destroy part of it, they turn to, and
immediately repair it.

Other species of ants again have no covered way; but
travel, exposed to view, upon the surface of the earth. You
will sometimes see a string of these ants a mile long, each

carrying in its mouth to its nest a green leaf, the size of a sixpence. It is wonderful to observe the order in which they move, and with what pains and labour they surmount the obstructions of the path.

The ants have their enemies, as well as the rest of animated nature. Amongst the foremost of these stand the three species of Ant-bears. The smallest is not much larger than a rat; the next is nearly the size of a fox; and the third a stout and powerful animal, measuring about six feet from the snout to the end of the tail. He is the most inoffensive of all animals, and never injures the property of man. He is chiefly found in the inmost recesses of the forest, and seems partial to the low and swampy parts near creeks, where the troely-tree grows. There he goes up and down in quest of ants, of which there is never the least scarcity; so that he soon obtains a sufficient supply of food, with very little trouble. He cannot travel fast; man is superior to him in speed. Without swiftness to enable him to escape from his enemies, without teeth, the possession of which would assist him in self-defence, and without the power of burrowing in the ground, by which he might conceal himself from his pursuers, he still is capable of ranging through these wilds in perfect safety ; nor does he fear the fatal pressure of the serpent's fold, or the teeth of the famished jaguar. Nature has formed his fore-legs wonderfully thick, and strong, and muscular, and armed his feet with three tremendous sharp and crooked claws. Whenever he seizes an animal with these formidable weapons, he hugs it close to his body, and keeps it there till it dies through pressure, or through want of food. Nor does the ant-bear, in the meantime, suffer much from loss of aliment, as it is a well-known fact, that he can go longer without food than, perhaps, any other animal, except the land-tortoise. His skin is of a texture that perfectly resists the bite of a dog; his hinder parts are protected by thick and shaggy hair, while his immense tail is large enough to cover his whole body.

The Indians have a great dread of coming in contact with the ant-bear; and after disabling him in the chase, never think of approaching him till he be quite dead. It is perhaps on account of this caution, that naturalists have never yet given to the world a true and correct drawing of this singular animal, or described the peculiar position of his fore-feet when he walks or stands. If, in taking a drawing from a dead ant-bear, you judge of the position in which he stands from that of all other terrestrial animals the sloth excepted, you will be in error. Examine only a figure of this animal, in books of natural history, or inspect a stuffed specimen in the best museums, and you will see that the fore-claws are just in the same forward attitude as those of a dog, or a common bear when he walks or stands. But this is a distorted and unnatural position; and in life, would be a painful and intolerable attitude for the ant-bear. The length and curve of his claws cannot admit of such a position. When he walks or stands, his feet have somewhat the appearance of a club-hand. He goes entirely on the outer side of his fore-feet, which are quite bent inwards; the claws collected into a point, and going under the foot. In this position he is quite at ease; while his long claws are disposed of in a manner to render them harmless to him, and are prevented from becoming dull and worn, like those of the dog, which would inevitably be the case, did their points come in actual contact with the ground; for his claws have not that retractile power which is given to animals of the feline species by which they are enabled to preserve the sharpness of their claws on the most flinty path. A slight inspection of the fore-feet of the ant-bear, will immediately convince you of the mistake artists and naturalists have fallen into, by putting his fore-feet in the same position as those of other quadrupeds ; for you will perceive that the whole outer side of his foot is not only deprived of hair, but is hard and callous ; proof positive of its being in perpetual contact with the ground. Now, on the contrary, the inner side of the bottom of his foot is soft and rather hairy.

There is another singularity in the anatomy of the ant-bear, I believe, as yet unnoticed in the page of natural history. He has two very large glands situated below the root of the tongue. From these is emitted a glutinous liquid, with which his long tongue is lubricated when he puts it into the ants' nests. These glands are of the same substance as those found in the lower jaw of the woodpecker. The secretion from them, when wet, is very clammy and adhesive, but on being dried it loses these qualities, and you can pulverize it betwixt your finger and thumb ; so that, in dissection, if any of it has got upon the fur of the animal, or the feathers of the bird, allow it to dry there, and then it may be removed without leaving the least stain behind.

The ant-bear is a pacific animal. He is never the first to begin the attack. His motto may be, " Noli me tangere." As his habits and his haunts differ materially from those of every other animal in the forest, their interests never clash, and thus he might live to a good old age, and die at last in peace, were it not that his flesh is good food. On this account the Indian wages perpetual war against him, and as he cannot escape by flight, he falls an easy prey to the poisoned arrow, shot from the Indian's bow at a distance. If ever he be closely attacked by dogs, he immediately throws himself on his back, and if he be fortunate enough to catch hold of his enemy with his tremendous claws, the invader is sure to pay for his rashness with the loss of life.

We will now take a view of the vampire. As there was a free entrance and exit to the vampire in the loft where I slept, I had many a fine opportunity of paying attention to this nocturnal surgeon. He does not always live on blood. When the moon shone bright, and the fruit of the banana-tree was ripe, I could see him approach and eat it. He would also bring into the loft, from the forest, a green round fruit, something like the wild guava, and about the size of a nutmeg. There was something also, in the blossom of the sawarri nut-tree, which was grateful to him ; for on coming up Waratilla creek, in a moonlight night, I saw several vampires fluttering round the top of the sawarri tree, and every now and then the blossoms, which they had broken off fell into the water. They certainly did not drop off naturally, for on examining several of them, they appeared quite fresh and blooming. So I concluded the vampires pulled them from the tree, either to get at the incipient fruit, or to catch the insects which often take up their abode in flowers.

The vampire, in general, measures about twenty-six inches from wing to wing, extended, though I once killed one which measured thirty-two inches. He frequents old abandoned houses and hollow trees ; and sometimes a cluster of them may be seen in the forest hanging head downwards, from the branch of a tree.

Goldsmith seems to have been aware that the vampire hangs in clusters ; for in the *Deserted Village*, speaking of America, he says,—

"And matted woods, where birds forget to sing,
But silent bats in drowsy clusters cling."

The vampire has a curious membrane, which rises from

the nose, and gives it a very singular appearance. It has been remarked before, that there are two species of vampire in Guiana, a larger and a smaller. The larger sucks men and other animals ; the smaller seems to confine himself chiefly to birds. I learnt from a gentleman, high up in the river Demerara, that he was completely unsuccessful with his fowls, on account of the small vampire. He showed me some that had been sucked the night before, and they were scarcely able to walk.

Some years ago I went to the river Paumaron with a Scotch gentleman, by name Tarbet. We hung our hammocks in the thatched loft of a planter's house. Next morning I heard this gentleman muttering in his hammock, and now and then letting fall an imprecation or two, just about the time he ought to have been saying his morning prayers. " What is the matter, Sir," said I, softly ; " is any thing amiss ? " " What's the matter ? " answered he, surlily ; " why, the vampires have been sucking me to death." As soon as there was light enough, I went to his hammock, and saw it much stained with blood. " There," said he, thrusting his foot out of the hammock, " see how these infernal imps have been drawing my life's blood." On examining his foot, I found the vampire had tapped his great toe : there was a wound somewhat less than that made by a leech ; the blood was still oozing from it ; I conjectured he might have lost from ten to twelve ounces of blood. Whilst examining it, I think I put him into a worse humour by remarking, that an European surgeon would not have been so generous as to have blooded him without making a charge. He looked up in my face, but did not say a word : I saw he was of opinion that I had better have spared this piece of ill-timed levity.

It was not the last punishment of this good gentleman in the river Paumaron. The next night he was doomed to undergo a kind of ordeal unknown in Europe. There is a species of large red ant in Guiana, sometimes called Ranger, sometimes Coushie. These ants march in millions through the country, in compact order, like a regiment of soldiers; they eat up every insect in their march; and if a house obstruct their route, they do not turn out of the way, but go quite through it. Though they sting cruelly when molested, the planter is not sorry to see them in his house; for it is but a passing visit, and they destroy every kind of insect vermin that has taken shelter under his roof.

Now, in the British plantations of Guiana, as well as in Europe, there is always a little temple dedicated to the goddess Cloacina. Our dinner had chiefly consisted of crabs, dressed in rich and different ways. Paumaron is famous for crabs, and strangers who go thither consider them the greatest luxury. The Scotch gentleman made a very capital dinner on crabs; but this change of diet was productive of unpleasant circumstances: he awoke in the night in that state in which Virgil describes Cæleno to have been, viz. "fædissima ventris proluvies." Up he got, to verify the remark,

"Serius aut citius, sedem properamus ad unam."

Now, unluckily for himself, and the nocturnal tranquillity of the planter's house, just at that unfortunate hour, the Coushie Ants were passing across the seat of Cloacina's temple; he had never dreamed of this; and so, turning his face to the door, he placed himself in the usual situation which the votaries of the goddess generally take. Had a lighted match dropped upon a pound of gunpowder, as he afterwards remarked, it could not have caused a greater recoil. Up he jumped, and forced his way out, roaring for help and for a light, for he was worried alive by ten thousand devils. The fact is, he had sat down upon an intervening body of coushie ants. Many of those which escaped being crushed to death, turned again, and, in revenge, stung the unintentional intruder most severely. The watchman had fallen asleep, and it was some time before a light could be procured, the fire having gone out ; in the mean time, the poor gentleman was suffering an indescribable martyrdom, and would have found himself more at home in the Augean stable than in the planter's house.

I had often wished to have been once sucked by the vampire. in order that I might have it in my power to say it had really happened to me. There can be no pain in the operation, for the patient is always asleep when the vampire is sucking him ; and as for the loss of a few ounces of blood, that would be a trifle in the long run. Many a night have I slept with my foot out of the hammock to tempt this winged surgeon, expecting that he would be there; but it was all in vain ; the vampire never sucked me, and I could never account for his not doing so, for we were inhabitants of the same loft for months together.

The armadillo is very common in these forests ; he burrows in the sand-hills like a rabbit. As it often takes a considerable time to dig him out of his hole, it would be a long and laborious business to attack each hole indiscriminately without knowing whether the animal were there or not. To prevent disappointment, the Indians carefully examine the mouth of the hole, and put a short stick down it. Now if, on introducing the stick, a number of mosquitos come out, the Indians know to a certainty that the armadillo is in it : wherever there are no mosquitos in the hole there is no armadillo. The Indian having satisfied himself that the armadillo is there, by the mosquitos which come out, he immediately cuts a long and slender stick, and introduces it into the hole : he carefully observes the line the stick takes, and then sinks a pit in the sand to catch the end of it: this done, he puts it farther into the hole, and digs another pit, and so on, till at last he comes up with the armadillo, which had been making itself a passage in the sand till it had exhausted all its strength through pure exertion. I have been sometimes three quarters of a day in digging out one armadillo, and obliged to sink half a dozen pits, seven feet deep, before I got up to it. The Indians and negroes are very fond of the flesh, but I considered it strong and rank.

On laying hold of the armadillo you must be cautious not to come in contact with his feet: they are armed with sharp claws, and with them he will inflict a severe wound in self-defence: when not molested, he is very harmless and innocent; he would put you in mind of the hare in Gay's fables,—

> "Whose care was never to offend,
> And every creature was her friend."

The armadillo swims well in time of need, but does not go into the water by choice. He is very seldom seen abroad during the day; and when surprised, he is sure to be near the mouth of his hole. Every part of the armadillo is well protected by his shell, except his ears. In life, this shell is very limber, so that the animal is enabled to go at full stretch, or roll himself up into a ball, as occasion may require.

On inspecting the arrangement of the shell, it puts you very much in mind of a coat of armour; indeed it is a natural coat of armour to the armadillo, and being composed both of scale and bone, it affords ample security, and has a pleasing effect.

Often, when roving in the wilds, I would fall in with the Land Tortoise; he too adds another to the list of unoffending animals; he subsists on the fallen fruits of the forest. When an enemy approaches he never thinks of moving, but quietly draws himself under his shell, and there awaits his doom in patience: he only seems to have two enemies who can do him any damage ; one of these is the Boa Constrictor : this snake swallows the tortoise alive, shell and all. But a boa large enough to do this is very scarce, and thus there is not much to apprehend from that quarter ; the other enemy is man, who takes up the tortoise, and carries him away. Man also is scarce in these never-ending wilds, and the little depredations he may commit upon the tortoise will be nothing, or a mere trifle. The tiger's teeth cannot penetrate its shell, nor can a stroke of his paws do it any damage. It is of so compact and strong a nature, that there is a common saying, a London waggon might roll over it and not break it.

Ere we proceed, let us take a retrospective view of the five animals just enumerated ; they are all quadrupeds, and have some very particular mark, or mode of existence, different from all other animals. The sloth has four feet, but never can use them, to support his body on the earth ; they want soles, which are a marked feature in the feet of other animals. The ant-bear has not a tooth in his head, still he roves fearless on, in the same forests with the Jaguar and boa constrictor. The vampire does not make use of his feet to walk, but to stretch a membrane, which enables him to go up into an element where no other quadruped is seen. The armadillo has only here and there a straggling hair, and has neither fur, nor wool, nor bristles, but in lieu of them has received a movable shell, on which are scales very much like those of fishes. The tortoise is oviparous, entirely without any appearance of hair, and is obliged to accommodate itself to a shell which is quite hard and inflexible, and in no point of view whatever obedient to the will or pleasure of the bearer. The egg of the tortoise has a very hard shell, while that of the turtle is quite soft.

CHAPTER II.

IN some parts of these forests I saw the Vanilla growing
luxuriantly. It creeps up the trees to the height of
thirty or forty feet. I found it difficult to get a ripe pod,
as the monkeys are very fond of it, and generally took
care to get there before me. The pod hangs from the
tree in the shape of a little scabbard. Vayna is the
Spanish for a scabbard, and Vanilla for a little scabbard.
Hence the name.

In Mibiri creek there was a cayman of the small species,
measuring about five feet in length ; I saw it in the same
place for months, but could never get a shot at it ; for the
moment I thought I was sure of it, it dived under the
water before I could pull the trigger. At last I got an
Indian with his bow and arrow ; he stood up in the canoe
with his bow ready bent, and as we drifted past the place,
he sent his arrow into the cayman's eye, and killed it
dead. The skin of this little species is much harder and

stronger than that of the large kind : it is good food, and tastes like veal.

My friend, Mr. Edmonstone, had very kindly let me have one of his old negroes, and he constantly attended me ; his name was Daddy Quashi ; he had a brave stomach for heterogeneous food ; it could digest, and relish too, cayman, monkies, hawks, and grubs. The Daddy made three or four meals on this cayman while it was not absolutely putrid, and salted the rest. I could never get him to face a snake ; the horror he betrayed on seeing one was beyond description ; I asked him why he was so terribly alarmed ; he said it was by seeing so many dogs, from time to time, killed by them.

Here I had a fine opportunity of examining several species of the caprimulgus. I am fully persuaded that these innocent little birds never suck the herds ; for when they approach them, and jump up at their udders, it is to catch the flies and insects there. When the moon shone bright, I would frequently go and stand within three yards of a cow, and distinctly see the caprimulgus catch the flies on its udder. On looking for them in the forest, during the day, I either found them on the ground, or else invariably sitting *longitudinally* on the branch of a tree, not *crosswise* like all other birds.

The Wasps' or Maribuntas, are great plagues in these forests, and require the naturalist to be cautious as he wanders up and down. Some make their nests pendent from the branches ; others have them fixed to the underside of a leaf. Now in passing on, if you happen to disturb one of these, they sally forth and punish you severely. The largest kind is blue ; it brings blood where its sting enters, and causes pain and inflammation enough to create a fever. The Indians make a fire under the nest, and after killing or driving away the old ones, they roast the young grubs in the comb and eat them. I tried them once by way of dessert after dinner, but my stomach was offended at their intrusion; probably it was more the idea than the taste that caused the stomach to rebel.

Time and experience have convinced me that there is not much danger in roving amongst snakes and wild beasts, provided only that you have self-command. You must never approach them abruptly; if so, you are sure to pay for your rashness; because the idea of self-defence is predominant in every animal, and thus the snake, to defend himself from what he considers an attack upon him, makes the intruder feel the deadly effect of his poisonous fangs. The jaguar flies at you and knocks you senseless with a stroke of his paw : whereas, if you had not come upon him too suddenly, it is ten to one but that he had retired, in lieu of disputing the path with you. The labarri snake is very poisonous, and I have often approached within two yards of him without fear. I took care to move very softly and gently without moving my arms, and he always allowed me to have a fine view of him, without showing the least inclination to make a spring at me. He would appear to keep his eye fixed on me, as though suspicious, but that was all. Sometimes I have taken a stick ten feet long, and placed it on the labarri's back. He would then glide away without offering resistance. But when I put the end of the stick abruptly to his head, he immediately opened his mouth, flew at it, and bit it.

One day, wishful to see how the poison comes out of the fangs of the snake, I caught a labarri alive. He was about eight feet long. I held him by the neck, and my hand was so near his jaw, that he had not room to move his head to bite it. This was the only position I could have held him in with safety and effect. To do so, it only required a little resolution and coolness. I then took a small piece of stick in the other hand, and pressed it against the fang, which is invariably in the upper jaw. Towards the point of the fang, there is a little oblong aperture on the convex side of it. Through this, there is a communication down the fang to the root, at which lies a little bag containing the poison. Now, when the point of the fang is pressed, the root of the fang also presses against the bag, and sends up a portion of the poison therein contained. Thus, when I applied a piece of stick to the point of the fang, there came out of the hole a liquor thick and yellow, like strong camomile tea. This was the poison which is so dreadful in its effects, as to render the labarri snake one of the most poisonous in the forests of Guiana. I once caught a fine labarri, and made it bite itself. I forced the poisonous fang into its belly. In a few minutes I thought it was going to die, for it appeared dull and heavy. However, in half an hour's time, he was as brisk and vigorous as ever, and in the course of the day showed no symptoms of being affected. Is then the life of the snake proof against its own poison ? This subject is not unworthy of the consideration of the naturalist.

In Guiana there is a little insect in the grass and on the shrubs, which the French call Bête-rouge. It is of a beautiful scarlet colour, and so minute, that you must bring your eye close to it before you can perceive it. It is most numerous in the rainy season. Its bite causes an intoler·able itching. The best way to get rid of it, is to rub the part affected with oil or rum. You must be careful not to scratch it. If you do so, and break the skin, you expose yourself to a sore. The first year I was in Guiana, the bête-rouge, and my own want of knowledge, and, I may add, the little attention I paid to it, created an ulcer above the ankle, which annoyed me for six months, and if I hobbled out into the grass, a number of bête-rouge would settle on the edges of the sore, and increase the inflammation.

Still more inconvenient, painful, and annoying is another little pest, called the Chegoe. It looks exactly like a very small flea, and a stranger would take it for one. However, in about four and twenty hours, he would have several broad hints that he had made a mistake in his ideas of the animal. It attacks different parts of the body, but chiefly the feet, betwixt the toe-nails and the flesh. There it buries itself, and at first causes an itching not unpleasant. In a day or so, after examining the part, you perceive a place about the size of a pea, somewhat discoloured, rather of a blue appearance. Sometimes it happens that the itching is so trivial, you are not aware that the miner is at work. Time, they say, makes great discoveries. The discoloured part turns out to be the nest of the chegoe containing hundreds of eggs, which, if allowed to hatch there, the young ones will soon begin to form other nests, and in time cause a spreading ulcer. As soon as you perceive that you have got the chegoe in your flesh, you must take a needle, or a sharp-pointed knife, and take it out. If the nest be formed, great care must be taken not to break it, otherwise some of the eggs remain in the flesh, and then you will soon be annoyed with more chegoes. After removing the nest, it is well to drop spirit of turpentine into the hole : that will most effectually destroy any chegoe that may be lurking there. Sometimes I have taken four nests out of my feet in the course of the day.

Every evening, before sundown, it was part of my toilette to examine my feet, and see that they were clear of chegoes. Now and then a nest would escape the scrutiny, and then I had to smart for it a day or two after. A chegoe once lit upon the back of my hand; wishful to see how he worked, I allowed him to take possession. He immediately set to work, head foremost, and in about half an hour he had completely buried himself in the skin. I then let him feel the point of my knife, and exterminated him.

More than once, after sitting down upon a rotten stump, I have found myself covered with Ticks. There is a short and easy way to get quit of these unwelcome adherents. Make a large fire and stand close to it, and if you be covered with ticks, they will all fall off.

Let us now forget for a while the quadrupeds, serpents, and insects, and take a transitory view of the native Indians of these forests.

There are five principal nations or tribes of Indians in *ci-devant* Dutch Guiana, commonly known by the name of Warow, Arowack, Acoway, Carib, and Macoushi. They live in small hamlets, which consist of a few huts, never exceeding twelve in number. These huts are always in the forest, near a river or some creek. They are open on all sides, (except those of the Macoushi,) and covered with a species of palm leaf.

Their principal furniture is the hammock. It serves them both for chair and bed. It is commonly made of cotton ; though those of the Warows are formed from the æta tree. At night they always make a fire close to it. The heat keeps them warm, and the smoke drives away the mosquitos and sand-flies. You sometimes find a table in the hut ; but it was not made by the Indians, but by some negro, or mulatto carpenter.

They cut down about an acre or two of the trees which surround the huts, and there plant Pepper, Papaws, Sweet and Bitter Cassava, Plantains, Sweet Potatoes, Yams, Pine-Apples, and Silk-Grass. Besides these, they generally have a few acres in some fertile part of the forest for their cassava, which is as bread to them. They make earthen pots to boil their provisions in; and they get from the white men flat circular plates of iron, on which they bake their cassava. They have to grate the cassava before it is pressed, preparatory to baking; and those Indians who are too far in the wilds to procure graters from the white men, make use of a flat piece of wood, studded with sharp stones. They have no cows, horses, mules, goats, sheep, or asses. The men hunt and fish, and the women work in the provision ground, and cook their victuals.

In each hamlet there is the trunk of a large tree, hollowed out like a trough. In this, from their cassava, they make an abominable ill-tasted and sour kind of fermented liquor, called piwarri. They are very fond of it, and never fail to get drunk after every brewing. The frequency of the brewing depends upon the superabundance of cassava.

Both men and women go without clothes. The men have a cotton wrapper, and the women a bead-ornamented square piece of cotton, about the size of your hand, for the fig-leaf. Those far away in the interior, use the bark of a tree for this purpose. They are very clean people, and wash in the river, or creek, at least twice every day. They paint themselves with the roucou, sweetly perfumed with hayawa or accaiari. Their hair is black and lank, and never curled. The women braid it up fancifully, something in the shape of Diana's head-dress in ancient pictures. They have very few diseases. Old age and pulmonary complaints seem to be the chief agents for removing them to another world. The pulmonary complaints are generally brought on by a severe cold, which they do not know how to arrest in its progress, by the use of the lancet. I never saw an idiot amongst them, nor could I perceive any that were deformed from their birth.

Their women never perish in childbed, owing, no doubt, to their never wearing stays.

They have no public religious ceremony. They acknowledge two superior beings,—a good one, and a bad one. They pray to the latter not to hurt them, and they are of opinion that the former is too good to do them an injury. I suspect, if the truth were known, the individuals of the village never offer up a single prayer or ejaculation. They have a kind of a priest called a Pee-ay-man, who is an enchanter. He finds out things lost. He mutters prayers to the evil spirit over them and their children when they are sick. If a fever be in the village, the Pee-ay-man goes about all night long, howling, and making dreadful noises, and begs the bad spirit to depart. But he has very seldom to perform this part of his duty, as fevers seldom visit the Indian hamlets. However, when a fever does come, and his incantations are of no avail, which I imagine is most commonly the case, they abandon the place for ever, and make a new settlement elsewhere. They consider the owl and the goatsucker as familiars of the evil spirit, and never destroy them.

I could find no monuments or marks of antiquity amongst these Indians; so that after penetrating to the Rio Branco, from the shores of the Western Ocean, had any body questioned me on this subject, I should have answered, I have seen nothing amongst these Indians which tells me that they have existed here for a century; though, for aught I know to the contrary, they may have been here before the Redemption, but their total want of civilization has assimilated them to the forests in which they wander. Thus, an aged tree falls and moulders into dust and you cannot tell what was its appearance, its beauties, or its diseases amongst the neighbouring trees; another has shot up in its place, and after nature has had her course, it will make way for a successor in its turn. So it is with the Indian of Guiana; he is now laid low in the dust; he has left no record behind him, either on parchment, or on a stone, or in earthenware, to say what he has done. Perhaps the place where his buried ruins lie was unhealthy, and the survivors have left it long ago, and gone far away into the wilds. All that you can say is, the trees where I stand appear lower and smaller than the rest, and from this I conjecture, that some Indians may have had a settlement here formerly. Were I by chance to meet the son of the father who moulders here, he could tell me that his father was famous for slaying tigers and serpents and caymen, and noted in the chase of the tapir and wild boar, but that he remembers little or nothing of his grandfather.

They are very jealous of their liberty, and much attached to their own mode of living. Though those in the neighbourhood of the European settlements have constant communication with the whites, they have no inclination to become civilized. Some Indians who have accompanied white men to Europe, on returning to their own land, have thrown off their clothes, and gone back into the forests.

In George-town, the capital of Demerara, there is a large shed, open on all sides, built for them by order of government. Hither the Indians come with monkies, parrots, bows and arrows, and pegalls. They sell these to the white men for money, and too often purchase rum with it, to which they are wonderfully addicted.

Government allows them annual presents in order to have their services, when the colony deems it necessary to scour the forests in quest of runaway negroes. Formerly these expeditions were headed by Charles Edmonstone, Esq., now of Cardross Park, near Dumbarton. This brave colonist never returned from the woods without being victorious. Once, in an attack upon the rebel negroes' camp, he led the way, and received two balls in his body; at the same moment that he was wounded, two of his Indians fell dead by his side; he recovered after his life was despaired of, but the balls could never be extracted.

Since the above appeared in print, I have had the account of this engagement with the negroes in the forest from Mr. Edmonstone's own mouth.

He received four slugs in his body, as will be seen in the sequel.

The plantations of Demerara and Essequibo are bounded by an almost interminable extent of forest. Hither the runaway negroes repair, and form settlements, from whence they issue to annoy the colonists, as occasion may offer.

In 1801, the runaway slaves had increased to an alarming extent. The Governor gave orders that an expedition should be immediately organized, and proceed to the woods, under the command of Charles Edmonstone, Esq. General Hislop sent him a corporal, a sergeant, and eleven men, and he was joined by a part of the colonial militia, and by sixty Indians.

With this force Mr. Edmonstone entered the forest, and proceeded in a direction towards Mahaica.

He marched for eight days through swamps, and over places obstructed by fallen trees and the bush-rope; tormented by myriads of mosquitos, and ever in fear of treading on the poisonous snakes, which can scarcely be distinguished from the fallen leaves.

At last he reached a wooded sand-hill, where the Maroons had intrenched themselves in great force. Not expecting to come so soon upon them, Mr. Edmonstone, his faithful man Coffee, and two Indian chiefs, found themselves considerably ahead of their own party. As

yet, they were unperceived by the enemy, but, unfortunately, one of the Indian chiefs fired a random shot at a
distant Maroon.   Immediately the whole negro camp
turned out, and formed themselves in a crescent, in front
of Mr. Edmonstone.   Their chief was an uncommonly fine
negro, about six feet in height; and his head-dress was
that of an African warrior, ornamented with a profusion
of small shells.   He advanced undauntedly with his gun
in his hand, and, in insulting language, called out to Mr.
Edmonstone to come on and fight him.

Mr. Edmonstone approached him slowly, in order to
give his own men time to come up; but they were yet too
far off for him to profit by this manœuvre.   Coffee, who
carried his master's gun, now stepped up behind him, and
put the gun into his hand, which Mr. Edmonstone received,
without advancing it to his shoulder.

He was now within a few yards of the Maroon chief,
who seemed to betray some symptoms of uncertainty; for
instead of firing directly at Mr. Edmonstone, he took a step
sideways, and rested his gun against a tree; no doubt with
the intention of taking a surer aim.   Mr. Edmonstone, on
perceiving this, immediately cocked his gun, and fired it
off, still holding it in the position in which he had received
it from Coffee.

The whole of the contents entered the negro's body, and
ne dropped dead on his face.

The negroes, who had formed in a crescent, now in their
turn fired a volley, which brought Mr. Edmonstone and
his two Indian chiefs to the ground.   The Maroons did
not stand to reload, but on Mr. Edmonstone's party
coming up, they fled precipitately into the surrounding
forest.

Four slugs had entered Mr. Edmonstone's body.   After
coming to himself, on looking around, he saw one of the

fallen Indian chiefs bleeding by his side. He accosted him by name, and said he hoped he was not much hurt. The dying Indian had just strength enough to answer, "Oh no,"—and then expired. The other chief was lying quite dead. He must have received his mortal wound just as he was in the act of cocking his gun to fire on the negroes; for it appeared that the ball which gave him his death wound, had carried off the first joint of his thumb, and passed through his forehead. By this time his wife, who had accompanied the expedition, came up. She was a fine young woman, and had her long black hair fancifully braided in a knot on the top of her head, fastened with a silver ornament. She unloosed it, and, falling on her husband's body, covered it with her hair, bewailing his untimely end with the most heartrending cries.

The blood was now running out of Mr. Edmonstone's shoes. On being raised up, he ordered his men to pursue the flying Maroons, requesting at the same time that he might be left where he had fallen, as he felt that he was mortally wounded. They gently placed him on the ground, and after the pursuit of the Maroons had ended, the corporal and sergeant returned to their commander, and formed their men. On his asking what this meant, the sergeant replied, "I had the General's orders, on setting out from town, not to leave you in the forest, happen what might." By slow and careful marches, as much as the obstructions in the woods would admit of, the party reached Plantation Alliance, on the bank of the Demerara, and from thence it crossed the river to Plantation Vredestein.

The news of the rencounter had been spread far and wide by the Indians, and had already reached town. The General, Captains Macrai and Johnstone, and Doctor Dunkin, proceeded to Vredestein. On examining Mr. Edmonstone's wounds, four slugs were found to have

entered the body; one was extracted, the rest remained
there till the year 1824, when another was cut out by a
professional gentleman of Port Glasgow. The other two
still remain in the body; and it is supposed that either
one or both have touched a nerve, as they cause almost
continual pain. Mr. Edmonstone has commanded fifteen
different expeditions in the forest in quest of the Maroons.
The Colonial Government has requited his services, by
freeing his property from all taxes, and presenting him a
handsome sword, and a silver urn, bearing the following
inscription:

" Presented to CHARLES EDMONSTONE, Esq. by the Governor and
Court of Policy of the Colony of Demerara, as a token of their
esteem, and the deep sense they entertain of the very great activity
and spirit manifested by him on various occasions in his successful
exertions for the internal security of the Colony.—*January* 1*st*,
1809."

I do not believe that there is a single Indian in *ci-devant*
Dutch Guiana who can read or write, nor am I aware that
any white man has reduced their language to the rules
of grammar; some may have made a short manuscript
vocabulary of the few necessary words, but that is all.
Here and there a white man, and some few people of
colour, talk the language well. The temper of the Indian
of Guiana is mild and gentle, and he is very fond of his
children.

Some ignorant travellers and colonists call these Indians
a lazy race. Man in general will not be active without an
object. Now when the Indian has caught plenty of fish,
and killed game enough to last him for a week, what need
has he to range the forest? He has no idea of making
pleasure-grounds. Money is of no use to him, for in these
wilds there are no markets for him to frequent, nor milliners' shops for his wife and daughters; he has no taxes to

pay, no highways to keep up, no poor to maintain, nor army nor navy to supply; he lies in his hammock both night and day (for he has no chair or bed, neither does he want them), and in it he forms his bow, and makes his arrows, and repairs his fishing tackle. But as soon as he has consumed his provisions, he then rouses himself, and, like the lion, scours the forest in quest of food. He plunges into the river after the deer and tapir, and swims across it; passes through swamps and quagmires, and never fails to obtain a sufficient supply of food. Should the approach of night stop his career, while he is hunting the wild boar, he stops for the night, and continues the chase the next morning. In my way through the wilds to the Portuguese frontier, I had a proof of this: we were eight in number, six Indians, a negro, and myself. About ten o'clock in the morning, we observed the feet-mark of the wild boars; we judged by the freshness of the marks that they had passed that way early the same morning. As we were not gifted, like the hound, with scent, and as we had no dog with us, we followed their track by the eye. The Indian after game is as sure with his eye as the dog is with his nose. We followed the herd till three in the afternoon, then gave up the chase for the present; made our fires close to a creek where there was plenty of fish, and then arranged the hammocks. In an hour the Indians shot more fish with their arrows than we could consume. The night was beautifully serene and clear, and the moon shone as bright as day. Next morn we rose at dawn, got breakfast, packed up, each took his burden, and then we put ourselves on the track of the wild boars, which we had been following the day before. We supposed that they, too, would sleep that night in the forest, as we had done; and thus the delay on our part would be no disadvantage to us. This was just the case, for about nine o'clock their feet-marks became fresher and fresher: we now doubled our pace, but did not give mouth like hounds. We pushed on in silence, and soon came up with them; there were above one hundred of them; we killed six, and the rest took off in different directions. But to the point.

Amongst us the needy man works from light to dark for a maintenance. Should this man chance to acquire a fortune, he soon changes his habits. No longer under "strong necessity's supreme command," he contrives to get out of bed betwixt nine and ten in the morning. His servant helps him to dress, he walks on a soft carpet to his breakfast table, his wife pours out his tea, and his servant hands him his toast. After breakfast, the doctor advises a little gentle exercise in the carriage for an hour or so. At dinner-time he sits down to a table groaning beneath the weight of heterogeneous luxury: there he rests upon a chair for three or four hours, eats, drinks, and talks (often unmeaningly) till tea is announced. He proceeds slowly to the drawing-room, and there spends the best part of his time in sitting, till his wife tempts him with something warm for supper. After supper, he still remains on his chair at rest, till he retires to rest for the night. He mounts leisurely up stairs upon a carpet, and enters his bed-room : there, one would hope, that at least he mutters a prayer or two, though perhaps not on bended knee: he then lets himself drop into a soft and downy bed, over which has just passed the comely Jenny's warming-pan. Now, could the Indian in his turn see this, he would call the white men a lazy, indolent set.

Perhaps then, upon due reflection, you would draw this conclusion ; that men will always be indolent where there is no object to rouse them.

As the Indian of Guiana has no idea whatever of communicating his intentions by writing, he has fallen upon a plan of communication sure and simple. When two or three families have determined to come down the river and pay you a visit, they send an Indian beforehand with a string of beads. You take one bead off every day; and on the day that the string is beadless, they arrive at your house.

In finding their way through these pathless wilds, the sun is to them what Ariadne's clue was to Theseus. When he is on the meridian, they generally sit down, and rove onwards again as soon as he has sufficiently declined to the west; they require no other compass. When in chase, they break a twig on the bushes as they pass by every three or four hundred paces, and this often prevents them from losing their way on their return.

You will not be long in the forests of Guiana, before you perceive how very thinly they are inhabited. You may wander for a week together without seeing a hut. The wild beasts, snakes, the swamps, the trees, the uncurbed luxuriance of everything around you, conspire to inform you that man has no habitation here—man has seldom passed this way.

CHAPTER III.

LET us now return to natural history. There was a person making shingles, with twenty or thirty negroes, not far from Mibiri-hill. I had offered a reward to any of them who would find a good-sized snake in the forest, and come and let me know where it was. Often had these negroes looked for a large snake, and as often been disappointed.

One Sunday morning I met one of them in the forest, and asked him which way he was going : he said he was going towards Warratilla creek to hunt an armadillo : and he had his little dog with him. On coming back, about noon, the dog began to bark at the root of a large tree, which had been upset by the whirlwind, and was lying there in a gradual state of decay. The negro said, he thought his dog was barking at an acouri, which had probably taken refuge under the tree, and he went up with an intention to kill it : he there saw a snake, and hastened back to inform me of it.

The sun had just passed the meridian in a cloudless sky ; there was scarcely a bird to be seen, for the winged inhabitants of the forest, as though overcome by heat, had retired to the thickest shade : all would have been like midnight silence, were it not for the shrill voice of the Pi-pi-yo, every now and then resounding from a distant tree. I was sitting with a little Horace in my hand, on what had once been the steps which formerly led up to the now mouldering and dismantled building. The negro and his little dog came down the hill in haste, and I was soon informed that a snake had been discovered; but it was a young one, called the Bush-master, a rare and poisonous snake.

I instantly rose up, and laying hold of the eight-foot lance, which was close by me, " Well then, Daddy," said I, " we'll go and have a look at the snake." I was barefoot, with an old hat, and check shirt, and trousers on, and a pair of braces to keep them up.   The negro had his cutlass, and as we ascended the hill, another negro, armed with a cutlass, joined us, judging, from our pace, that there was something to do. The little dog came along with us, and when we had got about half a mile in the forest, the negro stopped, and pointed to the fallen tree : all was still and silent : I told the negroes not to stir from the place where they were, and keep the little dog in, and that I would go in and reconnoitre.

I advanced up to the place slow and cautious. The snake was well concealed, but at last I made him out; it was a Coulacanara, not poisonous, but large enough to have crushed any of us to death. On measuring him afterwards, he was something more than fourteen feet long. This species of snake is very rare, and much thicker, in proportion to his length, than any other snake in the forest. A coulacanara of fourteen feet in length is as thick as a common boa of twenty-four. After skinning this snake I could easily get my head into his mouth, as the singular formation of the jaws admits of wonderful extension.

A Dutch friend of mine, by name Brouwer, killed a Boa, twenty-two feet long, with a pair of stag's horns in his mouth : he had swallowed the stag, but could not get the horns down: so he had to wait in patience with that uncomfortable mouthful till his stomach digested the body, and then the horns would drop out. In this plight the Dutchman found him as he was going in his canoe up the river, and sent a ball through his head.

On ascertaining the size of the serpent which the negro had just found, I retired slowly the way I came, and promised four dollars to the negro who had shown it to me, and one to the other who had joined us. Aware that the day was on the decline, and that the approach of night would be detrimental to the dissection, a thought struck me that I could take him alive. I imagined if I could strike him with the lance behind the head, and pin him to the ground, I might succeed in capturing him. When I told this to the negroes, they begged and entreated me to let them go for a gun, and bring more force, as they were sure the snake would kill some of us.

I had been at the siege of Troy for nine years, and it would not do now to carry back to Greece, " nil decimo nisi dedecus anno." I mean, I had been in search of a large serpent for years, and now having come up with one, it did not become me to turn soft. So, taking a cutlass from one of the negroes, and then ranging both the sable slaves behind me, I told them to follow me, and that I would cut them down if they offered to fly. I smiled as I said this, but they shook their heads in silence, and seemed to have but a bad heart of it.

When we got up to the place, the serpent had not stirred, but I could see nothing of his head, and I judged by the folds of his body that it must be at the farthest side of his den. A species of woodbine had formed a complete mantle over the branches of the fallen tree, almost impervious to the rain, or the rays of the sun. Probably he had resorted to this sequestered place for a length of time, as it bore marks of an ancient settlement.

I now took my knife, determining to cut away the woodbine, and break the twigs in the gentlest manner possible, till I could get a view of his head. One negro stood guard close behind me with the lance; and near him the other with a cutlass. The cutlass which I had taken from the first negro was on the ground close by me in case of need.

After working in dead silence for a quarter of an hour, with one knee all the time on the ground, I had cleared away enough to see his head. It appeared coming out betwixt the first and second coil of his body, and was flat on the ground. This was the very position I wished it to be in.

I rose in silence and retreated very slowly, making a sign to the negroes to do the same. The dog was sitting at a distance in mute observance. I could now read in the face of the negroes, that they considered this a very unpleasant affair; and they made another attempt to persuade me to let them go for a gun. I smiled in a good-natured manner, and made a feint to cut them down with the weapon I had in my hand. This was all the answer I made to their request, and they looked very uneasy.

It must be observed, we were now about twenty yards from the snake's den. I now ranged the negroes behind me, and told him who stood next to me to lay hold of the lance the moment I struck the snake, and that the other must attend my movements. It now only remained to take their cutlasses from them, for I was sure, if I did not disarm them, they would be tempted to strike the snake in time of danger, and thus for ever spoil his skin. On taking their cutlasses from them, if I might judge from their physiognomy, they seemed to consider it as a most intolerable act of tyranny in me. Probably nothing kept them from bolting, but the consolation that I was to be betwixt them and the snake. Indeed, my own heart, in spite of all I could do, beat quicker than usual ; and I felt those sensations which one has on board a merchant-vessel in war time, when the captain orders all hands on deck to prepare for action, while a strange vessel is coming down upon us under suspicious colours.

We went slowly on in silence, without moving our arms or heads, in order to prevent all alarm as much as possible, lest the snake should glide off, or attack us in self-defence. I carried the lance perpendicularly before me, with the point about a foot from the ground. The snake had not moved; and on getting up to him, I struck him with the lance on the near side, just behind the neck, and pinned him to the ground. That moment, the negro next to me seized the lance, and held it firm in its place, while I dashed head foremost into the den to grapple with the snake, and to get hold of his tail before he could do any mischief.

On pinning him to the ground with the lance, he gave a tremendous loud hiss, and the little dog ran away, howling as he went. We had a sharp fray in the den, the rotten sticks flying on all sides, and each party struggling for superiority. I called out to the second negro to throw himself upon me, as I found I was not heavy enough. He did so, and the additional weight was of great service. I had now got firm hold of his tail ; and after a violent struggle or two, he gave in, finding himself overpowered. This was the moment to secure him. So, while the first negro continued to hold the lance firm to the ground, and the other was helping me, I contrived to unloose my braces, and with them tied up the snake's mouth.

The snake now finding himself in an unpleasant situation, tried to better himself, and set resolutely to work, but we overpowered him. We contrived to make him twist himself round the shaft of the lance, and then prepared to convey him out of the forest. I stood at his head and held it firm under my arm, one negro supported the belly, and the other the tail. In this order we began to move slowly towards home, and reached it after resting ten times ; for the snake was too heavy for us to support him without stopping to recruit our strength. As we proceeded onwards with him, he fought hard for freedom, but it was all in vain. The day was now too far spent to think of dissecting him. Had I killed him, a partial putrefaction would have taken place before morning. I had brought with me up into the forest a strong bag, large enough to contain any animal that I should want to dissect. I considered this the best mode of keeping live wild animals when I was pressed for daylight ; for the bag yielding in every direction to their efforts, they would have nothing solid or fixed to work on, and thus would be prevented from making a hole through it. I say fixed, for after the mouth of the bag was closed, the bag itself was not fastened or tied to anything, but moved about wherever the animal inside caused it to roll. After securing afresh the mouth of the coulacanara, so that he could not open it, he was forced into this bag, and left to his fate till morning.

I cannot say he allowed me to have a quiet night. My hammock was in the loft just above him, and the floor betwixt us, half gone to decay, so that in parts of it no boards intervened betwixt his lodging-room and mine. He was very restless and fretful ; and had Medusa been my wife, there could not have been more continued and disagreeable hissing in the bedchamber that night. At day-break, I sent to borrow ten of the negroes who were cutting wood at a distance; I could have done with half that number, but judged it most prudent to have a good force, in case he should try to escape from the house when we opened the bag. However, nothing serious occurred.

We untied the mouth of the bag, kept him down by main force, and then I cut his throat. He bled like an ox. By six o'clock the same evening, he was completely dissected. On examining his teeth, I observed that they were all bent like tenter-hooks, pointing down his throat, and not so large or strong as I expected to have found them; but they are exactly suited to what they are intended by nature to perform. The snake does not masticate his food, and thus the only service his teeth have to perform is to seize his prey, and hold it till he swallows it whole.

In general, the skins of snakes are sent to museums without the head: for when the Indians and Negroes kill a snake, they seldom fail to cut off the head, and then they run no risk from its teeth. When the skin is stuffed in the museum, a wooden head is substituted, armed with teeth which are large enough to suit a tiger's jaw; and this tends to mislead the spectator, and give him erroneous ideas.

During this fray with the serpent, the old negro, Daddy Quashi, was in Georgetown procuring provisions, and just returned in time to help to take the skin off. He had spent best part of his life in the forest with his old master, Mr. Edmonstone, and amused me much in recounting their many adventures amongst the wild beasts. The Daddy had a particular horror of snakes, and frankly declared he could never have faced the one in question.

The week following, his courage was put to the test, and he made good his words. It was a curious conflict, and took place near the spot where I had captured the large snake. In the morning I had been following a new species of paroquet, and the day being rainy, I had taken an umbrella to keep the gun dry, and had left it under a tree; in the afternoon I took Daddy Quashi with me to look for it. Whilst he was searching about, curiosity took me towards the place of the late scene of action. There was a path where timber had formerly been dragged along. Here I observed a young coulacanara, ten feet long, slowly moving onwards; I saw he was not thick enough to break my arm in case he got twisted round it. There was not a moment to be lost. I laid hold of his tail with the left hand, one knee being on the ground; with the right I took my hat, and held it as you would hold a shield for defence.

The snake instantly turned, and came on at me, with his head about a yard from the ground, as if to ask me, what business I had to take liberties with his tail. I let him come, hissing and open-mouthed, within two feet of my face, and then, with all the force I was master of, I drove my fist, shielded by my hat, full in his jaws. He was stunned and confounded by the blow, and ere he could recover himself, I had seized his throat with both hands, in such a position that he could not bite me; I then allowed him to coil himself round my body, and marched off with him as my lawful prize. He pressed me hard, but not alarmingly so.

In the meantime, Daddy Quashi having found the umbrella, and having heard the noise which the fray occasioned, was coming cautiously up. As soon as he saw me, and in what company I was, he turned about and ran off home, I after him, and shouting to increase his fear. On scolding him for his cowardice, the old rogue begged that I would forgive him, for that the sight of the snake had positively turned him sick at stomach.

When I had done with the carcass of the large snake, it
was conveyed into the forest, as I expected that it would
attract the king of the vultures, as soon as time should
have rendered it sufficiently savoury. In a few days it
sent forth that odour which a carcass should send forth,
and about twenty of the common vultures came and
perched on the neighbouring trees ; the king of the
vultures came too ; and I observed that none of the
common ones seemed inclined to begin breakfast till his
majesty had finished. When he. had consumed as much
snake as nature informed him would do him good, he
retired to the top of a high mora-tree, and then all the
common vultures fell to, and made a hearty meal.

The head and neck of the king of the vultures are bare
of feathers ; but the beautiful appearance they exhibit
fades in death. The throat and the back of the neck are
of a fine lemon colour; both sides of the neck, from the
ears downwards, of a rich scarlet ; behind the corrugated
part there is a white spot. The crown of the head is
scarlet ; betwixt the lower mandible and the eye, and close
by the ear, there is a part which has a fine silvery blue
appearance ; the corrugated part is of a dirty light brown ;
behind it, and just above the white spot, a portion of the
skin is blue, and the rest scarlet ; the skin which juts out
behind the neck, and appears like an oblong caruncle, is
blue in part, and part orange.

The bill is orange and black, the caruncles on his forehead orange, and the cere orange ; the orbits scarlet, and
the irides white. Below the bare part of the neck there is
a cinereous ruff. The bag of the stomach, which is only
seen when distended with food, is of a most delicate
white, intersected with blue veins, which appear on it just
like the blue veins on the arm of a fair-complexioned
person.

The tail and long wing-feathers are black, the belly white, and the rest of the body a fine satin colour.

I cannot be persuaded that the vultures ever feed upon live animals, not even upon lizards, rats, mice, or frogs; I have watched them for hours together, but never could see them touch any living animals, though innumerable lizards, frogs, and small birds swarmed all around them. I have killed lizards and frogs, and put them in a proper place for observation; as soon as they began to stink, the Aura vulture invariably came and took them off. I have frequently observed, that the day after the planter had burnt the trash in a cane-field, the aura vulture was sure to be there, feeding on the snakes, lizards, and frogs which had suffered in the conflagration. I often saw a large bird (very much like the common gregarious vulture at a distance) catch and devour lizards; after shooting one, it turned out to be not a vulture, but a hawk, with a tail squarer and shorter than hawks have in general. The vultures, like the goatsucker and woodpecker, seem to be in disgrace with man. They are generally termed a voracious, stinking, cruel, and ignoble tribe. Under these impressions, the fowler discharges his gun at them, and probably thinks he has done well in ridding the earth of such vermin.

Some governments impose a fine on him who kills a vulture. This is a salutary law, and it were to be wished that other governments would follow so good an example. I would fain here say a word or two in favour of this valuable scavenger.

Kind Providence has conferred a blessing on hot countries in giving them the vulture; he has ordered it to consume that which, if left to dissolve in putrefaction, would infect the air, and produce a pestilence. When full of food, the vulture certainly appears an indolent bird; he will stand for hours together on the branch of a tree, or on the top of a house, with his wings drooping, and, after rain, with them spread and elevated to catch the rays of the sun. It has been remarked by naturalists, that the flight of this bird is laborious. I have paid attention to the vulture in Andalusia, and to those in Guiana, Brazil, and the West Indies, and conclude that they are birds of long, even, and lofty flight. Indeed, whoever has observed the aura vulture, will be satisfied that his flight is wonderfully majestic, and of long continuance.

The bird is above five feet from wing to wing extended. You will see it soaring aloft in the aerial expanse on pinions which never flutter, and which at the same time carry him through the fields of ether with a rapidity equal to that of the golden eagle. In Paramaribo the laws protect the vulture, and the Spaniards of Angustura never think of molesting him. In 1808, I saw the vultures in that city as tame as domestic fowls; a person who had never seen a vulture would have taken them for turkeys. They were very useful to the Spaniards; and had it not been for them, the refuse of the slaughter-houses in Angustura would have caused an intolerable nuisance.

The common black, short, square-tailed vulture, is gregarious; but the aura vulture is not so; for, though you may see fifteen or twenty of them feeding on the dead vermin in a cane-field, after the trash has been set fire to, still, if you have paid attention to their arrival, you will have observed that they came singly and retired singly, and thus their being all together in the same field was merely accidental, and caused by each one smelling the effluvia as he was soaring through the sky to look out for food. I have watched twenty come into a cane-field; they arrived one by one, and from different parts of the heavens. Hence we may conclude, that though the other species of vulture are gregarious, the aura vulture is not.

If you dissect a vulture that has just been feeding on carrion, you must expect that your olfactory nerves will be somewhat offended with the rank effluvia from his craw; just as they would be were you to dissect a citizen after the Lord Mayor's dinner. If, on the contrary, the vulture be empty at the time you commence the operation, there will be no offensive smell, but a strong scent of musk.

I had long wished to examine the native haunts of the Cayman; but as the river Demerara did not afford a specimen of the large kind, I was obliged to go to the river Essequibo to look for one.

I got the canoe ready, and went down in it to George-town; where, having put in the necessary articles for the expedition, not forgetting a couple of large shark-hooks, with chains attached to them, and a coil of strong new rope, I hoisted a little sail, which I had got made on purpose, and at six o'clock in the morning shaped our course for the river Essequibo. I had put a pair of shoes on to prevent the tar at the bottom of the canoe from sticking to my feet. The sun was flaming hot, and from eleven o'clock till two beat perpendicularly upon the top of my feet, betwixt the shoes and the trousers. Not feeling it disagreeable, or being in the least aware of painful consequences, as I had been barefoot for months, I neglected to put on a pair of short stockings which I had with me. I did not reflect, that sitting still in one place, with your feet exposed to the sun, was very different from being exposed to the sun while in motion.

We went ashore in the Essequibo, about three o'clock in the afternoon, to choose a place for the night's residence, to collect firewood, and to set the fish-hooks. It was then that I first began to find my legs very painful: they soon became much inflamed and red and blistered; and it required considerable caution not to burst the blisters, otherwise sores would have ensued. I immediately got into the hammock, and there passed a painful and sleepless night, and for two days after I was disabled from walking.

About midnight, as I was lying awake, and in great pain, I heard the Indian say, "Massa, massa, you no hear tiger?" I listened attentively, and heard the softly sounding tread of his feet as he approached us. The moon had gone down; but every now and then we could get a glance of him by the light of our fire: he was the jaguar, for I could see the spots on his body. Had I wished to have fired at him, I was not able to take a sure aim, for I was in such pain that I could not turn myself in my hammock. The Indian would have fired, but I would not allow him to do so, as I wanted to see a little more of our new visitor; for it is not every day or night that the traveller is favoured with an undisturbed sight of the jaguar in his own forests.

Whenever the fire got low, the jaguar came a little nearer, and when the Indian renewed it, he retired abruptly; sometimes he would come within twenty yards, and then we had a view of him, sitting on his hind legs like a dog; sometimes he moved slowly to and fro, and at other times we could hear him mend his pace, as if impatient. At last the Indian, not relishing the idea of having such company in the neighbourhood, could contain himself no longer, and set up a most tremendous yell. The jaguar bounded off like a racehorse, and returned no more; it appeared by the print of his feet the next morning that he was a full-grown jaguar.

In two days after this we got to the first falls in the Essequibo. There was a superb barrier of rocks quite across the river. In the rainy season these rocks are for the most part under water ; but it being now dry weather, we had a fine view of them, while the water from the river above them rushed through the different openings in majestic grandeur. Here, on a little hill, jutting out into the river, stands the house of Mrs. Peterson, the last house of people of colour up this river ; I hired a negro from her, and a coloured man, who pretended that they knew the haunts of the cayman, and understood everything about taking him. We were a day in passing these falls and rapids, celebrated for the Pacou, the richest and most delicious fish in Guiana. The coloured man was now in his element ; he stood in the head of the canoe, and with his bow and arrow shot the pacou as they were swimming in the stream. The arrow had scarcely left the bow before he had plunged headlong into the river, and seized the fish as it was struggling with it. He dived and swam like an otter, and rarely missed the fish he aimed at.

Did my pen, gentle reader, possess descriptive powers, I would here give thee an idea of the enchanting scenery of the Essequibo ; but that not being the case, thou must be contented with a moderate and well-intended attempt.

Nothing could be more lovely than the appearance of the forest on each side of this noble river. Hills rose on hills in fine gradation, all covered with trees of gigantic height and size. Here their leaves were of a lively purple, and there of the deepest green. Sometimes the Caracara extended its scarlet blossoms from branch to branch, and gave the tree the appearance as though it had been hung with garlands.

This delightful scenery of the Essequibo made the soul overflow with joy, and caused you to rove in fancy through fairy-land ; till, on turning an angle of the river, you were recalled to more sober reflections on seeing the once grand and towering mora, now dead and ragged in its topmost branches, while its aged trunk, undermined by the rushing torrent, hung as though in sorrow over the river, which, ere long, would receive it, and sweep it away for ever.

During the day, the trade-wind blew a gentle and refreshing breeze, which died away as the night set in, and then the river was as smooth as glass.

The moon was within three days of being full, so that we did not regret the loss of the sun, which set in all its splendour. Scarce had he sunk behind the western hills, when the Goatsuckers sent forth their soft and plaintive cries; some often repeating, "Who are you—who, who, who are you?" and others, "Willy, Willy, Willy come go."

The Indian and Daddy Quashi often shook their heads at this, and said they were bringing talk from Yabahou, who is the evil spirit of the Essequibo. It was delightful to sit on the branch of a fallen tree, near the water's edge, and listen to these harmless birds as they repeated their evening song; and watch the owls and vampires as they every now and then passed up and down the river.

The next day, about noon, as we were proceeding onwards, we heard the Campanero tolling in the depth of the forest. Though I should not then have stopped to dissect even a rare bird, having a greater object in view, still I could not resist the opportunity offered of acquiring the campanero. The place where he was tolling was low and swampy, and my legs not having quite recovered from the effects of the sun, I sent the Indian to shoot the campanero. He got up to the tree, which he described as very high, with a naked top, and situated in a swamp. He fired at the bird, but either missed it, or did not wound it sufficiently to bring it down. This was the only opportunity I had of getting a campanero during this expedition. We had never heard one toll before this morning, and never heard one after.

CHAPTER IV.

ABOUT an hour before sunset, we reached the place which
the two men who had joined us at the falls pointed out
as a proper one to find a Cayman. There was a large
creek close by, and a sand-bank gently sloping to the
water. Just within the forest on this bank, we cleared a
place of brushwood, suspended the hammocks from the
trees, and then picked up enough of decayed wood for
fuel.

The Indian found a large land tortoise, and this, with
plenty of fresh fish which we had in the canoe, afforded a
supper not to be despised.

The tigers had kept up a continued roaring every night
since we had entered the Essequibo. The sound was
awfully fine. Sometimes it was in the immediate neighbourhood; at other times it was far off, and echoed
amongst the hills like distant thunder.

It may, perhaps, not be amiss to observe here, that when
the word tiger is used, it does not mean the Bengal tiger.

It means the jaguar, whose skin is beautifully spotted, and not striped like that of the tiger in the East. It is, in fact, the tiger of the new world, and receiving the name of tiger from the discoverers of South America, it has kept it ever since. It is a cruel, strong, and dangerous beast, but not so courageous as the Bengal tiger.

We now baited a shark-hook with a large fish, and put it upon a board about a yard long, and one foot broad, which we had brought on purpose. This board was carried out in the canoe, about forty yards into the river. By means of a string, long enough to reach the bottom of the river, and at the end of which string was fastened a stone, the board was kept, as it were, at anchor. One end of the new rope I had bought in town was reeved through the chain of the shark-hook, and the other end fastened to a tree on the sand-bank.

It was now an hour after sunset. The sky was cloudless, and the moon shone beautifully bright. There was not a breath of wind in the heavens, and the river seemed like a large plain of quicksilver. Every now and then a huge fish would strike and plunge in the water; then the owls and goatsuckers would continue their lamentations, and the sound of these was lost in the prowling tiger's growl. Then all was still again, and silent as midnight.

The caymen were now upon the stir, and at intervals their noise could be distinguished amid that of the jaguar, the owls, the goatsuckers, and frogs. It was a singular and awful sound. It was like a suppressed sigh, bursting forth all of a sudden, and so loud that you might hear it above a mile off. First one emitted this horrible noise, and then another answered him; and on looking at the countenances of the people around me, I could plainly see that they expected to have a cayman that night.

We were at supper, when the Indian, who seemed to

have had one eye on the turtle-pot and the other on the bait in the river, said he saw the cayman coming.

Upon looking towards the place, there appeared something on the water like a black log of wood. It was so unlike anything alive, that I doubted if it were a cayman; but the Indian smiled, and said he was sure it was one, for he remembered seeing a cayman, some years ago, when he was in the Essequibo.

At last it gradually approached the bait, and the board began to move. The moon shone so bright that we could distinctly see him open his huge jaws, and take in the bait. We pulled the rope. He immediately let drop the bait; and then we saw his black head retreating from the board, to the distance of a few yards, and there it remained quite motionless.

He did not seem inclined to advance again; and so we finished our supper. In about an hour's time he again put himself in motion, and took hold of the bait. But, probably, suspecting that he had to deal with knaves and cheats, he held it in his mouth but did not swallow it. We pulled the rope again, but with no better success than the first time.

He retreated as usual, and came back again in about an hour. We paid him every attention till three o'clock in the morning; when, worn out with disappointment, we went to the hammocks, turned in, and fell asleep.

When day broke, we found that he had contrived to get the bait from the hook, though we had tied it on with string. We had now no more hopes of taking a cayman till the return of night. The Indian took off into the woods, and brought back a noble supply of game. The rest of us went into the canoe, and proceeded up the river to shoot fish. We got even more than we could use.

As we approached the shallows, we could see the large

Sting-rays moving at the bottom. The coloured man never failed to hit them with his arrow. The weather was delightful. There was scarcely a cloud to intercept the sun's rays.

I saw several scarlet aras, anihingas, and ducks, but could not get a shot at them. The parrots crossed the river in innumerable quantities, always flying in pairs. Here, too, I saw the Sun-bird, called Tirana by the Spaniards in the Oroonoque, and shot one of them. The black and white Scarlet-headed Finch was very common here. I could never see this bird in the Demerara, nor hear of its being there.

We at last came to a large sand-bank, probably two miles in circumference. As we approached it we could see two or three hundred Fresh-water Turtle on the edge of the bank. Ere we could get near enough to let fly an arrow at them, they had all sunk into the river and appeared no more.

We went on the sand-bank to look for their nests, as this was the breeding season. The coloured man showed us how to find them. Wherever a portion of the sand seemed smoother than the rest, there was sure to be a turtle's nest. On digging down with our hands, about nine inches deep, we found from twenty to thirty white eggs; in less than an hour we got above two hundred. Those which had a little black spot or two on the shell we ate the same day, as it was a sign that they were not fresh, and of course would not keep: those which had no speck were put into dry sand, and were good some weeks after.

At midnight, two of our people went to this sand-bank, while the rest stayed to watch the cayman. The turtle had advanced on to the sand to lay their eggs, and the men got betwixt them and the water ; they brought off half a dozen very fine and well-fed turtle. The egg-shell of the fresh-water turtle is not hard like that of the land tortoise, but appears like white parchment and gives way to the pressure of the fingers; but it is very tough, and does not break. On this sand-bank, close to the forest, we found several Guana's nests; but they had never more than fourteen eggs a-piece. Thus passed the day in exercise and knowledge, till the sun's declining orb reminded us it was time to return to the place from whence we had set out.

The second night's attempt upon the cayman was a repetition of the first, quite unsuccessful. We went a fishing the day after, had excellent sport, and returned to experience a third night's disappointment. On the fourth evening, about four o'clock, we began to erect a stage amongst the trees, close to the water's edge. From this we intended to shoot an arrow into the cayman: at the end of this arrow was to be attached a string, which would be tied to the rope, and as soon as the cayman was struck we were to have the canoe ready and pursue him in the river.

While we were busy in preparing the stage, a tiger began to roar. We judged by the sound that he was not above a quarter of a mile from us, and that he was close to the side of the river. Unfortunately, the Indian said it was not a jaguar that was roaring, but a couguar. The couguar is of a pale, brownish red colour, and not as large as the jaguar. As there was nothing particular in this animal, I thought it better to attend to the apparatus for catching the cayman than to go in quest of the couguar. The people, however, went in the canoe to the place where the couguar was roaring. On arriving near the spot, they saw it was not a couguar, but an immense jaguar, standing on the trunk of an aged mora-tree, which bended over the river; he growled and showed his teeth as they approached; the coloured man fired at him with a ball, but probably missed him, and the tiger instantly descended, and took off into the woods. I went to the place before dark, and we searched the forest for about half a mile in the direction he had fled, but we could see no traces of him, or any marks of blood; so I concluded that fear had prevented the man from taking steady aim.

We spent best part of the fourth night in trying for the cayman, but all to no purpose. I was now convinced that something was materially wrong. We ought to have been successful, considering our vigilance and attention, and that we had repeatedly seen the cayman. It was useless to tarry here any longer; moreover, the coloured man began to take airs, and fancied that I could not do without him. I never admit of this in any expedition where I am commander; and so I convinced the man, to his sorrow, that I could do without him; for I paid him what I had agreed to give him, which amounted to eight dollars, and ordered him back in his own curial to Mrs. Peterson's, on the hill at the first falls. I then asked the negro if there were any Indian settlements in the neighbourhood; he said he knew of one, a day and a half off. We went in quest of it, and about one o'clock the next day the negro showed us the creek where it was.

The entrance was so concealed by thick bushes that a stranger would have passed it without knowing it to be a creek. In going up it we found it dark, winding, and intricate beyond any creek that I had ever seen before When Orpheus came back with his young wife from Styx, his path must have been similar to this, for Ovid says it was

"Arduus, obliquus, caligine densus opaca,"

and this creek was exactly so.

When we had got about two-thirds up it, we met the Indians going a fishing. I saw, by the way their things were packed in the curial, that they did not intend to return for some days. However, on telling them what we wanted, and by promising handsome presents of powder, shot, and hooks, they dropped their expedition, and invited us up to the settlement they had just left, and where we laid in a provision of cassava.

They gave us for dinner boiled ant-bear and red monkey; two dishes unknown even at Beauvilliers in Paris, or at a London city feast. The monkey was very good indeed, but the ant-bear had been kept beyond its time; it stunk, as our venison does in England; and so, after tasting it, I preferred dining entirely on monkey. After resting here, we went back to the river. The Indians, three in number, accompanied us in their own curial, and, on entering the river, pointed to a place a little way above, well calculated to harbour a cayman. The water was deep and still, and flanked by an immense sand-bank; there was also a little shallow creek close by.

On this sand-bank, near the forest, the people made a shelter for the night. My own was already made; for I always take with me a painted sheet, about twelve feet by ten. This, thrown over a pole, supported betwixt two trees, makes you a capital roof with very little trouble.

We showed one of the Indians the shark-hook. He shook his head and laughed at it, and said it would not do. When he was a boy, he had seen his father catch the caymen, and on the morrow he would make something that would answer.

In the meantime, we set the shark-hook, but it availed us nought; a cayman came and took it, but would not swallow it.

Seeing it was useless to attend the shark-hook any

longer, we left it for the night, and returned to our hammocks.

Ere I fell asleep, a reflection or two broke in upon me. I considered, that as far as the judgment of civilized man went, everything had been procured and done to ensure success. We had hooks, and lines, and baits, and patience; we had spent nights in watching, had seen the cayman come and take the bait, and after our expectations had been wound up to the highest pitch, all ended in disappointment. Probably this poor wild man of the woods would succeed by means of a very simple process; and thus prove to his more civilized brother that, notwithstanding books and schools, there is a vast deal of knowledge to be picked up at every step, whichever way we turn ourselves.

In the morning, as usual, we found the bait gone from the shark-hook. The Indians went into the forest to hunt, and we took the canoe to shoot fish and get another supply of turtles' eggs, which we found in great abundance on this large sand-bank.

We went to the little shallow creek, and shot some young caymen, about two feet long. It was astonishing to see what spite and rage these little things showed when the arrow struck them; they turned round and bit it, and snapped at us when we went into the water to take them up. Daddy Quashi boiled one of them for his dinner, and found it very sweet and tender. I do not see why it should not be as good as frog or veal.

The day was now declining apace, and the Indian had made his instrument to take the cayman. It was very simple. There were four pieces of tough hard wood, a foot long, and about as thick as your little finger, and barbed at both ends; they were tied round the end of the rope, in such a manner, that if you conceive the rope to be an

arrow, these four sticks would form the arrow's head; so
that one end of the four united sticks answered to the
point of the arrow-head, while the other ends of the
sticks expanded at equal distances round the rope, thus—

Now it is evident, that if the cayman swallowed this, (the
other end of the rope, which was thirty yards long, being
fastened to a tree,) the more he pulled, the faster the barbs
would stick into his stomach.   This wooden hook, if you
may so call it, was well baited with the flesh of the
acouri, and the entrails were twisted round the rope for
about a foot above it.

Nearly a mile from where we had our hammocks, the
sand-bank was steep and abrupt, and the river very still
and deep; there the Indian pricked a stick into the sand.
It was two feet long, and on its extremity was fixed the
machine; it hung suspended about a foot from the water,
and the end of the rope was made fast to a stake driven
well into the sand.

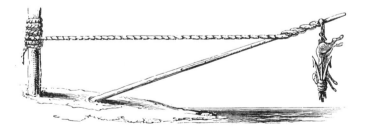

The Indian then took the empty shell of a land tortoise
and gave it some heavy blows with an axe.   I asked him

why he did that. He said it was to let the cayman hear that something was going on. In fact the Indian meant it as the cayman's dinner-bell.

Having done this, we went back to the hammocks, not intending to visit it again till morning. During the night, the jaguars roared and grumbled in the forest, as though the world was going wrong with them, and at intervals we could hear the distant cayman. The roaring of the jaguars was awful; but it was music to the dismal noise of these hideous and malicious reptiles.

About half-past five in the morning, the Indian stole off silently to take a look at the bait. On arriving at the place he set up a tremendous shout. We all jumped out of our hammocks, and ran to him. The Indians got there before me, for they had no clothes to put on, and I lost two minutes in looking for my trousers and in slipping into them.

We found a cayman, ten feet and a half long, fast to the end of the rope. Nothing now remained to do, but to get him out of the water without injuring his scales, "hoc opus, hic labor." We mustered strong: there were three Indians from the creek, there was my own Indian Yan, Daddy Quashi, the negro from Mrs. Peterson's, James, Mr. R. Edmonstone's man, whom I was instructing to preserve birds, and lastly, myself.

I informed the Indians that it was my intention to draw him quietly out of the water, and then secure him. They looked and stared at each other, and said I might do it myself; but they would have no hand in it; the cayman would worry some of us. On saying this, "consedere duces," they squatted on their hams with the most perfect indifference.

The Indians of these wilds have never been subject to the least restraint; and I knew enough of them to be aware, that if I tried to force them against their will, they would take off, and leave me and my presents unheeded, and never return.

Daddy Quashi was for applying to our guns, as usual, considering them our best and safest friends. I immediately offered to knock him down for his cowardice, and he shrunk back, begging that I would be cautious, and not get myself worried ; and apologizing for his own want of resolution. My Indian was now in conversation with the others, and they asked if I would allow them to shoot a dozen arrows into him, and thus disable him. This would have ruined all. I had come above three hundred miles on purpose to get a cayman uninjured, and not to carry back a mutilated specimen. I rejected their proposition with firmness, and darted a disdainful eye upon the Indians.

Daddy Quashi was again beginning to remonstrate, and I chased him on the sand-bank for a quarter of a mile. He told me afterwards, he thought he should have dropped down dead with fright, for he was firmly persuaded, if I had caught him, I should have bundled him into the cayman's jaws. Here then we stood, in silence, like a calm before a thunder-storm. " Hoc res summa loco. Scinditur in contraria vulgus." They wanted to kill him, and I wanted to take him alive.

I now walked up and down the sand, revolving a dozen projects in my head. The canoe was at a considerable distance, and I ordered the people to bring it round to the place where we were. The mast was eight feet long, and not much thicker than my wrist. I took it out of the canoe, and wrapped the sail round the end of it. Now it appeared clear to me, that if I went down upon one knee, and held the mast in the same position as the soldier holds his bayonet when rushing to the charge, I could force it

down the cayman's throat, should he come open-mouthed
at me. When this was told to the Indians, they brightened
up, and said they would help me to pull him out of the
river.

"Brave squad!" said I to myself, "'Audax omnia
perpeti,' now that you have got me betwixt yourselves
and danger." I then mustered all hands for the last
time before the battle. We were, four South American
savages, two negroes from Africa, a creole from Trinidad,
and myself a white man from Yorkshire. In fact, a little
tower of Babel group, in dress, no dress, address, and
language.

Daddy Quashi hung in the rear; I showed him a large
Spanish knife, which I always carried in the waistband of
my trousers: it spoke volumes to him, and he shrugged
up his shoulders in absolute despair. The sun was just
peeping over the high forests on the eastern hills, as if
coming to look on, and bid us act with becoming fortitude.
I placed all the people at the end of the rope, and ordered
them to pull till the cayman appeared on the surface of
the water; and then, should he plunge, to slacken the rope
and let him go again into the deep.

I now took the mast of the canoe in my hand (the sail
being tied round the end of the mast) and sunk down upon
one knee, about four yards from the water's edge, determining to thrust it down his throat, in case he gave me
an opportunity. I certainly felt somewhat uncomfortable
in this situation, and I thought of Cerberus on the other
side of the Styx ferry. The people pulled the cayman to
the surface; he plunged furiously as soon as he arrived in
these upper regions, and immediately went below again
on their slackening the rope. I saw enough not to fall
in love at first sight. I now told them we would run all
risks, and have him on land immediately. They pulled

again, and out he came,—"monstrum horrendum, informe."
This was an interesting moment. I kept my position
firmly, with my eye fixed steadfast on him.

By this time the cayman was within two yards of me.
I saw he was in a state of fear and perturbation; I instantly dropped the mast, sprang up, and jumped on his
back, turning half round as I vaulted, so that I gained my
seat with my face in a right position. I immediately
seized his fore legs, and, by main force, twisted them on
his back; thus they served me for a bridle.

He now seemed to have recovered from his surprise, and
probably fancying himself in hostile company, he began to
plunge furiously, and lashed the sand with his long and
powerful tail. I was out of reach of the strokes of it, by
being near his head. He continued to plunge and strike,
and made my seat very uncomfortable. It must have been
a fine sight for an unoccupied spectator.

The people roared out in triumph, and were so vociferous,
that it was some time before they heard me tell them to
pull me and my beast of burden farther inland. I was
apprehensive the rope might break, and then there would
have been every chance of going down to the regions under
water with the cayman. That would have been more
perilous than Arion's marine morning ride :—

"Delphini insidens vada cærula sulcat Arion."

The people now dragged us above forty yards on the
sand : it was the first and last time I was ever on a
cayman's back. Should it be asked, how I managed to
keep my seat, I would answer,—I hunted some years with
Lord Darlington's fox-hounds.

After repeated attempts to regain his liberty, the cayman
gave in, and became tranquil through exhaustion. I now
managed to tie up his jaws, and firmly secured his fore-

feet in the position I had held them. We had now another severe struggle for superiority, but he was soon overcome and again remained quiet. While some of the people were pressing upon his head and shoulders, I threw myself on his tail, and by keeping it down to the sand, prevented him from kicking up another dust. He was finally conveyed to the canoe, and then to the place where we had suspended our hammocks. There I cut his throat; and, after breakfast was over, commenced the dissection.

Now that the affray had ceased, Daddy Quashi played a good finger and thumb at breakfast; he said he found himself much revived, and became very talkative and useful, as there was no longer any danger. He was a faithful, honest negro. His master, my worthy friend Mr. Edmonstone, had been so obliging as to send out particular orders to the colony, that the Daddy should attend me all the time I was in the forest. He had lived in the wilds of Demerara with Mr. Edmonstone for many years; and often amused me with the account of the frays his master had had in the woods with snakes, wild beasts, and runaway negroes. Old age was now coming fast upon him; he had been an able fellow in his younger days, and a gallant one too, for he had a large scar over his eyebrow, caused by the stroke of a cutlass, from another negro, while the Daddy was engaged in an intrigue.

The back of the cayman may be said to be almost impenetrable to a musket-ball, but his sides are not near so strong; and are easily pierced with an arrow; indeed, were they as strong as the back and the belly, there would be no part of the cayman's body soft and elastic enough to admit of expansion after taking in a supply of food.

The cayman has no grinders; his teeth are entirely made for snatch and swallow; there are thirty-two in each jaw. Perhaps no animal in existence bears more decided marks in his countenance of cruelty and malice than the cayman. He is the scourge and terror of all the large rivers in South America near the line.

One Sunday evening, some years ago, as I was walking with Don Felipe de Ynciarte, governor of Angustura, on the bank of the Oroonoque, " Stop here a minute or two, Don Carlos," said he to me, " while I recount a sad accident. One fine evening last year, as the people of Angustura were sauntering up and down here, in the Alameda, I was within twenty yards of this place, when I saw a large cayman rush out of the river, seize a man, and carry him down, before anybody had it in his power to assist him. The screams of the poor fellow were terrible as the cayman was running off with him. He plunged into the river with his prey; we instantly lost sight of him, and never saw or heard him more."

I was a day and a half in dissecting our cayman, and then we all got ready to return to Demerara.

It was much more perilous to descend than to ascend the falls in the Essequibo.

The place we had to pass had proved fatal to four Indians about a month before. The water foamed, and dashed and boiled, amongst the steep and craggy rocks, and seemed to warn us to be careful how we ventured there.

I was for all hands to get out of the canoe, and then after lashing a long rope ahead and astern, we might have climbed from rock to rock, and tempered her in her passage down, and our getting out would have lightened her much. But the negro who had joined us at Mrs. Peterson's said he was sure it would be safer to stay in the canoe while she went down the fall. I was loath to give way to him; but I did so this time against my better judgment, as he assured me that he was accustomed to pass and repass these falls.

Accordingly we determined to push down: I was at the helm, the rest at their paddles. But before we got half way through, the rushing waters deprived the canoe of all power of steerage, and she became the sport of the torrent; in a second she was half full of water, and I cannot comprehend to this day why she did not go down; luckily the people exerted themselves to the utmost,—she got headway, and they pulled through the whirlpool; I being quite in the stern of the canoe, part of a wave struck me, and nearly knocked me overboard.

We now paddled to some rocks at a distance, got out, unloaded the canoe, and dried the cargo in the sun, which was very hot and powerful. Had it been the wet season, almost everything would have been spoiled.

After this, the voyage down the Essequibo was quick and pleasant till we reached the sea-coast; there we had a trying day of it; the wind was dead against us, and the sun remarkably hot; we got twice aground upon a mud-flat, and were twice obliged to get out, up to the middle in mud, to shove the canoe through it. Half way betwixt the Essequibo and Demerara the tide of flood caught us; and after the utmost exertions, it was half-past six in the evening before we got to Georgetown.

We had been out from six in the morning in an open canoe on the sea-coast, without umbrella or awning, exposed all day to the fiery rays of a tropical sun. My face smarted so that I could get no sleep during the night, and the next morning my lips were all in blisters. The Indian Yan went down to the Essequibo a copper colour, but the reflection of the sun from the sea, and from the sand-banks in the river, had turned him nearly black. He laughed at himself, and said that the Indians in the Demerara would not know him again. I stayed one day in Georgetown, and then set off the next morning for head-quarters in Mibiri creek, where I finished the cayman.

Here the remaining time was spent in collecting birds, and in paying particular attention to their haunts and economy. The rainy season having set in, the weather became bad and stormy; the lightning and thunder were incessant: the days cloudy, and the nights cold and misty. I had now been eleven months in the forests, and collected some rare insects, two hundred and thirty birds, two land tortoises, five armadillas, two large serpents, a sloth, an ant-bear, and a cayman.

I left the wilds and repaired to Georgetown to spend a few days with Mr. R. Edmonstone previous to embarking for Europe. I must here return my sincerest thanks to this worthy gentleman for his many kindnesses to me; his friendship was of the utmost service to me, and he never failed to send me supplies up into the forest by every opportunity.

I embarked for England, on board the *Dee* West-India-man, commanded by Captain Grey.

Sir Joseph Banks had often told me, he hoped that I would give a lecture in public, on the new mode I had discovered of preparing specimens in natural history for museums. I always declined to do so, as I despaired of ever being able to hit upon a proper method of doing quadrupeds; and I was aware that it would have been an imperfect lecture to treat of birds only. I imparted what little knowledge I was master of, at Sir Joseph's, to the unfortunate gentlemen who went to Africa to explore the Congo; and that was all that took place in the shape of a lecture. Now that I had hit upon the way of doing quadrupeds, I drew up a little plan on board the *Dee*, which I trusted would have been of service to naturalists; and by proving to them the superiority of the new plan, they would probably be induced to abandon the old and common way, which is a disgrace to the present age, and renders hideous every specimen in every museum that I have as yet visited. I intended to have given three lectures; one on insects and serpents; one on birds; and one on quadrupeds. But, as it will be shortly seen, this little plan was doomed not to be unfolded to public view. Illiberality blasted it in the bud.

We had a pleasant passage across the Atlantic, and arrived in the Mersey in fine trim and good spirits. Great was the attention I received from the commander of the *Dee.* He and his mate, Mr. Spence, took every care of my collection.

On our landing, the gentlemen of the Liverpool Customhouse received me as an old friend and acquaintance, and obligingly offered their services.

Twice before had I landed in Liverpool, and twice had I reason to admire their conduct and liberality. They knew I was incapable of trying to introduce anything contraband, and they were aware that I never dreamed of turning to profit the specimens I had procured. They considered that I had left a comfortable home in quest of science; and that I had wandered into far-distant climes, and gone barefooted, ill-clothed, and ill-fed, through swamps and woods, to procure specimens, some of which had never been seen in Europe. They considered that it would be difficult to fix a price upon specimens which had never been bought or sold, and which never were to be, as they were intended to ornament my own house. It was hard, they said, to have exposed myself, for years, to danger, and then be obliged to pay on returning to my native land. Under these considerations, they fixed a moderate duty, which satisfied all parties.

However, this last expedition ended not so. It taught me how hard it is to learn the grand lesson, " æquam memento rebus in arduis servare mentem."

But my good friends in the Custom-house of Liverpool were not to blame. On the contrary, they did all in their power to procure balm for me instead of rue. But it would not answer.

They appointed a very civil officer to attend me to the ship. While we were looking into some of the boxes, to see that the specimens were properly stowed, previous to their being conveyed to the king's depôt, another officer entered the cabin. He was an entire stranger to me, and seemed wonderfully aware of his own consequence. Without preface or apology, he thrust his head over my shoulder, and said, we had no business to have opened a single box without his permission. I answered, they had been opened almost every day since they had come on board, and that I considered there was no harm in doing so.

He then left the cabin, and I said to myself as he went out, " I suspect I shall see that man again at Philippi." The boxes, ten in number, were conveyed in safety from the ship to the depôt. I then proceeded to the Custom-house. The necessary forms were gone through, and a proportionate duty, according to circumstances, was paid.

This done, we returned from the Custom-house to the depôt, accompanied by several gentlemen who wished to see the collection. They expressed themselves highly gratified. The boxes were closed, and nothing now remained but to convey them to the cart, which was in attendance at the door of the depôt. Just as one of the inferior officers was carrying a box thither, in stepped the man whom I suspected I should see again at Philippi. He abruptly declared himself dissatisfied with the valuation which the gentlemen of the Customs had put upon the collection, and said he must detain it. I remonstrated, but it was all in vain.

After this pitiful stretch of power, and bad compliment to the other officers of the Customs, who had been satisfied with the valuation, this man had the folly to take me aside, and after assuring me that he had a great regard for the arts and sciences, he lamented that conscience obliged him to do what he had done, and he wished he had been fifty miles from Liverpool at the time that it fell to his lot to detain the collection. Had he looked in my face as he said this, he would have seen no marks of credulity there.

I now returned to the Custom-house, and after expressing my opinion of the officer's conduct at the depôt, I pulled a bunch of keys (which belonged to the detained boxes) out of my pocket, laid them on the table, took my leave of the gentlemen present, and soon after set off for Yorkshire.

I saved nothing from the grasp of the stranger officer but a pair of live Malay fowls, which a gentleman in Georgetown had made me a present of. I had collected in the forest several eggs of curious birds, in hopes of introducing the breed into England, and had taken great pains in doing them over with gum-arabic, and in packing them in charcoal, according to a receipt I had seen in the gazette, from the *Edinburgh Philosophical Journal.* But these were detained in the depôt, instead of being placed under a hen ; which utterly ruined all my hopes of rearing a new species of birds in England. Titled personages in London interested themselves in behalf of the collection, but all in vain. And vain also were the public and private representations of the first officer of the Liverpool Custom-house in my favour.

At last there came an order from the Treasury to say, that any specimens Mr. Waterton intended to present to public institutions might pass duty free ; but those which he intended to keep for himself must pay the duty !

A friend now wrote to me from Liverpool, requesting that I would come over and pay the duty, in order to save the collection, which had just been detained there six weeks. 1 did so. On paying an additional duty, (for the moderate duty first imposed had already been paid,) the man who had detained the collection delivered it up to me, assuring me that it had been well taken care of, and that a fire had been frequently made in the room. It is but justice to add, that on opening the boxes, there was nothing injured.

I could never get a clue to these harsh and unexpected measures, except that there had been some recent smuggling discovered in Liverpool ; and that the man in question had been sent down from London to act the part of Argus. If so, I landed in an evil hour; " nefasto die ; " making good the Spanish proverb, " Pagan a las veces, justos por pecadores ; " at times the innocent suffer for the guilty. After all, a little encouragement, in the shape of exemption from paying the duty on this collection, might have been expected ; but it turned out otherwise ; and after expending large sums in pursuit of natural history, on my return home I was doomed to pay for my success :—

> " Hic finis, Caroli fatorum, hic exitus illum,
>   Sorte tulit ! "

Thus, my fleece, already ragged and torn with the thorns and briers, which one must naturally expect to find in distant and untrodden wilds, was shorn, I may say, on its return to England.

However, this is nothing new ; Sancho Panza must have heard of similar cases ; for he says, " Muchos van por

lana, y vuelven trasquilados;" many go for wool, and
come home shorn.   In order to pick up matter for natural
history, I have wandered through the wildest parts of
South America's equatorial regions.   I have attacked and
slain a modern Python, and rode on the back of a cayman
close to the water's edge; a very different situation from
that of a Hyde-park dandy on his Sunday prancer before
the ladies.   Alone and barefoot I have pulled poisonous
snakes out of their lurking-places; climbed up trees to
peep into holes for bats and vampires, and for days together
hastened through sun and rain to the thickest parts of the
forest to procure specimens I had never got before.   In
fine, I have pursued the wild beasts over hill and dale,
through swamps and quagmires, now scorched by the
noon-day sun, now drenched by the pelting shower, and
returned to the hammock, to satisfy the cravings of
hunger, often on a poor and scanty supper.

These vicissitudes have turned to chestnut hue a once
English complexion, and changed the colour of my hair,
before father Time had meddled with it.   The detention of
the collection after it had fairly passed the Customs, and
the subsequent order from the Treasury that I should pay
duty for the specimens, unless they were presented to
some public institution, have cast a damp upon my energy,
and forced, as it were, the cup of Lethe to my lips, by
drinking which I have forgot my former intention of
giving a lecture in public on preparing specimens to
adorn museums.   In fine, it is this ungenerous treatment
that has paralyzed my plans, and caused me to give up
the idea I once had of inserting here the newly-discovered
mode of preparing quadrupeds and serpents; and without
it, the account of this last expedition to the wilds of
Guiana is nothing but a— fragment.

                              Farewell, Gentle Reader.

FOURTH JOURNEY.

CHAPTER I.

"Nunc huc, nunc illuc et utrinque sine ordine curro."

Three years in England.—Sail for New York.—Nomenclature.—Alteration of scenery.—A sprained ankle.—Magnificent cure.—Feats of
climbing. — Quebec. — Irish emigrants.— Ticonderago.— Saratoga.—
Philadelphia.—White-headed Eagle.—Form and fashion.—Climate.—
Forebodings of the civil war.—Sail for Antigua.

COURTEOUS reader, when I bade thee last farewell, I
thought these Wanderings were brought to a final close ;
afterwards I often roved in imagination through distant
countries famous for natural history, but felt no strong
inclination to go thither, as the last adventure had terminated in such unexpected vexation. The departure of
the Cuckoo and Swallow, and summer birds of passage,
for warmer regions, once so interesting to me, now scarcely
caused me to turn my face to the south ; and I continued
in this cold and dreary climate for three years. During
this period, I seldom or ever mounted my hobby-horse ;
indeed it may be said, with the old song—

"The saddle and bridle were laid on the shelf,"

and only taken down once, on the night that I was
induced to give a lecture in the philosophical hall of

Leeds. A little after this, Wilson's *Ornithology of the United States* fell into my hands.

The desire I had of seeing that country, together with the animated description which Wilson had given of the birds, fanned up the almost expiring flame. I forgot the vexations already alluded to, and set off for New York, in the beautiful packet *John Wells,* commanded by Captain Harris. The passage was long and cold; but the elegant accommodations on board, and the polite attention of the commander, rendered it very agreeable; and I landed, in health and merriment, in the stately capital of the new world.

We will soon pen down a few remarks on this magnificent city, but not just now. I want to venture into the north-west country, and get to their great canal, which the world talks so much about, though I fear it will be hard work to make one's way through bugs, bears, brutes, and buffaloes, which we Europeans imagine are so frequent and ferocious in these never-ending western wilds.

I left New York on a fine morning in July, without one letter of introduction, for the city of Albany, some hundred and eighty miles up the celebrated Hudson. I seldom care about letters of introduction, for I am one of those who depend much upon an accidental acquaintance. Full many a face do I see, as I go wandering up and down the world, whose mild eye, and sweet and placid features, seem to beckon. to me, and say, as it were, "Speak but civilly to me, and I will do what I can for you." Such a face as this is worth more than a dozen letters of introduction; and such a face, gentle reader, I found on board the steam-boat from New York to the city of Albany.

There was a great number of well-dressed ladies and gentlemen in the vessel, all entire strangers to me. I fancied I could see several whose countenances invited an unknown wanderer to come and take a seat beside them; but there was one who encouraged me more than the rest. I saw clearly that he was an American, and I judged, by his manners and appearance, that he had not spent all his time upon his native soil. I was right in this conjecture, for he afterwards told me that he had been in France and England. I saluted him as one stranger gentleman ought to salute another when he wants a little information; and soon after, I dropped in a word or two by which he might conjecture that I was a foreigner; but I did not tell him so; I wished him to make the discovery himself.

He entered into conversation with the openness and candour which is so remarkable in the American; and in a little time observed that he presumed I was from the old country. I told him that I was, and added, that I was an entire stranger on board. I saw his eye brighten up at the prospect he had of doing a fellow-creature a kind turn or two, and he completely won my regard by an affability which I shall never forget. This obliging gentleman pointed out everything that was grand and interesting as the steam-boat plied her course up the majestic Hudson Here the Catskill mountains raised their lofty summit; and there the hills came sloping down to the water's edge. Here he pointed to an aged and venerable oak, which having escaped the levelling axe of man, seemed almost to defy the blasting storm and desolating hand of time; and there, he bade me observe an extended tract of wood, by which I might form an idea how rich and grand the face of the country had once been. Here it was that, in the great and momentous struggle, the colonists lost the day; and there, they carried all before them :—

> ⁴ They closed full fast, on every side
> No slackness there was found ;
> And many a gallant gentleman
> Lay gasping on the ground."

Here, in fine, stood a noted regiment; there, moved their great captain; here, the fleets fired their broadsides; and there, the whole force rushed on to battle:—

> "Hic Dolopum manus, hic magnus tendebat Achilles,
> Classibus hic locus, hic acies certare solebat."

At tea-time we took our tea together, and the next morning this worthy American walked up with me to the inn in Albany, shook me by the hand, and then went his way. I bade him farewell, and again farewell, and hoped that fortune might bring us together again once more. Possibly she may yet do so; and should it be in England, I will take him to my house, as an old friend and acquaintance, and offer him my choicest cheer.

It is at Albany that the great canal opens into the Hudson, and joins the waters of this river to those of Lake Erie. The Hudson, at the city of Albany, is distant from Lake Erie about three hundred and sixty miles. The level of the lake is five hundred and sixty-four feet higher than the Hudson, and there are eighty-one locks on the canal. It is to the genius and perseverance of De Witt Clinton that the United States owe the almost incalculable advantages of this inland navigation. "Exegit monumentum ære perennius." You may either go along it all the way to Buffalo, on Lake Erie, or by the stage; or sometimes on one and then in the other, just as you think fit. Grand, indeed, is the scenery by either route, and capital the accommodations. Cold and phlegmatic must he be who is not warmed into admiration by the surrounding scenery, and charmed with the affability of the travellers he meets on the way.

This is now the season of roving, and joy and merriment for the gentry of this happy country. Thousands are on the move from different parts of the Union for the springs and lakes, and the falls of Niagara. There is nothing haughty or forbidding in the Americans; and wherever you meet them, they appear to be quite at home. This is exactly what it ought to be, and very much in favour of the foreigner who journeys amongst them. The immense number of highly polished females who go in the stages to visit the different places of amusement, and see the stupendous natural curiosities of this extensive country, incontestably proves that safety and convenience are ensured to them, and that the most distant attempt at rudeness would, by common consent, be immediately put down.

By the time I had got to Schenectady, I began strongly to suspect that I had come into the wrong country to look for bugs, bears, brutes, and buffaloes. It is an enchanting journey from Albany to Schenectady, and from thence to Lake Erie. The situation of the city of Utica is particularly attractive; the Mohawk running close by it, the fertile fields and woody mountains, and the falls of Trenton, forcibly press the stranger to stop a day or two here before he proceeds onward to the lake.

At some far-distant period, when it will not be possible to find the place where many of the celebrated cities of the East once stood, the world will have to thank the United States of America for bringing their names into the western regions. It is, indeed, a pretty thought of these people to give to their rising towns the names of places so famous and conspicuous in former times.

As I was sitting one evening under an oak, in the high grounds behind Utica, I could not look down upon the city without thinking of Cato and his misfortunes. Had the town been called Crofton, or Warmfield, or Dewsbury, there would have been nothing remarkable in it; but Utica at once revived the scenes at school long past and half forgotten, and carried me with full speed

back again to Italy, and from thence to Africa. I crossed
the Rubicon with Cæsar; fought at Pharsalia; saw poor
Pompey into Larissa, and tried to wrest the fatal sword
from Cato's hand in Utica. When I perceived he was no
more, I mourned over the noble-minded man who took
that part which he thought would most benefit his country. There is something magnificent in the idea of a man
taking by choice the conquered side. The Roman gods
themselves did otherwise.

" *Victrix* causa Diis placuit, sed *victa* Catoni."

"In this did Cato with the Gods divide,
   They chose the conquering, *he* the conquer'd side."

The whole of the country from Utica to Buffalo is
pleasing; and the intervening of the inland lakes, large
and deep and clear, adds considerably to the effect. The
spacious size of the inns, their excellent provisions, and
the attention which the traveller receives in going from
Albany to Buffalo, must at once convince him that this
country is very much visited by strangers; and he will
draw the conclusion that there must be something in it
uncommonly interesting to cause so many travellers to
pass to and fro.

Nature is losing fast her ancient garb, and putting on a
new dress in these extensive regions. Most of the stately
timber has been carried away; thousands of trees are
lying prostrate on the ground; while meadows, corn-fields,
villages, and pastures are ever and anon bursting upon the
traveller's view as he journeys on through the remaining
tracts of wood. I wish I could say a word or two for the
fine timber which is yet standing. Spare it, gentle inhabitants, for your country's sake; these noble sons of the
forest beautify your landscapes beyond all description;
when they are gone, a century will not replace their loss :

they cannot, they must not fall; their vernal bloom, their summer richness and autumnal tints, please and refresh the eye of man; and even when the days of joy and warmth are fled, the wintry blast soothes the listening ear with a sublime and pleasing melancholy as it howls through their naked branches.

> " Around me trees unnumber'd rise,
> Beautiful in various dyes:
> The gloomy pine, the poplar blue,
> The yellow beech, the sable yew;
> The slender fir, that taper grows,
> The sturdy oak, with broad-spread boughs."

A few miles before you reach Buffalo, the road is low and bad, and in stepping out of the stage I sprained my foot very severely; it swelled to a great size, and caused me many a day of pain and mortification, as will be seen in the sequel.

Buffalo looks down on Lake Erie, and possesses a fine and commodious inn. At a little distance is the Black Rock, and there you pass over to the Canada side. A stage is in waiting to convey you some sixteen or twenty miles down to the falls. Long before you reach the spot you hear the mighty roar of waters, and see the spray of the far-famed falls of Niagara, rising up like a column to the heavens, and mingling with the passing clouds.

At this stupendous cascade of nature, the waters of the lake fall one hundred and seventy-six feet perpendicular. It has been calculated, I forget by whom, that the quantity of water discharged down this mighty fall, is six hundred and seventy thousand two hundred and fifty-five tons per minute. There are two large inns on the Canada side; but, after you have satisfied your curiosity in viewing the falls, and in seeing the rainbow in the foam far below where you are standing, do not, I pray you, tarry long at

either of them. Cross over to the American side, and
there you will find a spacious inn, which has nearly all the
attractions: there you meet with great attention, and
every accommodation.

The day is passed in looking at the falls, and in sauntering up and down the wooded and rocky environs of the
Niagara; and the evening is often enlivened by the merry
dance.

Words can hardly do justice to the unaffected ease and
elegance of the American ladies who visit the falls of
Niagara. The traveller need not rove in imagination
through Circassia in search of fine forms, or through
England, France, and Spain, to meet with polished
females. The numbers who are continually arriving here
from all parts of the Union confirm the justness of this
remark.

I was looking one evening at a dance, being unable to
join in it on account of the accident I had received near
Buffalo, when a young American entered the ball-room
with such a becoming air and grace, that it was impossible
not to have been struck with her appearance.

> " Her bloom was like the springing flower
>   That sips the silver dew,
> The rose was budded in her cheek,
>   Just opening to the view."

I could not help feeling a wish to know where she had

> " Into such beauty spread, and blown so fair."

Upon inquiry, I found that she was from the city of
Albany. The more I looked at the fair Albanese, the
more I was convinced, that in the United States of America
may be found grace and beauty and symmetry equal to
anything in the old world.

I now for good and all (and well I might) gave up the idea of finding bugs, bears, brutes, and buffaloes in this country, and was thoroughly satisfied that I had laboured under a great mistake in suspecting that I should ever meet with them.

I wished to join in the dance where the fair Albanese was " to brisk notes in cadence beating," but the state of my unlucky foot rendered it impossible; and as I sat with it reclined upon a sofa, full many a passing gentleman stopped to inquire the cause of my misfortune, presuming at the same time that I had got an attack of gout. Now this surmise of theirs always mortified me; for I never had a fit of gout in my life, and moreover, never expect, to have one.

In many of the inns in the United States, there is an album on the table, in which travellers insert their arrival and departure, and now and then indulge in a little flash or two of wit.

I thought, under existing circumstances, that there would be no harm in briefly telling my misadventure; and so, taking up the pen, I wrote what follows; and was never after asked a single question about the gout.

" C. Waterton, of Walton-Hall, in the county of York, England, arrived at the Falls of Niagara in July, 1824, and begs leave to pen down the following dreadful accident :—

> " He sprained his foot, and hurt his toe,
> On the rough road near Buffalo.
> It quite distresses him to stagger a-
> Long the sharp rocks of famed Niagara.
> So thus he's doomed to drink the measure
> Of pain, in lieu of that of pleasure.
> On Hope's delusive pinions borne,
> He came for wool, and goes back shorn.
> *N. B.*—Here he alludes to nothing but
> Th' adventure of his toe and foot ;

Save this,—he sees all that which can
Delight and charm the soul of man,
But feels it not,—because his toe
And foot together plague him so."

I remember once to have sprained my ankle very violently, many years ago, and that the doctor ordered me to hold it under the pump two or three times a day. Now, in the United States of America, all is upon a grand scale, except taxation; and I am convinced that the traveller's ideas become much more enlarged as he journeys through the country. This being the case, I can easily account for the desire I felt to hold my sprained foot under the fall of Niagara. I descended the winding staircase which has been made for the accommodation of travellers, and then hobbled on to the scene of action. As I held my leg under the fall, I tried to meditate on the immense difference there was betwixt a house-pump and this tremendous cascade of nature, and what effect it might have upon the sprain; but the magnitude of the subject was too overwhelming, and I was obliged to drop it.

Perhaps, indeed, there was an unwarrantable tincture of vanity in an unknown wanderer wishing to have it in his power to tell the world, that he had held his sprained foot under a fall of water which discharges six hundred and seventy thousand two hundred and fifty-five tons per minute. A gentle purling stream would have suited better. Now, it would have become Washington to have quenched his battle-thirst in the fall of Niagara; and there was something royal in the idea of Cleopatra drinking pearl-vinegar, made from the grandest pearl in Egypt; and it became Caius Marius to send word, that he was sitting upon the ruins of Carthage. Here, we have the person suited to the thing, and the thing to the person.

If, gentle reader, thou wouldst allow me to indulge a little longer in this harmless pen-errantry, I would tell thee, that I have had my ups and downs in life, as well as other people; for I have climbed to the point of the conductor above the cross on the top of St. Peter's, in Rome, and left my glove there. I have stood on one foot, upon the Guardian Angel's head, on the castle of St. Angelo; and, as I have just told thee, I have been low down under the fall of Niagara. But this is neither here nor there; let us proceed to something else.

When the pain of my foot had become less violent, and the swelling somewhat abated, I could not resist the inclination I felt to go down Ontario, and so on to Montreal and Quebec, and take Lakes Champlain and George in my way back to Albany.

Just as I had made up my mind to it, a family from the Bowling-green, in New York, who was going the same route, politely invited me to join their party. Nothing could be more fortunate. They were highly accomplished. The young ladies sang delightfully; and all contributed their portion, to render the tour pleasant and amusing.

Travellers had already filled the world with descriptions of the bold and sublime scenery from Lake Erie to Quebec:—

> " The fountain's fall, the river's flow,
> The woody valleys, warm and low ;
> The windy summit, wild and high,
> Roughly rushing to the sky."

And there is scarce one of them who has not described the achievements of former and latter times, on the different battle-grounds. Here, great Wolfe expired. Brave Montcalm was carried, mortally wounded, through yonder gate. Here fell the gallant Brock; and there General Sheaffee captured all the invaders. And in yonder harbour may be seen the mouldering remnants of British vessels. Their hour of misfortune has long passed away. The victors have now no use for them in an inland lake. Some have already sunk, while others, dismantled and half-dismasted, are just above the water, waiting, in shattered state, that destiny which must sooner or later destroy the fairest works of man.

The excellence and despatch of the steam-boats, together with the company which the traveller is sure to meet with at this time of the year, render the trip down to Montreal and Quebec very agreeable.

The Canadians are a quiet, and apparently a happy people. They are very courteous and affable to strangers. On comparing them with the character which a certain female traveller, a journalist, has thought fit to give them, the stranger might have great doubts whether or not he were amongst the Canadians.

Montreal, Quebec, and the falls of Montmorency, are well worth going to see. They are making tremendous fortifications at Quebec. It will be the Gibraltar of the new world. When one considers its distance from Europe, and takes a view of its powerful and enterprising neighbour, Virgil's remark at once rushes into the mind,

"Sic vos non vobis nidificatis aves."

I left Montreal with regret. I had the good fortune to be introduced to the Professors of the College. These fathers are a very learned and worthy set of gentlemen ; and on my taking leave of them, I felt a heaviness at heart, in reflecting that I had not more time to cultivate their acquaintance.

In all the way from Buffalo to Quebec, I only met with one bug ; and I cannot even swear that it belonged to the United States. In going down the St. Lawrence, in the steam-boat, I felt something crossing over my neck; and on laying hold of it with my finger and thumb, it turned out to be a little half-grown, ill-conditioned bug. Now, whether it were going from the American to the Canada side, or from the Canada to the American, and had taken the advantage of my shoulders to ferry itself across, I could not tell. Be this as it may, I thought of my uncle Toby and the fly; and so, in lieu of placing it upon the deck, and then putting my thumb-nail vertically upon it, I quietly chucked it amongst some baggage that was close by, and recommended it to get ashore by the first opportunity.

When we had seen all that was worth seeing in Quebec and at the falls of Montmorency, and had been on board the enormous ship *Columbus*, we returned for a day or two to Montreal, and then proceeded to Saratoga by Lakes Champlain and George.

The steam-boat from Quebec to Montreal had above five hundred Irish emigrants on board. They were going " they hardly knew whither," far away from dear Ireland. It made one's heart ache to see them all huddled together, without any expectation of ever revisiting their native soil. We feared that the sorrow of leaving home for ever, the miserable accommodation on board the ship which had brought them away, and the tossing of the angry ocean, in a long and dreary voyage, would have rendered them callous to good behaviour. But it was quite otherwise. They conducted themselves with great propriety. Every American on board seemed to feel for them. And then " they were so full of wretchedness. Need and oppression stared in their eyes. Upon their backs hung ragged misery. The world was not their friend." ` Poor dear Ireland, exclaimed an aged female, as I was talking to her, I shall never see it any more ! and then her tears began to

flow.   Probably the scenery on the banks of the St.
Lawrence recalled to her mind the remembrance of spots
once interesting to her :

" The lovely daughter,—lovelier in her tears,
The fond companion of her father's years,
Here silent stood,—neglectful of her charms,
And left her lover's for her father's arms.
With louder plaints the mother spoke her woes,
And blessed the cot where every pleasure rose ;
And pressed her thoughtless babes with many a tear,
And clasped them close, in sorrow doubly dear,
While the fond husband strove to lend relief,
In all the silent manliness of grief."

We went a few miles out of our route to take a look at
the once formidable fortress of Ticonderoga.   It has long
been in ruins, and seems as if it were doomed to moulder
quite away.

" Ever and anon there falls
Huge heaps of hoary moulder'd walls.
But time has seen, that lifts the low
And level lays the lofty brow,
Has seen this ruin'd pile complete,
Big with the vanity of state ;
But transient is the smile of fate."

The scenery of Lake George is superb ; the inn remarkably spacious and well attended ; and the conveyance
from thence to Saratoga very good.   He must be sorely
afflicted with spleen and jaundice, who, on his arrival at
Saratoga, remarks, there is nothing here worth coming to
see.   It is a gay and fashionable place ; has four uncommonly fine hotels ; its waters, for medicinal virtues, are
surpassed by none in the known world ; and it is resorted
to, throughout the whole of the summer, by foreigners
and natives of the first consideration.   Saratoga pleased
me much ; and afforded a fair opportunity of forming a
pretty correct idea of the gentry of the United States.

There is a pleasing frankness, and ease and becoming dignity, in the American ladies; and the good humour, and absence of all haughtiness and puppyism in the gentlemen, must, no doubt, impress the traveller with elevated notions of the company who visit this famous spa.

During my stay here, all was joy, and affability, and mirth. In the mornings the ladies played and sang for us; and the evenings were generally enlivened with the merry dance. Here I bade farewell to the charming family, in whose company I had passed so many happy days, and proceeded to Albany.

The stage stopped a little while in the town of Troy. The name alone was quite sufficient to recall to the mind scenes long past and gone. Poor king Priam! Napoleon's sorrows, sad and piercing as they were, did not come up to those of this ill-fated monarch. The Greeks first set his town on fire, and then began to bully :—

"Incensâ Danai dominantur in urbe."

One of his sons was slain before his face; "ante ora parentum, concidit." Another was crushed to mummy by boa-constrictors; "immensis orbibus angues." His city was rased to the ground, "jacet Ilion ingens." And Pyrrhus ran him through with his sword, "capulo tenus abdidit ensem." This last may be considered as a fortunate stroke for the poor old king. Had his life been spared at this juncture he could not have lived long. He must have died broken-hearted. He would have seen his son-in-law, once master of a noble stud, now, for want of a horse, obliged to carry off his father, up hill, on his own back, "cessi et sublato, montem genitore petivi." He would have heard of his grandson being thrown neck and heels from a high tower, " mittitur Astyanax illis de turribus." He would have been informed of his wife tearing out the eyes of king Odrysius with her finger nails, "digitos in perfida lumina condit." Soon after this, losing all appearance of woman, she became a bitch,

> "Perdidit infelix, hominis post omnia formam,"

and rent the heavens with her howlings,

> Externasque novo latratu terruit auras."

Then, becoming distracted with the remembrance of her misfortunes, "veterum memor illa malorum," she took off howling into the fields of Thrace,—

> "Tum quoque Sithonios, ululavit mœsta per agros."

Juno, Jove's wife and sister, was heard to declare, that poor Hecuba did not deserve so terrible a fate,—

> "Ipsa Jovis conjuxque sororque,
> Eventus Hecubam meruisse negaverit illos."

Had poor Priam escaped from Troy, one thing, and only one thing, would have given him a small ray of satisfaction, viz., he would have heard of one of his daughters nobly preferring to leave this world, rather than live to become servant-maid to old Grecian ladies :—

> "Non ego Myrmidonum sedes, Dolopumve superbas,
> Adspiciam, aut Graiis servitum matribus ibo."

At some future period, should a foreign armed force, or intestine broils, (all which heaven avert,) raise Troy to the dignity of a fortified city, Virgil's prophecy may then be fulfilled,

> "Atque iterum ad Trojam magnus mittetur Achilles."

After leaving Troy, I passed through a fine country to Albany; and then proceeded by steam down the Hudson to New York.

Travellers hesitate whether to give the preference to Philadelphia or to New York. Philadelphia is certainly a noble city, and its environs beautiful; but there is a degree of quiet and sedateness in it, which, though no doubt very agreeable to the man of calm and domestic habits, is not so attractive to one of speedy movements. The quantity of white marble which is used in the buildings, gives to Philadelphia a gay and lively appearance; but the sameness of the streets, and their crossing each other at right angles, are somewhat tiresome. The water-works which supply the city, are a proud monument of the skill and enterprise of its inhabitants; and the market is well worth the attention of the stranger.

When you go to Philadelphia, be sure not to forget to visit the Museum. It will afford you a great treat. Some of Mr. Peale's family are constantly in it, and are ever ready to show the curiosities to strangers, and to give them every necessary information. Mr. Peale has now passed his eightieth year, and appears to possess the vivacity, and, I may almost add, the activity of youth.

To the indefatigable exertions of this gentleman is the western world indebted for the possession of this splendid museum. Mr. Peale is, moreover, an excellent artist. Look attentively, I pray you, at the portrait he has taken of himself, by desire of the State of Pennsylvania. On entering the room he appears in the act of holding up a curtain, to show you his curiosities. The effect of the light upon his head is infinitely striking. I have never seen anything finer in the way of light and shade. The skeleton of the mammoth is a national treasure. I could form but a faint idea of it by description, until I had seen it. It is the most magnificent skeleton in the world. The city ought never to forget the great expense Mr. Peale was put to, and the skill and energy he showed, during the many months he spent in searching the swamps, where these enormous bones had been concealed from the eyes of the world for centuries.

The extensive squares of this city are ornamented with well-grown and luxuriant trees. Its unremitting attention to literature might cause it to be styled the Athens of the United States. Here, learning and science have taken up their abode. The literary and philosophical associations, the enthusiasm of individuals, the activity of the press, and the cheapness of the publications, ought to raise the name of Philadelphia to an elevated situation in the temple of knowledge.

From the press of this city came Wilson's famous "Ornithology." By observing the birds in their native haunts, he has been enabled to purge their history of numberless absurdities, which inexperienced theorists had introduced into it. It is a pleasing and a brilliant work. We have no description of birds in any European publication that can come up to this. By perusing Wilson's "Ornithology" attentively before I left England, I knew where to look for the birds, and immediately recognised them in their native land.

Since his time, I fear the White-headed Eagles have been much thinned. I was perpetually looking out for them, but saw very few. One or two came now and then, and soared in lofty flight over the falls of Niagara. The Americans are proud of this bird in effigy, and their hearts rejoice when its banner is unfurled. Could they not then be persuaded to protect the white-headed eagle, and allow it to glide in safety over its own native forests? Were I an American, I should think I had committed a kind of sacrilege in killing the white-headed eagle. The Ibis was held sacred by the Egyptians; the Hollanders protect the Stork; the Vulture sits unmolested on the top of the

houses in the city of Angustura ; and Robin-red-breast,
for his charity, is cherished by the English :—

> " No burial these pretty babes
>   Of any man receives,
>   Till robin-red-breast painfully
>   Did cover them with leaves." [1]

Poor Wilson was smote by the hand of death, before he
had finished his work.   Prince Charles Buonaparte, nephew
to the late emperor Napoleon, aided by some of the most
scientific gentlemen of Pennsylvania, is continuing this
valuable and interesting publication.

New York, with great propriety, may be called the commercial capital of the new world :—

> " Urbs augusta potens, nulli cessura."

Ere long, it will be on the coast of North America what
Tyre once was on that of Syria.   In her port are the ships
of all nations ; and in her streets is displayed merchandise
from all parts of the known world. And then the approach
to it is so enchanting ! The verdant fields, the woody hills,
the farms, and country houses, form a beautiful landscape
as you sail up to the city of New York.

Broadway is the principal street.   It is three miles and
a half long.   I am at a loss to know where to look for a
street, in any part of the world, which has so many attractions as this.   There are no steam-engines to annoy you
by filling the atmosphere full of soot and smoke ; the
houses have a stately appearance ; while the eye is relieved
from the perpetual sameness, which is common in most
streets, by lofty and luxuriant trees.

Nothing can surpass the appearance of the American
ladies, when they take their morning walk, from twelve to

---

[1] The fault against grammar is lost in the beauty of the idea.

three, in Broadway. The stranger will at once see that they have rejected the extravagant superfluities which appear in the London and Parisian fashions; and have only retained as much of those costumes, as is becoming to the female form. This, joined to their own just notions of dress, is what renders the New York ladies so elegant in their attire. The way they wear the Leghorn hat deserves a remark or two. With us, the formal hand of the milliner binds down the brim to one fixed shape, and that none of the handsomest. The wearer is obliged to turn her head full ninety degrees before she can see the person who is standing by her side. But in New York the ladies have the brim of the hat not fettered with wire, or tape, or ribbon, but quite free and undulating; and by applying the hand to it, they can conceal or expose as much of the face as circumstances require. This hiding and exposing of the face, by the bye, is certainly a dangerous movement, and often fatal to the passing swain. I am convinced in my own mind, that many a determined and unsuspecting bachelor, has been shot down by this sudden manœuvre, before he was aware that he was within reach of the battery.

The American ladies seem to have an abhorrence (and a very just one too) of wearing caps. When one considers for a moment, that women wear the hair long, which nature has given them both for an ornament and to keep the head warm, one is apt to wonder, by what perversion of good taste they can be induced to enclose it in a cap. A mob cap, a lace cap, a low cap, a high cap, a flat cap, a cap with ribbons dangling loose, a cap with ribbons tied under the chin, a peak cap, an angular cap, a round cap, and a pyramid cap! How would Canova's Venus look in a mob cap? If there be any ornament to the head in wearing a cap, it must surely be a false ornament. The American ladies are persuaded that the head can be ornamented without a cap. A rose-bud or two, a woodbine, or a sprig of eglantine, look well in the braided hair; and if there be raven locks, a lily or a snowdrop may be interwoven with effect.

Now that the packets are so safe, and make such quick passages to the United States, it would be as well if some of our head milliners would go on board of them, in lieu of getting into the Diligence for Paris. They would bring back more taste, and less caricature. And if they could persuade a dozen or two of the farmers' servant girls to return with them, we should soon have proof positive, that as good butter and cheese may be made with the hair braided up, and a daisy or primrose in it, as butter and cheese made in a cap of barbarous shape; washed, perhaps, in soap-suds last new moon.

New York has very good hotels, and genteel boarding-houses. All charges included, you do not pay above two dollars a day. Little enough, when you consider the capital accommodations, and the abundance of food.

In this city, as well as in others which I visited, every body seemed to walk at his ease. I could see no inclination for jostling; no impertinent staring at you; nor attempts to create a row in order to pick your pocket. I would stand for an hour together in Broadway, to observe the passing multitude. There is certainly a gentleness in these people, both to be admired and imitated. I could see very few dogs, still fewer cats, and but a very small proportion of fat women in the streets of New York. The climate was the only thing that I had really to find fault with; and as the autumn was now approaching, I began to think of preparing for warmer regions.

Strangers are apt to get violent cold, on account of the sudden change of the atmosphere. The noon would often be as warm as tropical weather, and the close of day cold and chilly. This must sometimes act with severity upon the newly-arrived stranger; and it requires more care and circumspection than I am master of to guard against it I contracted a bad and obstinate cough, which did not quite leave me till I had got under the regular heat of the sun, near the equator.

I may be asked, was it all good fellowship and civility during my stay in the United States? Did no forward person cause offence? was there no exhibition of drunkenness, or swearing, or rudeness; or display of conduct which disgraces civilized man in other countries? I answer, very few indeed: scarce any worth remembering, and none worth noticing. These are a gentle and a civil people. Should a traveller, now and then in the long run, witness a few of the scenes elluded to, he ought not, on his return home, to adduce a solitary instance or two, as the custom of the country. In roving through the wilds of Guiana, I have sometimes seen a tree hollow at heart, shattered and leafless; but I did not on that account condemn its vigorous neighbours, and put down a memorandum that the woods were bad; on the contrary, I made allowances: a thunder-storm, the whirlwind, a blight from heaven might have robbed it of its bloom, and caused its present forbidding appearance. And, in leaving the forest, I carried away the impression, that though some few of the trees were defective, the rest were an ornament to the wilds, full of uses and virtues, and capable of benefiting the world in a superior degree.

A man generally travels into foreign countries for his own ends; and I suspect there is scarcely an instance to be found of a person leaving his own home solely with the intention of benefiting those amongst whom he is about to travel. A commercial speculation, curiosity, a wish for information, a desire to reap benefit from an acquaintance with our distant fellow-creatures, are the general inducements for a man to leave his own fire-side. This ought never to be forgotten ; and then the traveller will journey on under the persuasion that it rather becomes him to court than expect to be courted, as his own interest is the chief object of his travels. With this in view, he will always render himself pleasant to the natives ; and they are sure to repay his little acts of courtesy with ample interest, and with a fund of information which will be of great service to him.

While in the United States, I found our western brother a very pleasant fellow ; but his portrait has been drawn in such different shades, by different travellers who have been through his territory, that it requires a personal interview before a correct idea can be formed of his true colours. He is very inquisitive ; but it is quite wrong on that account to tax him with being of an impertinent turn. He merely interrogates you for information ; and when you have satisfied him on that score, only ask him in your turn for an account of what is going on in his own country, and he will tell you everything about it with great good humour, and in excellent language. He has certainly hit upon the way (but I could not make out by what means) of speaking a much purer English language than that which is in general spoken on the parent soil. This astonished me much ; but it is really the case. Amongst his many good qualities, he has one unenviable, and, I may add, a bad propensity : he is immoderately fond of smoking. He may say, that he learned it from his nurse, with whom it was once much in vogue. In Dutch William's time (he was a man of bad taste), the English gentleman could not do without his pipe. During the short space of time that corporal Trim was at the inn inquiring after poor Lefevre's health, my uncle Toby had knocked the ashes out of three pipes. " It was not till my uncle Toby had knocked the ashes out of his third pipe," &c. Now these times have luckily gone by, and the custom of smoking amongst genteel Englishmen has nearly died away with them; it is a foul custom; it makes a foul mouth, and a foul place where the smoker stands; however, every nation has its whims. John Bull relishes stinking venison; a French-man depopulates whole swamps in quest of frogs; a Dutchman's pipe is never out of his mouth; a Russian will eat tallow candles; and the American indulges in the cigar. " De gustibus non est disputandum."

Our western brother is in possession of a country replete with everything that can contribute to the happiness and comfort of mankind. His code of laws, purified by ex-perience and common sense, has fully answered the expec-tations of the public. By acting up to the true spirit of this code, he has reaped immense advantages from it. His advancement, as a nation, has been rapid beyond all calcu-lation ; and, young as he is, it may be remarked, without any impropriety, that he is now actually reading a salutary lesson to the rest of the civilized world.

It is but some forty years ago, that he had the dispute with his nurse about a dish of tea. She wanted to force the boy to drink it according to her own receipt. He said, he did not like it, and that it absolutely made him ill. After a good deal of sparring, she took up the birch rod, and began to whip him with an uncommon degree of asperity. When the poor lad found that he must either drink the nauseous dish of tea or be flogged to death, he turned upon her in self-defence; showed her to the outside of the nursery door, and never more allowed her to meddle with his affairs.

Since the independence, the population has increased

from three to ten millions. A fine navy has been built; and everything attended to that could ensure prosperity at home, and respect abroad.

The former wilds of North America bear ample testimony to the achievements of this enterprising people. Forests have been cleared away, swamps drained, canals dug, and flourishing settlements established. From the shores of the Atlantic an immense column of knowledge has rolled into the interior. The Mississippi, the Ohio, the Missouri, and their tributary streams, have been wonderfully benefited by it. It now seems as if it were advancing towards the stony mountains · and probably will not become stationary till it reaches the Pacific Ocean. This almost immeasurable territory affords a shelter and a home to mankind in general: Jew or Gentile, king's-man or republican, he meets with a friendly reception in the United States. His opinions, his persecutions, his errors, or mistakes, however they may have injured him in other countries, are dead, and of no avail on his arrival here. Provided he keeps the peace, he is sure to be at rest.

Politicians of other countries imagine that intestine feuds will cause a division in this commonwealth; at present there certainly appears to be no reason for such a conjecture. Heaven forbid that it should happen! The world at large would suffer by it. For ages yet to come, may this great commonwealth continue to be the United States of North America.

The sun was now within a week or two of passing into the southern hemisphere, and the mornings and evenings were too cold to be comfortable. I embarked for the island of Antigua, with the intention of calling at the different islands in the Caribbean sea, on my way once more towards the wilds of Guiana.

CHAPTER II.

WE were thirty days in making Antigua, and thanked
Providence for ordering us so long a passage. A tremendous gale of wind, approaching to a hurricane, had
done much damage in the West Indies. Had our passage
been of ordinary length, we should inevitably have been
caught in the gale.

St. John's is the capital of Antigua. In better times it
may have had its gaieties and amusements. At present, it
appears sad and woe-begone. The houses, which are
chiefly of wood, seem as if they had not had a coat of
paint for many years; the streets are uneven and ill-
paved; and as the stranger wanders through them, he
might fancy that they would afford a congenial promenade
to the man who is about to take his last leave of surrounding worldly misery, before he hangs himself. There had
been no rain for some time, so that the parched and barren
pasture near the town might, with great truth, be called

Rosinante's own. The mules feeding on them, put you in mind of Ovid's description of famine :—

"Dura cutis, per quam spectari viscera possent."

It is somewhat singular, that there is not a single river or brook in the whole island of Antigua. In this it differs from Tartary in the other world; which, according to old writers, has five rivers ; viz. Acheron, Phlegethon, Cocytus, Styx, and Lethe.

In this island I found the Red Start, described in Wilson's " Ornithology of the United States." I wished to learn whether any of these birds remain the whole year in Antigua, and breed there ; or whether they all leave it for the north when the sun comes out of the southern hemisphere ; but, upon inquiry, I could get no information whatever.

After passing a dull week here, I sailed for Guadaloupe, whose bold and cloud-capped mountains have a grand appearance as you approach the island. Basseterre, the capital, is a neat town, with a handsome public walk in the middle of it, well shaded by a row of fine tamarind trees on each side. Behind the town, La Souffriere raises its high romantic summit; and on a clear day, you may see the volcanic smoke which issues from it.

Nearly midway, betwixt Guadaloupe and Dominica, you descry the Saintes. Though high, and bold, and rocky, they have still a diminutive appearance when compared with their two gigantic neighbours. You just see Marigalante to windward of them, some leagues off, about a yard high in the horizon.

Dominica is majestic in high and rugged mountains. As you sail along it, you cannot help admiring its beautiful coffee plantations, in places so abrupt and steep, that you would pronounce them almost inaccessible. Roseau, the capital, is but a small town, and has nothing attractive except the well-known hospitality of the present harbour-master, who is particularly attentive to strangers, and furnishes them with a world of information concerning the West Indies. Roseau has seen better days ; and you can trace good taste and judgment in the way in which the town has originally been laid out.

Some years ago it was visited by a succession of mis-fortunes, which smote it so severely, that it has never recovered its former appearance. A strong French fleet bombarded it; while a raging fire destroyed its finest buildings. Some time after, an overwhelming flood rolled down the gullies and fissures of the adjacent mountains, and carried all before it. Men, women, and children, houses, and property, were all swept away by this mighty torrent. The terrible scene was said to beggar all descrip-tion, and the loss was immense.

Dominica is famous for a large species of Frog, which the inhabitants keep in readiness to slaughter for the table. In the woods of this island, the large Rhinoceros Beetle is very common; it measures above six inches in length. In the same woods is found the beautiful Humming-bird, the breast and throat of which are of a brilliant changing purple. I have searched for this bird in Brazil, and through the whole of the wilds from the Rio Branco, which is a branch of the Amazons, to the river Paumaron, but never could find it. I was told by a man in the Egyptian-Hall, in Piccadilly, that this humming-bird is found in Mexico; but upon questioning him more about it, his information seemed to have been acquired by hearsay ; and so I concluded that it does not appear in Mexico. I suspect that it is never found out of the Antilles.

After leaving Dominica, you soon reach the grand

and magnificent island of Martinico.   St. Pierre, its capital, is a fine town, and possesses every comfort. The inhabitants seem to pay considerable attention to the cultivation of the tropical fruits.   A stream of water runs down the streets with great rapidity, producing a pleasing effect as you pass along.

Here I had an opportunity of examining a Cuckoo, which had just been shot.   It was exactly the same as the Metallic Cuckoo in Wilson's "Ornithology."   They told me it is a migratory bird in Martinico.   It probably repairs to this island after its departure from the United States.

At a little distance from Martinico, the celebrated Diamond Rock rises in insulated majesty out of the sea.   It was fortified during the last war with France, and bravely defended by an English captain.

In a few hours from Martinico, you are at St. Lucie, whose rough and towering mountains fill you with sublime ideas, as you approach its rocky shore.   The town Castries is quite embayed.   It was literally blown to pieces by the fatal hurricane, in which the unfortunate governor and his lady lost their lives.   Its present forlorn and gloomy appearance, and the grass which is grown up in the streets, too plainly show that its hour of joy is passed away ; and that it is in mourning, as it were, with the rest of the British West Indies.

From St. Lucie, I proceeded to Barbadoes in quest of a conveyance to the island of Trinidad.

Near Bridgetown, the capital of Barbadoes, I saw the metallic cuckoo, already alluded to.

Barbadoes is no longer the merry island it was when I visited it some years ago :—

"Infelix habitum, temporis hujus habet."

There is an old song, to the tune of La Belle Catharine, which must evidently have been composed in brighter times :—

> " Come let us dance and sing,
> While Barbadoes bells do ring ;
> Quashi scrapes the fiddle-string,
> And Venus plays the lute."

Quashi's fiddle was silent; and mute was the lute of Venus during my stay in Barbadoes. The difference betwixt the French and British islands was very striking. The first appeared happy and content ; the second were filled with murmurs and complaints. The late proceedings in England, concerning slavery, and the insurrection in Demerara, had evidently caused the gloom. The abolition of slavery is a question full of benevolence and fine feelings, difficulties and danger :—

> "Tantum ne noceas, dum vis prodesse videto."

It requires consummate prudence, and a vast fund of true information, in order to draw just conclusions on this important subject. Phaeton, by awkward driving, set the world on fire: " Sylvæ cum montibus ardent." Dædalus gave his son a pair of wings without considering the consequence ; the boy flew out of all bounds, lost his wings, and tumbled into the sea :—

> "Icarus, Icariis nomina fecit aquis."

When the old man saw what had happened, he damned his own handicraft in wing-making ; " devovitque suas artes." Prudence is a cardinal virtue :—

> "Omnia consultâ mente gerenda tegens."

Foresight is half the battle. " Hombre apercebido, medio combatido," says Don Quixote, or Sancho, I do not

remember which. Had queen Bess weighed well in her own
mind the probable consequences of this lamentable traffic,
it is likely she would not have been owner of two vessels
in Sir John Hawkins's squadron, which committed the
first robbery in negro flesh on the coast of Africa. As
philanthropy is the very life and soul of this momentous
question on slavery, which is certainly fraught with great
difficulties and danger, perhaps it would be as well at
present for the nation to turn its thoughts to poor ill-fated
Ireland, where oppression, poverty, and rags make a heartrending appeal to the feelings of the benevolent.

But to proceed. There was another thing which added
to the dulness of Barbadoes, and which seemed to have
considerable effect in keeping away strangers from the
island. The legislature had passed a most extraordinary
bill, by virtue of which every person who arrives at
Barbadoes is obliged to pay two dollars, and two dollars
more on his departure from it. It is called the alien bill;
and every Barbadian who leaves or returns to the island,
and every Englishman too, pays the tax!

Finding no vessel here for Trinidad, I embarked in
a schooner for Demerara, landed there after being nearly
stranded on a sand-bank, and proceeded without loss of
time to the forests in the interior. It was the dry
season, which renders a residence in the woods very
delightful.

There are three species of Jacamar to be found on the
different sand-hills and dry savannas of Demerara; but
there is another much larger and far more beautiful to be
seen when you arrive in that part of the country where
there are rocks. The jacamar has no affinity to the woodpecker or kingfisher, (notwithstanding what travellers
affirm,) either in its haunts or anatomy. The jacamar
lives entirely on insects, but never goes in search of them.

It sits patiently for hours together on the branch of a tree, and when the incautious insect approaches, it flies at it with the rapidity of an arrow, seizes it, and generally returns to eat it on the branch which it had just quitted. It has not the least attempt at song, is very solitary, and so tame that you may get within three or four yards of it before it takes flight. The males of all the different species which I have examined have white feathers on the throat. I suspect that all the male jacamars hitherto discovered have this distinctive mark. I could learn nothing of its incubation. The Indians informed me that one species of jacamar lays its eggs in the Wood-Ants' nests, which are so frequent in the trees of Guiana, and appear like huge black balls. I wish there had been proof positive of this; but the breeding time was over; and in the ants' nests which I examined, I could find no marks of birds having ever been in them. Early in January the jacamar is in fine plumage for the cabinet of the naturalist. The largest species measures ten inches and a half from the point of the beak to the end of the tail; its name amongst the Indians is Una-waya-adoucati, that is, grandfather of the jacamar. It is certainly a splendid bird; and in brilliancy and changeableness of its metallic colours, it yields to none of the Asiatic and African feathered tribe. The colours of the female are nearly as bright as those of the male, but she wants the white feathers on the throat. The large jacamar is pretty common about two hundred miles up the river Demerara.

Here I had a fine opportunity once more of examining the Three-toed Sloth. He was in the house with me for a day or two. Had I taken a description of him as he lay sprawling on the floor, I should have misled the world, and injured natural history. On the ground he appeared really a bungled composition, and faulty at all points; awkwardness and misery were depicted on his countenance ; and when I made him advance he sighed as though in pain. Perhaps it was, that by seeing him thus out of his element as it were, that the Count de Buffon, in his history of the sloth, asks the question—" Why should not some animals be created for misery, since, in the human species, the greatest number of individuals are devoted to pain from the moment of their existence ? " Were the question put to me, I would answer, I cannot conceive that any of them are created for misery. That thousands live in misery there can be no doubt ; but then, misery has overtaken them in their path through life, and wherever man has come up with them, I should suppose they have seldom escaped from experiencing a certain proportion of misery.

After fully satisfying myself that it only leads the world into error to describe the sloth while he is on the ground, or in any place except in a tree, I carried the one I had in my possession to his native haunts. As soon as he came in contact with the branch of a tree, all went right with him. I could see as he climbed up into his own country, that he was on the right road to happiness ; and felt persuaded more than ever, that the world has hitherto erred in its conjectures concerning the sloth, on account of naturalists, not having given a description of him when he was in the only position in which he ought to have been described, namely, clinging to the branch of a tree.

As the appearance of this part of the country bears great resemblance to Cayenne, and is so near to it, I was in hopes to have found the Grande Gobe Mouche of Buffon, and the septicoloured Tangara, both of which were common in Cayenne ; but after many diligent searches, I did not succeed ; nor could I learn from the Indians that they had ever seen those two species of birds in these parts.

Here I procured the Grosbeak with a rich scarlet

body, and black head and throat.   Buffon mentions it as
coming from America.   I had been in quest of it for years,
but could never see it, and concluded that it was not to
be found in Demerara.   The bird is of a greenish brown
before it acquires its rich plumage.

Amongst the bare roots of the trees, alongside of this
part of the river, a red crab sometimes makes its appearance, as you are passing up and down.   It is preyed upon
by a large species of Owl, which I was fortunate enough
to procure.   Its head, back, wings, and tail, are of so dark
a brown as almost to appear black.   The breast is of a
somewhat lighter brown.   The belly and thighs are of a
dirty yellow white.   The feathers round the eyes are of
the same dark brown as the rest of the body; and then
comes a circle of white, which has the appearance of a
large pair of spectacles.   I strongly suspect that the dirty
yellow white of the belly and thighs has originally been
pure white ; and that it has come to its present colour by
means of the bird darting down upon its prey in the mud.
But this is mere conjecture.

Here too, close to the river, I frequently saw the bird
called Sun-bird by the English colonists, and Tirana by the
Spaniards in the Oroonoque.   It is very elegant ; and in
its outward appearance approaches near to the heron tribe ;
still it does not live upon fish.   Flies and insects are its
food ; and it takes them just as a heron takes fish, by
approaching near and then striking with its beak at its
prey so quick, that it has no chance to escape.   The
beautiful mixture of grey, yellow, green, black, white, and
chestnut in the plumage of this bird, baffles any attempt
to give a description of the distribution of them which
would be satisfactory to the reader.

There is something remarkable in the great Tinamou,
which I suspect has hitherto escaped notice.   It invariably

roosts in trees ; but the feet are so small in proportion
to the body of this bulky bird, that they can be of no
use to it in grasping the branch ; and, moreover, the hind
toe is so short, that it does not touch the ground when the
bird is walking.   The back part of the leg, just below the
knee, is quite flat, and somewhat concave.   On it are
strong pointed scales, which are very rough, and catch
your finger as you move it along from the knee to the toe.
Now, by means of these scales, and the particular flatness
of that part of the leg, the bird is enabled to sleep in safety
upon the branch of a tree.

At the close of day, the great tinamou gives a loud,
monotonous, plaintive whistle, and then immediately
springs into the tree.   By the light of the full moon, the
vigilant and cautious naturalist may see him sitting in the
position already described.

The small Tinamou has nothing that can be called a
tail.   It never lays more than one egg, which is of a
chocolate colour.   It makes no nests, but merely scratches
a little hollow in the sand, generally at the foot of a tree.

Here we have an instance of a bird, the size of a partridge,
and of the same tribe, laying only one egg, while the rest
of the family, from the peahen to the quail, are known to
lay a considerable number.   The foot of this bird is very
small in proportion, but the back part of the leg bears no
resemblance to that of the larger tinamou; hence one
might conclude that it sleeps upon the ground.

Independent of the hollow trees, the Vampires have
another hiding-place.   They clear out the inside of the
large ants' nests, and then take possession of the shell.
I had gone about half a day down the river, to a part
of the forest where the wallaba-trees were in great
plenty.   The seeds had ripened, and I was in hopes to have
got the large scarlet ara, which feeds on them.   But,

unfortunately, the time had passed away, and the seeds had fallen.

While ranging here in the forest, we stopped under an ants' nest; and, by the dirt below, conjectured that it had got new tenants. Thinking it no harm to dislodge them, "vi et armis," an Indian boy ascended the tree; but, before he reached the nest, out flew above a dozen Vampires.

I have formerly remarked, that I wished to have it in my power to say, that I had been sucked by the vampire. I gave them many an opportunity, but they always fought shy; and though they now sucked a young man of the Indian breed very severely, as he was sleeping in his hammock in the shed next to mine, they would have nothing to do with me. His great toe seemed to have all the attractions. I examined it minutely as he was bathing it in the river at daybreak. The midnight surgeon had made a hole in it, almost of a triangular shape, and the blood was then running from it apace. His hammock was so defiled and stained with clotted blood, that he was obliged to beg an old black woman to wash it. As she was taking it down to the river side, she spread it out before me, and shook her head. I remarked, that I supposed her own toe was too old and tough to invite the Vampire-doctor to get his supper out of it; and she answered, with a grin, that doctors generally preferred young people.

Nobody has yet been able to inform me how it is that the vampire manages to draw such a large quantity of blood, generally from the toe, and the patient, all the time, remain in a profound sleep. I have never heard of an instance of a man waking under the operation. On the contrary, he continues in a sound sleep, and at the time of rising, his eyes first inform him that there has been a thirsty thief on his toe.

The teeth of the vampire are very sharp, and not unlike those of the rat. If it be that he inflicts the wounds with his teeth, (and he seems to have no other instruments,) one would suppose that the acuteness of the pain would cause the person who is sucked, to awake. We are in darkness in this matter; and I know of no means by which one might be enabled to throw light upon it. It is to be hoped that some future wanderer through the wilds of Guiana, will be more fortunate than I have been, and catch this nocturnal depredator in the fact. I have once before mentioned that I killed a vampire which measured thirty-two inches from wing to wing extended; but others, which I have since examined, have generally been from twenty to twenty-six inches in dimension.

The large humming-bird, called by the Indians Karabimiti, invariably builds its nest in the slender branches of the trees which hang over the rivers and creeks. In appearance, it is like brown tanned leather, and without a particle of lining. The rim of the nest is double inwards, and I always conjectured that it had taken this shape on account of the body of the bird pressing against it while she was laying her eggs. But this is quite a wrong conjecture. Instinct has taught the bird to give it this shape, in order that the eggs may be prevented from rolling out.

The trees on the river's bank are particularly exposed to violent gusts of wind, and while I have been sitting in the canoe, and looking on, I have seen the slender branch of the tree which held the humming-bird's nest so violently shaken, that the bottom of the inside of the nest has appeared, and had there been nothing at the rim to stop the eggs, they must inevitably have been jerked into the water. I suspect the humming-bird never lays more than two eggs. I never found more than two in any of the many nests which have come in my way. The eggs were always white, without any spots on them.

Probably travellers have erred in asserting that the monkeys of South America throw sticks and fruit at their pursuers. I have had fine opportunities of narrowly watching the different species of monkeys which are found in the wilds, betwixt the Amazons and the Oroonoque. I entirely acquit them of acting on the offensive. When the monkeys are in the high trees over your head, the dead branches will now and then fall down upon you, having been broken off as the monkeys pass along them; but they are never hurled from their hands.

Monkeys, commonly so called, both in the old and new continent, may be classed into three grand divisions: namely, the ape, which has no tail whatever; the baboon, which has only a short tail; and the monkey, which has a long tail. There are no apes, and no baboons, as yet discovered in the new world. Its monkeys may be very well and very briefly ranged under two heads; namely, those with hairy and bushy tails; and those whose tails are bare of hair underneath, about six inches from the extremity. Those with hairy and bushy tails climb just like the squirrel, and make no use of the tail to help them from branch to branch. Those which have the tail bare underneath towards the end, find it of infinite advantage to them, in their ascent and descent. They apply it to the branch of the tree, as though it were a supple finger, and frequently swing by it from the branch like the pendulum of a clock. It answers all the purposes of a fifth hand to the monkey, as naturalists have already observed.

The large red monkey of Demerara is not a baboon, though it goes by that name, having a long prensile tail.[1]

[1] I believe *prensile* is a new-coined word. I have seen it, but do not remember where.

Nothing can sound more dreadful than its nocturnal howlings. While lying in your hammock in these gloomy and immeasurable wilds, you hear him howling at intervals, from eleven o'clock at night till daybreak. You would suppose that half the wild beasts of the forest were collecting for the work of carnage. Now, it is the tremendous roar of the jaguar, as he springs on his prey : now it changes to his terrible and deep-toned growlings as he is pressed on all sides by superior force; and now, you hear his last dying moan, beneath a mortal wound.

Some naturalists have supposed that these awful sounds, which you would fancy are those of enraged and dying wild beasts, proceed from a number of the red monkeys howling in concert. One of them alone is capable of producing all these sounds ; and the anatomists, on an inspection of his trachea, will be fully satisfied that this is the case. When you look at him, as he is sitting on the branch of a tree, you will see a lump in his throat, the size of a large hen's egg.   In dark and cloudy weather, and just before a squall of rain, this monkey will often howl in the daytime ; and if you advance cautiously, and get under the high and tufted tree where he is sitting, you may have a capital opportunity of witnessing his wonderful powers of producing these dreadful and discordant sounds.

His flesh is good food ; but when skinned, his appearance is so like that of a young one of our own species, that a delicate stomach might possibly revolt at the idea of putting a knife and fork into it.   However, I can affirm, from experience, that after a long and dreary march through these remote forests, the flesh of this monkey is not to be sneezed at, when boiled in Cayenne pepper, or roasted on a stick over a good fire.   A young one tastes not unlike a kid, and the old ones have somewhat the flavour of he-goat.

I mentioned, in a former adventure, that I had hit upon an entirely new plan of making the skins of quadrupeds retain their exact form and feature. Intense application to the subject has since that period enabled me to shorten the process, and hit the character of an animal to a very great nicety, even to the preservation of the pouting lip, dimples, warts, and wrinkles on the face. I got a fine specimen of the howling monkey; and took some pains with it, in order to show the immense difference that exists betwixt the features of this monkey, and those of man.

I also procured an animal which has caused not a little speculation and astonishment. In my opinion, his thick coat of hair, and great length of tail, put his species out of all question; but then his face and head cause the inspector to pause for a moment, before he ventures to pronounce his opinion of the classification. He was a large animal, and as I was pressed for daylight, and more-over, felt no inclination to have the whole weight of his body upon my back, I contented myself with his head and shoulders, which I cut off: and have brought them with me to Europe.[1]   I have since found, that I acted quite right in doing so, having had enough to answer for the head alone, without saying anything of his hands and feet, and of his tail, which appendage, Lord Kames asserts, belongs to us.

The features of this animal are quite of the Grecian cast; and he has a placidity of countenance which shows

---

[1] My young friend, Mr. J. H. Foljambe, eldest son of Thomas Foljambe, Esq. of Wakefield, has made a drawing of the head and shoulders of this animal, (see Frontispiece,) and it is certainly a most correct and striking likeness of the original.

that things went well with him when in life. Some gentlemen of great skill and talent, on inspecting his head, were convinced that the whole series of its features has been changed. Others again have hesitated, and betrayed doubts, not being able to make up their minds, whether it be possible, that the brute features of the monkey can be changed into the noble countenance of man.—" Scinditur vulgus." One might argue at considerable length on this novel subject; and perhaps, after all, produce little more than prolix pedantry. "Vox et præterea nihil."

Let us suppose for an instant, that it is a new species. Well; "Una golondrina no hace verano;" one swallow does not make summer, as Sancho Panza says. Still, for all that, it would be well worth while going out to search for it; and these times of Pasco-Peruvian enterprise are favourable to the undertaking. Perhaps, gentle readers, you would wish me to go in quest of another. I would beg leave respectfully to answer, that the way is dubious, long, and dreary; and though, unfortunately, I cannot allege the excuse of "me pia conjux detinet," still I would fain crave a little repose. I have already been a long while errant :—

> " Longa mihi exilia, et vastum maris æquor aravi,
> Ne mandate mihi, nam ego sum defessus agendo."

Should anybody be induced to go, great and innumerable are the discoveries yet to be made in those remote wilds; and should he succeed in bringing home, even a head alone, with features as perfect as those of that which I have brought, far from being envious of him, I should consider him a modern Alcides, fully entitled to register a thirteenth labour. Now if, on the other hand, we argue, that this head in question has had all its original features destroyed, and a set of new ones given to it, by what means has this hitherto unheard-of change been effected ? Nobody in our museums has as yet been able to restore the natural features to stuffed animals ; and he who has any doubts of this, let him take a living cat or dog, and compare them with a stuffed cat or dog in any of the first-rate museums.   A momentary glance of the eye would soon settle his doubts on this head.

If I have succeeded in effacing the features of a brute, and putting those of a man in their place, we might be entitled to say, that the sun of Proteus has risen to our museums :—

> " Unius hic faciem, facies transformat in omnes ;
> Nunc homo, nunc tigris ; nunc equa, nunc mulier."

If I have effected this, we can now give to one side of the skin of a man's face the appearance of eighty years, and to the other side that of blooming seventeen.   We could make the forehead and eyes serene in youthful beauty, and shape the mouth and jaws to the features of a malicious old ape.   Here is a new field opened to the adventurous and experimental naturalist :   I have trodden it up and down till I am almost weary.   To get at it myself I have groped through an alley, which may be styled, in the words of Ovid,—

> " Arduus, obliquus, caligine densus opaca."

I pray thee, gentle reader, let me out a while.   Time passes on apace ; and I want to take thee to have a peep at the spots where mines are supposed to exist in Guiana. As the story of this singular head has, probably, not been made out to thy satisfaction, perhaps, (I may say it nearly in Corporal Trim's words,) on some long and dismal winter's evening, but not now, I may tell thee more about it ;

together with that of another head, which is equally
striking.

It is commonly reported, and I think there is no reason to
doubt the fact, that when Demerara and Essequibo were
under the Dutch flag, there were mines of gold and silver
opened near to the river Essequibo. The miners were not
successful in their undertaking, and it is generally conjectured that their failure proceeded from inexperience.

Now, when you ascend the Essequibo, some hundred
miles above the place where these mines are said to be
found, you get into a high, rocky, and mountainous
country. Here many of the mountains have a very
barren aspect, producing only a few stinted shrubs, and
here and there a tuft of coarse grass. I could not learn
that they have ever been explored, and at this day their
mineralogy is totally unknown to us. The Indians are so
thinly scattered in this part of the country, that there
would be no impropriety in calling it uninhabited :—

"Apparent rari errantes in gurgite vasto."

It remains to be yet learnt, whether this portion of
Guiana be worth looking after, with respect to its supposed
mines. The mining speculations at present are flowing
down another channel. The rage in England for working
the mines of other states has now risen to such a pitch,
that it would require a considerable degree of caution in
a mere wanderer of the woods, in stepping forward to say
anything that might tend to raise or depress the spirits
of the speculators.

A question or two, however, might be asked. When
the revolted colonies shall have repaired in some measure
the ravages of war, and settled their own political economy upon a firm foundation, will they quietly submit to
see foreigners carrying away those treasures which are

absolutely part of their own soil, and which necessity
(necessity has no law) forced them to barter away in their
hour of need? Now, if it should so happen that the
masters of the country begin to repent of their bargain,
and become envious of the riches which foreigners carry
off, many a teasing law might be made, and many a vexatious enaction might be put in force, that would, in all
probability, bring the speculators into trouble and
disappointment.

Besides this consideration, there is another circumstance
which ought not to be overlooked. I allude to the change
of.masters nearly throughout the whole of America. It
is a curious subject for the European philosopher to
moralize upon, and for the politician to examine. The
more they consider it, the more they will be astonished.
If we may judge by what has already taken place, we are
entitled to predict, that in a very few years more, no
European banner will be seen to float in any part of the
new world. Let us take a cursory view of it.

England some years ago possessed a large portion of
the present United States. France had Louisiana; Spain
held the Floridas, Mexico, Darien, Terra Firma, Buenos
Ayres, Paraguay, Chili, Peru, and California; and Portugal
ruled the whole of Brazil. All these immense regions are
now independent states. England, to be sure, still has
Canada, Nova Scotia, and a few creeks on the coast of
Labrador; also a small settlement in Honduras, and the
wilds of Demerara and Essequibo; and these are all.
France has not a foot of ground except the forests of
Cayenne. Portugal has lost every province; Spain is
blockaded in nearly her last citadel; and the Dutch flag
is only seen in Surinam. Nothing more now remains to
Europe of this immense continent, where, but a very few
years ago, she reigned triumphant.

With regard to the West India Islands, they may be considered as the mere outposts of this mammoth domain. St. Domingo has already shaken off her old masters, and become a star of observation to the rest of the sable brethren. The anti-slavery associations of England, full of benevolence and activity, have opened a tremendous battery upon the last remaining forts, which the lords of the old continent still hold in the new world; and, in all probability, will not cease firing till they shall have caused the last flag to be struck, of Europe's late mighty empire in the Transatlantic regions. It cannot well be doubted, but that the sable hordes in the West Indies will like to follow good example, whenever they shall have it in their power to do so.

Now with St. Domingo as an example before them, how long will it be before they try to raise themselves into independent states? And if they should succeed in crushing us in these our last remaining tenements, I would bet ten to one that none of the new governments will put on mourning for our departure out of the new world. We must well remember, that our own government was taxed with injustice and oppression by the United States during their great struggle; and the British press for years past has, and is still teeming with every kind of abuse and unbecoming satire against Spain and Portugal for their conduct towards the now revolted colonies.

France also comes in for her share of obloquy. Now, this being the case, will not America at large wish most devoutly for the day to come when Europe shall have no more dominion over her? Will she not say to us, Our new forms of government are very different from your old ones? We will trade with you, but we shall always be very suspicious of you as long as you retain possession of the West Indies, which are, as we may say close to our door-steads. You must be very cautious how you interfere with our politics ; for, if we find you meddling with them, and by that means cause us to come to loggerheads, we shall be obliged to send you back to your own homes, three or four thousand miles across the Atlantic ; and then, with that great ditch betwixt us, we may hope we shall be good friends. He who casts his eye on the East Indies, will there see quite a different state of things. The conquered districts have merely changed one European master for another ; and I believe there is no instance of any portion of the East Indies throwing off the yoke of the Europeans and establishing a government of their own.

Ye who are versed in politics, and study the rise and fall of empires, and know what is good for civilized man, and what is bad for him, or in other words, what will make him happy and what will make him miserable—tell us how comes it that Europe has lost almost her last acre in the boundless expanse of territory which she so lately possessed in the west, and still contrives to hold her vast property in the extensive regions of the east ?

But whither am I going ? I find myself on a new and dangerous path. Pardon, gentle reader, this sudden deviation. Methinks I hear thee saying to me,—

"Tramite quo tendis, majoraque viribus audes."

I grant that I have erred, but I will do so no more. In general I avoid politics ; they are too heavy for me, and I am aware that they have caused the fall of many a strong and able man ; they require the shoulders of Atlas to support their weight.

When I was in the rocky mountains of Macoushia, in the month of June, 1812, I saw four young Cocks of the Rock in an Indian's hut ; they had been taken out of the nest that week. They were of a uniform dirty brown colour, and by the position of the young feathers upon the head, you might see that there would be a crest there when the bird arrived at maturity. By seeing young ones in the month of June, I immediately concluded that the old cock of the rock would be in fine plumage from the end of November to the beginning of May: and that the naturalist, who was in quest of specimens for his museum, ought to arrange his plans in such a manner as to be able to get into Macoushia during these months. However, I find now, that no exact period can be fixed; for, in December, 1824, an Indian, in the river Demerara, gave me a young cock of the rock not a month old, and it had just been brought from the Macoushi country. By having a young specimen at this time of the year, it puts it out of one's power to say at what precise time the old birds are in full plumage. I took it on board a ship with me for England, but it was so very susceptible of cold that it shivered and died, three days after we had passed Antigua.

If ever there should be a great demand for large supplies of gum-elastic, commonly called India-rubber, it may be procured in abundance far away in the wilds of Demerara and Essequibo.

Some years ago, when I was in the Macoushi country there was a capital trick played upon me about India-rubber. It is almost too good to be left out of these Wanderings, and it shows that the wild and uneducated Indian is not without abilities. Weary and sick, and feeble through loss of blood, I arrived at some Indian huts, which were about two hours distant from the place where the gum-elastic trees grew. After a day and a night's rest I went to them, and with my own hands made a fine ball of pure India-rubber; it hardened immediately it became exposed to the air, and its elasticity was almost incredible.

While procuring it, exposure to the rain, which fell in torrents, brought on a return of inflammation in the stomach, and I was obliged to have recourse again to the lancet, and to use it with an unsparing hand. I wanted another ball, but was not in a state the next morning to proceed to the trees. A fine interesting young Indian observing my eagerness to have it, tendered his services, and asked me two handsful of fish-hooks for his trouble.

Off he went, and to my great surprise returned in a very short time. Bearing in mind the trouble and time it had cost me to make a ball, I could account for this Indian's expedition in no other way except that, being an inhabitant of the forest, he knew how to go about his work in a much shorter way than I did. His ball, to be sure, had very little elasticity in it. I tried it repeatedly, but it never rebounded a yard high. The young Indian watched me with great gravity, and when I made him understand that I expected the ball would dance better, he called another Indian, who knew a little English, to assure me that I might be quite easy on that score. The young rogue, in order to render me a complete dupe, brought the new moon to his aid. He gave me to understand that the ball was like the little moon, which he pointed to, and by the time it grew big and old, the ball would bounce beautifully. This satisfied me, and I gave him the fish-hooks, which he received without the least change of countenance.

I bounced the ball repeatedly for two months after, but I found that it still remained in its infancy. At last I suspected that the savage (to use a vulgar phrase) had come Yorkshire over me; and so I determined to find out how he had managed to take me in. I cut the ball in two, and then saw what a taught trick he had played me. It seems he had chewed some leaves into a lump, the size

of a walnut, and then dipped them in the liquid gum-
elastic.   It immediately received a coat about as thick as
a sixpence.   He then rolled some more leaves round it,
and gave it another coat.   He seems to have continued
this process till he made the ball considerably larger than
the one I had procured; and in order to put his roguery
out of all chance of detection, he made the last and outer
coat thicker than a dollar.   This Indian would, no doubt,
have thriven well in some of our great towns.

Finding that the rainy season was coming on, I left the
wilds of Demerara and Essequibo with regret, towards the
close of December, 1824; and reached once more the
shores of England, after a long and unpleasant passage.

Ere we part, kind reader, I could wish to draw a little
of thy attention to the instructions which are to be found
at the end of this book.   Twenty years have now rolled
away since I first began to examine the specimens of
zoology in our museums.   As the system of preparation
is founded in error, nothing but deformity, distortion, and
disproportion, will be the result of the best intentions and
utmost exertions of the workman.   Canova's education,
taste, and genius enabled him to present to the world
statues so correct and beautiful that they are worthy of
universal admiration.   Had a common stonecutter tried
his hand upon the block out of which these statues were
sculptured, what a lamentable want of symmetry and
fine countenance there would have been.   Now, when we
reflect that the preserved specimens in our museums and
private collections are always done upon a wrong principle, and generally by low and illiterate people, whose
daily bread depends upon the shortness of time in which
they can get through their work, and whose opposition to
the true way of preparing specimens can only be surpassed
by their obstinacy in adhering to the old method; can we

any longer wonder at their want of success ; or hope to
see a single specimen produced that will be worth looking
at ?   With this I conclude, hoping that thou hast received
some information, and occasionally had a smile upon thy
countenance, while perusing these " Wanderings ; " and
begging, at the same time, to add that

Well I know thy penetration
  Many a stain and blot will see,
In the languid, long narration,
  Of my sylvan errantry.

For the pen too oft was weary
  In the wandering writer's hand,
As he roved through deep and dreary
  Forests, in a distant land.

Show thy mercy, gentle reader,
  Let him not entreat in vain ;
It will be his strength's best feeder.
  Should he ever go again.

And who knows how soon, complaining
  Of a cold and wifeless home,
He may leave it, and again in
  Equatorial regions roam ?

C. W.

ON PRESERVING BIRDS FOR CABINETS OF NATURAL HISTORY.

Faults in bird-stuffing.—Tools required.—Knowledge of anatomy.—
Attitudes of birds.—Flow of the plumage.—How to skin a bird.—
Inserting cotton.—Killing wounded birds.—Stuffing a hawk.—The
first incision.—The skin to be pushed, not pulled.—Arrangement of
wings.—Modelling the body.—Spreading the tail.—Constant attention
required.—Strength and elasticity.—Value of corrosive sublimate.—
Experience and patience.

WERE you to pay as much attention to birds as the sculptor does to the human frame, you would immediately see, on entering a museum, that the specimens are not well done.

This remark will not be thought severe when you reflect that that which once was a bird has probably been stretched, stuffed, stiffened, and wired by the hand of a common clown. Consider likewise how the plumage must have been disordered by too much stretching or drying, and perhaps sullied, or at least deranged, by the pressure of a coarse and heavy hand—plumage which, ere life had fled from within it, was accustomed to be touched by nothing rougher than the dew of heaven, and the pure and gentle breath of air.

In dissecting, three things are necessary to ensure success, viz., a penknife, a hand not coarse or clumsy, and practice. The first will furnish you with the means;

the second will enable you to dissect; and the third cause you to dissect well. These may be called the mere mechanical requisites.

In stuffing, you require cotton, a needle and thread, a little stick the size of a common knitting-needle, glass eyes, a solution of corrosive sublimate, and any kind of a common temporary box to hold the specimen. These also may go under the same denomination as the former. But if you wish to excel in the art, if you wish to be in ornithology what Angelo was in sculpture, you must apply to profound study and your own genius to assist you. And these may be called the scientific requisites.

You must have a complete knowledge of ornithological anatomy. You must pay close attention to the form and attitude of the bird, and know exactly the proportion each curve, or extension, or contraction, or expansion of any particular part bears to the rest of the body. In a word, you must possess Promethean boldness, and bring down fire and animation, as it were, into your preserved specimen.

Repair to the haunts of birds on plains and mountains, forests, swamps, and lakes, and give up your time to examine the economy of the different orders of birds.

Then you will place your eagle in attitude commanding, the same as Nelson stood in, in the day of battle, on the *Victory's* quarter-deck. Your pie will seem crafty, and just ready to take flight, as though fearful of being surprised in some mischievous plunder. Your sparrow will retain its wonted pertness by means of placing his tail a little elevated, and giving a moderate arch to the neck. Your vulture will show his sluggish habits by having his body nearly parallel to the earth, his wings somewhat drooping, and their extremities under the tail instead of above it—expressive of ignoble indolence.

Your dove will be in artless, fearless innocence, looking mildly at you, with its neck, not too much stretched, as if uneasy in its situation, or drawn too close into the shoulders, like one wishing to avoid a discovery; but in moderate, perpendicular length, supporting the head horizontally, which will set off the breast to the best advantage. And the breast ought to be conspicuous, and have this attention paid to it; for when a young lady is sweet and gentle in her manners, kind and affable to those around her; when her eyes stand in tears of pity for the woes of others, and she puts a small portion of what Providence has blessed her with into the hand of imploring poverty and hunger—then we say she has the breast of a turtle-dove.

You will observe how beautifully the feathers of a bird are arranged, one falling over the other in nicest order; and that, where this charming harmony is interrupted, the defect, though not noticed by an ordinary spectator, will appear immediately to the eye of a naturalist. Thus, a bird not wounded and in perfect feather must be procured if possible, for the loss of feathers can seldom be made good; and where the deficiency is great, all the skill of the artist will avail him little in his attempt to conceal the defect, because, in order to hide it, he must contract the skin, bring down the upper feathers, and shove in the lower ones, which would throw all the surrounding parts into contortion.

You will also observe that the whole of the skin does not produce feathers, and that it is very tender where the feathers do not grow. The bare parts are admirably formed for expansion about the throat and stomach, and they fit into the different cavities of the body at the wings, shoulders, rump, and thighs with wonderful exactness; so that in stuffing the bird, if you make an even rotund surface of the skin where these cavities existed, in lieu of reforming them, all symmetry, order, and proportion are lost for ever.

You must lay it down as an absolute rule that the bird is to be entirely skinned, otherwise you can never succeed in forming a true and pleasing specimen.

You will allow this to be just, after reflecting a moment on the nature of the fleshy parts and tendons, which are often left in : 1st, they require to be well seasoned with aromatic spices; 2dly, they must be put into an oven to dry ; 3dly, the heat of the fire and the natural tendency all cured flesh has to shrink and become hard renders the specimen withered, distorted, and too small; 4thly, the inside then becomes like a ham or any other dried meat. Ere long the insects claim it as their own; the feathers begin to drop off, and you have the hideous spectacle of death in ragged plumage.

Wire is of no manner of use, but, on the contrary, a great nuisance ; for where it is introduced, a disagreeable stiffness and derangement of symmetry follow.

The head and neck can be placed in any attitude, the body supported, the wings closed, extended or elevated, the tail depressed, raised or expanded, the thighs set horizontal or oblique, without any aid from wire.   Cotton will effect all this.

A very small proportion of the skull bone, say, from the forepart of the eyes to the bill, is to be left in; though even this is not absolutely necessary.   Part of the wing-bones, the jaw-bones, and half of the thigh-bones, remain. Everything else, flesh, fat, eyes, bones, brains, and tendons are all to be taken away.

While dissecting, it will be of use to keep in mind,— That, in taking off the skin from the body, by means of your fingers and a little knife, you must try to shove it, in lieu of pulling it, lest you stretch it.

That, you must press as lightly as possible on the bird, and every now and then take a view of it, to see that the feathers, &c., are all right.

That, when you come to the head, you must take care that the body of the skin rests on your knee; for if you allow it to dangle from your hand, its own weight will stretch it too much.

That, throughout the whole operation, as fast as you detach the skin from the body, you must put cotton immediately betwixt the body and it; and this will effectually prevent any fat, blood, or moisture from coming in contact with the plumage. Here it may be observed that, on the belly you find an inner skin, which keeps the bowels in their place. By a nice operation with the knife, you can cut through the outer skin, and leave the inner skin whole. Attention to this will render your work very clean; so that, with a little care in other parts, you may skin a bird without even soiling your finger ends.

As you can seldom get a bird without shooting it, a line or two on this head will be necessary. If the bird be still alive, press it hard with your finger and thumb, just behind the wings, and it will soon expire. Carry it by the legs, and then, the body being reversed, the blood cannot escape down the plumage through the shot-holes. As blood will often have issued out before you have laid hold of the bird, find out the shot-holes, by dividing the feathers with your fingers, and blowing on them, and then, with your penknife, or the leaf of a tree, carefully remove the clotted blood, and put a little cotton on the hole. If, after all, the plumage has not escaped the marks of blood; or if it has imbibed slime from the ground, wash the part in water, without soap, and keep gently agitating the feathers, with your fingers, till they are quite dry. Were you to wash them, and leave them to dry by themselves, they would have a very mean and shrivelled appearance.

In the act of skinning a bird, you must either have it upon a table, or upon your knee. Probably, you will prefer your knee; because when you cross one knee over the other, and have the bird upon the uppermost, you can raise it to your eye, or lower it, at pleasure, by means of the foot on the ground, and then your knee will always move in unison with your body, by which much stooping will be avoided and lassitude prevented.

With these precautionary hints in mind, we will now proceed to dissect a bird. Suppose we take a hawk. The little birds will thank us, with a song for his death, for he has oppressed them sorely; and in size he is just the thing. His skin is also pretty tough, and the feathers adhere to it.

We will put close by us a little bottle of the solution of corrosive sublimate in alcohol; also a stick like a common knitting-needle, and a handful or two of cotton. Now fill the mouth and nostrils of the bird with cotton, and place it upon your knee on its back, with its head pointing to your left shoulder. Take hold of the knife with your two first fingers and thumb, the edge upwards. You must not keep the point of the knife perpendicular to the body of the bird; because, were you to hold it so, you would cut the inner skin of the belly, and thus let the bowels out. To avoid this, let your knife be parallel to the body, and then you will divide the outer skin with great ease.

Begin on the belly below the breast-bone, and cut down the middle, quite to the vent. This done, put the bird in any convenient position, and separate the skin from the body, till you get at the middle joint of the thigh. Cut it through, and do nothing more there at present, except introducing cotton all the way on that side, from the vent to the breast-bone. Do exactly the same on the opposite side.

Now place the bird perpendicular, its breast resting on your knee, with its back towards you. Separate the skin from the body on each side at the vent, and never mind at present the part from the vent to the root of the tail. Bend the tail gently down to the back, and while your finger and thumb are keeping down the detached parts of the skin on each side of the vent, cut quite across, and deep, till you see the back-bone, near the oil-gland at the root of the tail. Sever the back-bone at the joint, and then you have all the root of the tail, together with the oil-gland, dissected from the body. Apply plenty of cotton.

After this, seize the end of the back bone with your finger and thumb: and now you can hold up the bird clear of your knee, and turn it round and round, as occasion requires. While you are holding it thus, contrive, with the help of your other hand and knife, by cutting and shoving, to get the skin pushed up till you come to where the wing joins on to the body.

Forget not to apply cotton; cut this joint through; do the same at the other wing, add cotton, and gently push the skin over the head; cut out the roots of the ears, which lie very deep in the head, and continue skinning till you reach the middle of the eye; cut the nictitating membrane quite through, otherwise you would tear the orbit of the eye; and after this, nothing difficult intervenes to prevent your arriving at the root of the bill.

When this is effected, cut away the body, leaving a little bit of skull, just as much as will reach to the fore-part of the eye; clean well the jaw-bones, fasten a little cotton at the end of your stick, dip it into the solution, and touch the skull and corresponding part of the skin, as you cannot well get to these places afterwards. From the time of pushing the skin over the head, you are supposed to have had the bird resting upon your knee; keep it there still, and with great caution and tenderness return the head through the inverted skin, and when you see the beak appearing, pull it very gently till the head comes out unruffled and unstained.

You may now take the cotton out of the mouth; cut away all the remaining flesh at the palate, and whatever may have remained at the under jaw.

Here is now before you the skin, without loss of any feathers, and all the flesh, fat, and uncleaned bones out of it, except the middle joint of the wings, one bone of the thighs, and the fleshy root of the tail. The extreme point of the wing is very small, and has no flesh on it, comparatively speaking, so that it requires no attention, except touching it with the solution from the outside. Take all the flesh from the remaining joint of the wing, and tie a thread about four inches long to the end of it; touch all with the solution, and put the wing-bone back into its place. In baring this bone you must by no means pull the skin; you would tear it to pieces beyond all doubt, for the ends of the long feathers are attached to the bone itself; you must push off the skin with your thumb-nail and forefinger. Now skin the thigh quite to the knee; cut away all flesh and tendons, and leave the bone: form an artificial thigh round it with cotton; apply the solution, and draw back the skin over the artificial thigh: the same to the other thigh.

Lastly, proceed to the tail; take out the inside of the oil-gland, remove all the remaining flesh from the root, till you see the ends of the tail-feathers; give it the solution, and replace it. Now take out all the cotton which you have been putting into the body from time to time to

preserve the feathers from grease and stains. Place the
bird upon your knee on its back; tie together the
two threads which you had fastened to the end of the
wing-joints, leaving exactly the same space betwixt them
as your knowledge in anatomy informs you existed there
when the bird was entire; hold the skin open with your
finger and thumb, and apply the solution to every part of
the inside. Neglect the head and neck at present; they
are to receive it afterwards.

Fill the body moderately with cotton, lest the feathers
on the belly should be injured whilst you are about the
following operation. You must recollect that half of the
thigh, or in other words, one joint of the thigh-bone, has
been cut away. Now, as this bone never moved perpendicular to the body, but, on the contrary, in an oblique
direction, of course, as soon as it is cut off, the remaining
part of the thigh and leg, having nothing now to support
them obliquely, must naturally fall to their perpendicular.
Hence the reason why the legs appear considerably too
long. To correct this, take your needle and thread, fasten
the end round the bone inside, and then push the needle
through the skin just opposite to it. Look on the outside,
and after finding the needle amongst the feathers, tack up
the thigh under the wing with several strong stitches.
This will shorten the thigh, and render it quite capable of
supporting the weight of the body without the help of
wire. This done, take out every bit of cotton, except the
artificial thighs, and adjust the wing-bones (which are connected by the thread) in the most even manner possible, so
that one joint does not appear to lie lower than the other;
for unless they are quite equal, the wings themselves will
be unequal when you come to put them in their proper
attitude. Here then rests the shell of the poor hawk,
ready to receive, from your skill and judgment, the size,

the shape, the features and expression it had, ere death, and your dissecting hand, brought it to its present still and formless state. The cold hand of death stamps deep its mark upon the prostrate victim. When the heart ceases to beat, and the blood no longer courses through the veins, the features collapse, and the whole frame seems to shrink within itself. If then you have formed your idea of the real appearance of the bird from a dead specimen, you will be in error. With this in mind, and at the same time forming your specimen a trifle larger than life, to make up for what it will lose in drying, you will reproduce a bird that will please you.

It is now time to introduce the cotton for an artificial body, by means of a little stick like a knitting-needle ; and without any other aid or substance than that of this little stick and cotton, your own genius must produce those swellings and cavities, that just proportion, that elegance and harmony of the whole, so much admired in animated nature, so little attended to in preserved specimens. After you have introduced the cotton, sew up the orifice you originally made in the belly, beginning at the vent. And from time to time, till your arrive at the last stitch, keep adding a little cotton, in order that there may be no deficiency there. Lastly, dip your stick into the solution, and put it down the throat three or four times, in order that every part may receive it.

When the head and neck are filled with cotton quite to your liking, close the bill as in nature. A little bit of bees' wax, at the point of it, will keep the mandibles in their proper place. A needle must be stuck into the lower mandible perpendicularly. You will shortly see the use of it. Bring also the feet together by a pin, and then run a thread through the knees, by which you may draw them to each other, as near as you judge proper. Nothing now remains to be added but the eyes. With your little stick make a hollow in the cotton within the orbit, and introduce the glass eyes through the orbit. Adjust the orbit to them, as in nature, and that requires no other fastener.

Your close inspection of the eyes of animals will already have informed you, that the orbit is capable of receiving a much larger body than that part of the eye which appears within it when in life. So that, were you to proportion your eye to the size the orbit is capable of receiving, it would be far too large. Inattention to this has caused the eyes of every specimen, in the best cabinets of natural history, to be out of all proportion. To prevent this, contract the orbit, by means of a very small delicate needle and thread, at that part of it farthest from the beak. This may be done with such nicety, that the stitch cannot be observed; and thus you have the artificial eye in true proportion.

After this, touch the bill, orbits, feet, and former oil-gland at the root of the tail, with the solution, and then you have given to the hawk everything necessary, except attitude, and a proper degree of elasticity, two qualities very essential.

Procure any common ordinary box, fill one end of it, about three-fourths up to the top, with cotton, forming a sloping plane. Make a moderate hollow in it to receive the bird. Now take the hawk in your hands, and, after putting the wings in order, place it in the cotton, with its legs in a sitting posture. The head will fall down. Never mind. Get a cork, and run three pins into the end, just like a three-legged stool. Place it under the bird's bill, and run the needle, which you formerly fixed there, into the head of the cork. This will support the bird's head admirably. If you wish to lengthen the neck, raise the

cork, by putting more cotton under it. If the head is to be
brought forward, bring the cork nearer to the end of the
box. If it requires to be set backwards on the shoulders,
move back the cork.

As in drying, the back-part of the neck will shrink more
than the fore-part, and thus throw the beak higher than
you wish it to be, putting you in mind of a stargazing
horse, prevent this fault, by tying a thread to the beak,
and fastening it to the end of the box with a pin or needle.
If you choose to elevate the wings, do so, and support
them with cotton; and should you wish to have them particularly high, apply a little stick under each wing, and
fasten the end of them to the side of the box with a little
bees' wax.

If you would have the tail expanded, reverse the order
of the feathers, beginning from the two middle ones.
When dry, replace them in their true order, and the tail
will preserve for ever the expansion you have given it. Is
the crest to be erect? move the feathers in a contrary
direction to that in which they lie, for a day or two, and
it will never fall down after.

Place the box anywhere in your room, out of the
influence of the sun, wind, and fire; for the specimen must
dry very slowly, if you wish to reproduce every feature.
On this account the solution of corrosive sublimate is uncommonly serviceable; for at the same time that it totally
prevents putrefaction, it renders the skin moist and flexible
for many days. While the bird is drying, take it out and
replace it in its position once every day. Then, if you see
that any part begins to shrink into disproportion, you can
easily remedy it.

The small covert feathers of the wings are apt to rise a
little, because the skin will come in contact with the bone
which remains in the wing. Pull gently the part that

rises, with your finger and thumb, for a day or two. Press the feathers down. The skin will adhere no more to the bone, and they will cease to rise.

Every now and then touch and retouch all the different parts of the features, in order to render them distinct and visible, correcting at the same time any harshness, or unnatural risings or sinkings, flatness or rotundity. This is putting the last finishing hand to it.

In three or four days the feet lose their natural elasticity, and the knees begin to stiffen. When you observe this, it is time to give the legs any angle you wish, and arrange the toes for a standing position, or curve them to your finger. If you wish to set the bird on a branch, bore a little hole under each foot, a little way up the leg ; and having fixed two proportional spikes on the branch, you can, in a moment, transfer the bird from your finger to it, and from it to your finger, at pleasure.

When the bird is quite dry, pull the thread out of the knees, take away the needle, &c., from under the bill, and all is done. In lieu of being stiff with wires, the cotton will have given a considerable elasticity to every part of your bird; so that, when perching on your finger, if you press it down with the other hand, it will rise again. You need not fear that your hawk will alter, or its colours fade. The alcohol has introduced the sublimate into every part and pore of the skin, quite to the roots of the feathers. Its use is twofold. 1st. It has totally prevented all tendency to putrefaction ; and thus a sound skin has attached itself to the roots of the feathers. You may take hold of a single one, and from it suspend five times the weight of the bird. You may jerk it ; it will still adhere to the skin, and, after repeated trials, often break short. 2dly. As no part of the skin has escaped receiving particles of sublimate contained in the alcohol, there is not a spot exposed

to the depredation of insects, for they will never venture
to attack any substance which has received corrosive
sublimate.

You are aware that corrosive sublimate is the most fatal
poison to insects that is known. It is antiputrescent ; so
is alcohol ; and they are both colourless; of course they
cannot leave a stain behind them. The spirit penetrates
the pores of the skin with wonderful velocity, deposits
invisible particles of the sublimate, and flies off. The sublimate will not injure the skin, and nothing can detach it
from the parts where the alcohol has left it.[1]

Furs of animals, immersed in this solution, will retain
their pristine brightness and durability in any climate.

Take the finest curled feather from a lady's head, dip it
in the solution, and shake it gently till it be dry ; you will
find that the spirit will fly off in a few minutes, not a curl
in the feather will be injured, and the sublimate will preserve it from the depredation of the insect.

Perhaps it may be satisfactory to add here, that, some
years ago, I did a bird upon this plan in Demerara. It
remained there two years. It was then conveyed to
England, where it stayed five months, and returned to
Demerara. After being four years more there, it was
conveyed back again through the West Indies to England,
where it has now been near five years, unfaded and
unchanged.

On reflecting that this bird has been twice in the temperate and torrid zone, and remained some years in the hot
and humid climate of Demerara, only six degrees from the
line, and where almost everything becomes a prey to the

---

[1] All the feathers require to be touched with the solution, in order that
they may be preserved from the depredation of the moth. The surest way
of proceeding is, to immerse the bird in the solution of corrosive sublimate,
and then dry it before you begin to dissect it.

insect, and that it is still as sound and bright as when it was first done, it will not be thought extravagant to surmise that this specimen will retain its pristine form and colours for years after the hand that stuffed it has mouldered into dust.

I have shown this art to the naturalists in Brazil, Cayenne, Demerara, Oroonoque, and Rome, and to the royal cabinets of Turin and Florence. A severe accident prevented me from communicating it to the cabinet of Paris, according to my promise. A word or two more, and then we will conclude.

A little time and experience will enable you to produce a finished specimen. "Mox similis volucri, mox vera volucris." If your early performance should not correspond with your expectations, do not let that cast you down. You cannot become an adept all at once. The poor hawk itself, which you have just been dissecting, waited to be fledged before it durst rise on expanded pinion; and had parental aid and frequent practice ere it could soar with safety and ease beyond the sight of man.

Little more remains to be added, except that what has been penned down with regard to birds may be applied, in some measure, to serpents, insects, and four-footed animals.

Should you find these instructions too tedious, let the wish to give you every information plead in their defence. They might have been shorter: but Horace says, by labouring to be brief you become obscure.

If, by their means, you should be enabled to procure specimens from foreign parts in better preservation than usual, so that the naturalist may have it in his power to give a more perfect description of them than has hitherto been the case; should they cause any unknown species to be brought into public view, and thus add a little more to the page of natural history, it will please me much. But should they, unfortunately, tend to cause a wanton expense of life; should they tempt you to shoot the pretty songster warbling near your door, or destroy the mother, as she is sitting on the nest to warm her little ones; or kill the father, as he is bringing a mouthful of food for their support;—oh, then!—deep indeed will be the regret that I ever wrote them.

Adieu,

CHARLES WATERTON.

EXPLANATORY INDEX.

EXPLANATORY INDEX

A.

ACAIARI.—This is the resinous gum of the Hayawa, or Hiawa, tree, *Icica heptaphylla.*

It is reddish-brown, rather translucent, and brittle. When placed on the fire, or, even better, laid on a piece of iron nearly red-hot, it melts and then forms bubbles, which on breaking throw out puffs of a highly perfumed smoke, very much resembling that of the purest incense. Mr. Waterton gave me a large piece of it, and when describing the manners and customs of Guiana to my guests I have often gratified them with the fragrant smoke of the Acaiari. The natives sometimes burn lumps of it as torches.

In his *Essays*, Waterton frequently gives disconnected pieces of information which are extremely useful when employed as additions to the *Wanderings*. For example, when treating of the trade winds, he makes the following remarks on the acaiari gum :—

" In Guiana there is a tree called Hayawa ; it produces a deliciously-smelling resin, fit for incense. When the Indians stop on the banks of a river for the night, they are much in the habit of burning this resin for its fine and wholesome scent. It is found in a hard and lumpy state, all down the side of the tree from which it has oozed. It is also seen on the foot of the tree, and incorporated with the sand.

" When we had taken up our nightly quarters on the bank of the Essequibo, many a time we perceived this delightful fragrance of the Hayawa, which came down the bed of the river to the place where we were, in a direction quite opposite to the trade wind. My Indians knew by this that other Indians were encamped for the night on the river side above us."

In appearance the Acaiari much resembles the kaurie or cowdie gum of New Zealand, which exudes from a species of pine, and, like the Acaiari, is often found in large lumps imbedded in the sand. It is imported in great quantities, as an excellent varnish is made of it.

The Hayawa tree grows plentifully on the Essequibo in loose sandy soil. The wood is not much used because it decays on exposure to weather, but, on account of its perfume, it is recommended for naturalist's boxes and cabinets. It runs to about fifty feet in height. The gum is sometimes known as Resin of Konima.

ACOURI (*Dasyprocta acouchi*).—This is one of a rodent group, of which there are several species. The teeth, which are used as sights for the blow-gun, are the two incisors of the lower jaw. A lump of "kurumanni" wax is heated and fixed to the tube. The teeth are then laid upon it nearly parallel to each other, with the convex side upwards, and pressed into the wax. When the weapon is brought to this country, the wax becomes brittle, and the teeth are apt to be broken off. In travelling, the only hope of preserving this ingenious backsight, is by wrapping it in a piece of linen, and then covering it with a thick layer of tow or cotton wool.

The size of the Acouri is about equal to that of a large rabbit, and its flesh can be eaten, although it is very dry and has scarcely a particle of fat.

ACUERO.—Sometimes called Aquiro (*Astrocaryon aculeatum*). A species of palm. The fruit is used in lieu of butter, and the seeds, which are spherical, very hard, and as black as ebony, are cut into table-napkin rings, &c., just like the nut of the vegetable ivory.

ÆTA (*Mauritia flexuosa*).—This is a palm, which, in favourable situations, attains an enormous size, sometimes being
upwards of a hundred feet in height before the branches, or
rather leaves, are reached. As this great palm is widely
spread and is conspicuous, it has received various names.
Waterton calls it Æta, spelt by others Ita or Itah. But
the name by which it is most generally known is Moriche, or
Murichi. Of this splendid palm, Kingsley writes as follows
in *At Last :* —

"The noble Moriche palm delights in wet, at least in
Trinidad and on the lower Orinoco; but Schomburgk describes
forests of them—if, indeed, it be the same species—as growing
in the mountains of Guiana up to an altitude of four thousand
feet.

"The soil in which they grow here is half pitch pavement,
half loose brown earth, and over both, shallow pools of water,
which will become much deeper in the wet season ; and all
about float or lie their pretty fruit, the size of an apple, and
scaled like a fir cone. They are last year's, empty and decayed. The ripe fruit contains first a rich pulpy nut, and at
last a hard cone, something like that of the vegetable ivory
palm (*Phytelephas macrocarpa*) which grows in the mainland,
but not here. Delicious they are, and precious to monkeys
and parrots, as well as to the Orinoco Indians, among whom
the Jamunacs, according to Humboldt, say, that when a man
and woman survived that great deluge, which the Mexicans
call the age of water, they cast behind them, over their heads,
the fruits of the Moriche palm, as Deucalion and Pyrrha cast
stones, and saw the seeds in them produce men and women,
who re-peopled the earth. No wonder, indeed that certain
tribes look on this tree as sacred, or that the missionaries
should have named it the tree of life."

Humboldt gives the following eloquent account of this
palm in his *Personal Narrative :*—

"In the season of inundations these clumps of Mauritia,
with their leaves in the form of a fan, have the appearance

of a forest rising from the bosom of the waters. The navigator in proceeding along the channels of the delta of the Orinoco at night, sees with surprise the summit of the palm-trees illumined by large fires. These are the habitations of the Guaraons (Tivitivas and Waraweties of Raleigh), which are suspended from the trunks of the trees. These tribes hang up mats in the air, which they fill with earth, and kindle on a layer of moist clay the fire necessary for their household wants. They have owed their liberty and their political independence for ages to the quaking and swampy soil, which they pass over in the time of drought, and on which they alone know how to walk in security to their solitude in the delta of the Orinoco, to their abode on the trees, where religious enthusiasm will probably never lead any American Stylites.

"The Mauritia palm-tree, the *tree of life* of the missionaries, not only affords the Guaraons a safe dwelling during the risings of the Orinoco, but its shelly fruit, its farinaceous pith, its juice, abounding in saccharine matter, and the fibres of its petioles, furnish them with food, wine, and thread proper for making cords and weaving hammocks. These customs of the Indians of the delta of the Orinoco were found formerly in the Gulf of Darien (Uraba), and in the greater part of the inundated lands between the Guerapiche and the mouths of the Amazon. It is curious to observe in the lowest degree of human civilization the existence of a whole tribe depending on one single species of palm-tree, similar to those insects which feed on one and the same flower, or on one and the same part of a plant."

The word Guaraon, here used by Humboldt, is another rendering of the word Warow, one of the native tribes, a branch of which chooses this curious life.

Travellers in the country where the Moriche grows, are in the habit of using sandals made of the basal part of the leaf-stalk. They do not last long, and have to be renewed every third day. But, as the Moriche is always plentiful, and any native can make these sandals as well as twist the thongs from the outer fibres of the same leaf, there is no difficulty in keeping up the supply.

AI.—See Sloth, Three-toed.

ALBICORE (*Thynnus pacificus*).—As its scientific name implies, it is closely related to the celebrated tunny. It is a voracious fish, and is easily taken by a hook when there is a smart breeze, and the ship is going swiftly through the water, but in a calm, the Albicore becomes suspicious, and will not come near the ship.

ALLIGATOR.—See Cayman.

ANHINGA (*Plotus anhinga*).—This very remarkable bird belongs to the important group of the Pelicans, and is a mighty catcher of fish. It pursues its prey in a most singular

ANHINGA.

fashion. It crawls along some rock or tree-stump, which overhangs the water, and sits so motionless that it is scarcely distinguishable. When it sees a fish within reach, it drops into the water so silently that the river seems as if it were made of oil. It is an excellent swimmer, keeping its body submerged, and writhing its long and pliant neck in so serpentine a manner that it has often been mistaken for a water-snake.

In consequence of a habit of darting its long neck and pointed beak through the foliage among which it is resting, it has been called the Darter. Sometimes it is known by the name of Ducklar.

ANT, Black (*Ponera grandis*).—It is one of the largest and most venomous of the Ants, and is here given of its natural size.

The sting of this Ant is not only painful, but absolutely dangerous. Mr. Brown mentions that one of his men nearly lost his life from the stings of three of these terrible Ants.

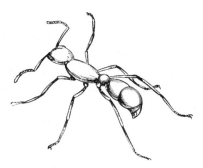

GREAT BLACK ANT (MUNIRI).

Indeed, so much are they dreaded, that travellers have been fairly turned out of their houses by the entrance of only a few Muniris, as they are called.

ANT, Coushie (*Œcodoma cephalotes*).—Coushies are veritable plagues in tropical America. They make burrows in all directions, sometimes entering houses and giving no notice of their presence until their tunnel is broken, in which case, the inhabitants have to vacate the premises for a time. I know of an instance where the Coushies ruined a gold mine for a time, breaking into it with a tunnel some eighty yards in length, and letting in a torrent of water, which broke down the machinery, and washed away all the supports, so that the mine had to be dug afresh.

Moreover, the stronghold of the Coushies had to be discovered and destroyed, a long and costly task, only to be undertaken by men who make it their special business.

COUSHIE ANT

When a tunnel has been traced to the nest, a large dome is built over it, filled with wood and sulphur, and closed except a few openings for the admission of air.

The wood is then lighted, bellows are inserted into the holes, and negro slaves work the bellows day and night until all the fuel is exhausted. Perhaps there may be a dozen burrows radiating from the nest. These are discovered by the smoke rising from their entrances, which are stopped up and marked.

When the fire has ceased, the holes for the bellows are stopped, and the nest is left for several days, so that not one Ant is left in it alive. Then the tunnels are laid open from beginning to end, and filled up with clay rammed into them. The tropical sun soon bakes the clay as hard as brick, and not until then is the locality considered as safe.

Mr. C. B. Brown met with rather a ludicrous incident in which the Coushies were caught in their own trap :—

" I had a small tin can, shaped like a sandwich box, with a layer of cork in the bottom, in which I pinned any curious insects met with. One night our camp was not far from the large earth-mounds of the Cushi ant (*Œcodoma cephalotes*), and a band of these creatures got into the insect case, deposited their loads of earth, and then set to work to destroy all my small but choice collection in the most heartless manner. They were unable to carry off the insects, after cutting them up, owing to the curved shape of the sides of the box preventing their egress, and were thus neatly trapped."

This insect is sometimes called by the name of Saüba.

ANT, Small Red (*Myrmica sœvissima*).—This is popularly called the Fire Ant, on account of the sharpness of its sting. The same traveller, who trapped the coushies, himself fell a victim to the Fire Ant :—

"At this place I observed a tall, straight sapling, with a regularly arranged style of branches in one or two sets near its top. Taking a machete, or cutlass, I gave the tree a blow with the intention of cutting it down, and was in the act of raising my hand to deliver another, when I received two or three sharp stings on the back of the neck, which felt like sparks of fire, and produced such a demoralizing effect upon my nerves, that I dropped the cutlass and fled.

"I hastily raised my hand to my neck, and seized two or three long-bodied, amber-coloured Ants, which had been dislodged from the tree by the jar produced by the blow, and had fallen upon me. These Ants always inhabit this kind of tree, living at the base of its leaf-stalks. The pain did not leave me for over an hour afterwards, and made me feel exceedingly ruffled and wroth."

Several travellers have told me that each sting feels like a red-hot needle thrust into the skin, the only difference being that the pain of the needle would soon die away, while that of the sting remains.

There is much more to be said about the Ants of Guiana, but space is too limited for further description.

ANTS' nests in trees.—These are evidently Termites, so generally miscalled White Ants. One of their nests is well described by C. Kingsley :—

"We passed too, in the path, an object curious enough, if not beautiful. Up a smooth stem ran a little rib, seemingly of earth and dead wood, almost straight, and about half an inch across, leading to a great brown lump among the branches, as big as a bushel basket. We broke it open, and found it a covered gallery, swarming with life. Brown, ant-like creatures, white, maggot-like creatures, of several shapes and sizes, were hurrying up and down, as busy as human beings in Cheapside. They were Termites, "white ants"—of which of the many species I know not—and the lump above was their nest. But why they should find it wisest to pack their nest aloft is as difficult to guess, as to guess why they take the trouble to build this gallery up to it, instead of walking up the stem in the open air. It may be that they are afraid of birds. It may be, too, that they actually dislike the light. At all events, the majority of them—the workers and soldiers, I believe, without exception—are blind, and do all their work by an intensely developed sense of touch, and it may be of smell and hearing also. Be that as it may, we should have seen them, had we had time to wait, repair the breach in the gallery, with as much discipline and division of labour as average human workmen in a manufactory."

ANTS' nests on ground. Also Termites.

ANT-BEAR, OR GREAT ANT-EATER, (*Myrmecophaga jubata*). —Waterton's statement that it could be a dangerous foe was long discredited. Now, as Waterton has rescued so many animals from the evil report that they were dangerous, he might have been believed when he said that the Ant-bear, though it never attacks without provocation, is a terrible antagonist when irritated. As usual, Waterton was right and the critics wrong. In Brown's *Canoe Life in Guiana* there is a story of a doubly fatal fight between an Ant-bear and a native, which completely corroborates Waterton's statement.

"We had not gone many miles before the guide lost the path, and we all scattered to look for it. In doing so, I walked almost on the top of a sleeping Ant-bear, which, springing up, sat on its hind legs, and grasped at me with its huge fore-claws. I sprang quickly to one side, and thus escaped. Thinking that it was good eating, I shot it, but the Indians said that it was not wholesome food, although, from the great interest they took in seeing it killed, I thought it was. [Waterton says that its flesh is good eating.]

"These large Ant-eaters are very dangerous customers, and have been known to kill men. William told me that an

GREAT ANT-BEAR.

Indian, living near Roraima, was hunting in the forest to the north of that mountain with some others, armed with his long blow-pipe. In returning home, considerably in advance of the rest of the party, it is supposed that he saw a young Ant-eater, and, taking it up in his arms, was carrying it home, when its mother gave chase, overtook, and killed him ; for, when his companions came up, they found him lying dead on his face in the embrace of the Ant-bear, one of its large claws having entered his heart. In the struggle he had managed to stick his knife behind his back into the animal, which bled to death, but not before the poor fellow had succumbed to its terrible hug.

"It was evident that he had only heard the Ant-eater coming when it was close upon him, and in turning round to look, his blow-pipe got caught across the path in front of him; then, as he turned to run, it formed a bar to his pro-

LITTLE ANT-BEAR.

gress, and he fell over it as the animal seized him. So firmly had the animal grappled him, that to separate it from the corpse the Indians had to cut off its fore-legs.".

ANT-BEAR (Smaller.)—(" *Cyclothurus didactylus*.")

This is a very much smaller animal than the Great Ant-bear, and while the one feeds on insects which it finds in the ground, so does the other subsist on the ants and termites which live in trees. Its tail is long and prehensile, and when dissected its ribs are seen to be so flat, so thin, and so wide that this part of the skeleton reminds the observer of the bands of an armadillo. The very characteristic sketch of a Little Ant-eater in repose was drawn by a lady, and lent to the late C. Kingsley, from whose delightful *At Last* it is taken.

ANT-BIRDS.—These are also called Ant-Thrushes, and belong to the *Formicarinæ*. They are all thick-bodied birds, with large heads, long legs, short tails, and very strong bills, as perhaps is needful, considering the food on which they almost entirely subsist. The largest of them is called the Giant Pitta, and is about equal in size to our English rook. It is a native of Surinam.

Several species of Ant-Thrush are to be found in India They find an English representative in the well-known Dipper of our streams and lakes.

APRON.—This ornament, for it can hardly be called a dress, is made of various sizes, the average being that of the beautiful example shown in the illustration, and drawn from a specimen in my collection. It is eight inches in width, and four in depth, and the colours are most artistically arranged, so as to produce definite patterns in blue, yellow, green, carmine chalk-white, and opaque vermilion. Other specimens are rather larger, and some are not half the size. According to Mr. C. B. Brown, the Accoway tribe seem to be the best Apron makers.

" I started from the Weynamou landing and walked to the village, which consisted of four or five palm-thatched houses with open sides, situated in a clearing, in which dwelt some Ackawoise Indians.

" I was struck with the manner in which the men of the place wore their hair, allowing it to grow long and fall far below their shoulders, giving them a very feminine appearance. The head man had his hair bound round at the end with cord in such a manner that it stuck out at a right angle behind. The old fellow's corporation projected in front quite as far as his pig-tail did behind, and gave him a most ridiculous appearance. Neither men nor women had eyebrows, having, according to Indian custom, plucked them out. Their upper lips and both sides of the mouth were tattooed with blue curved lines. The dress of the women was exceedingly simple, consisting only of a small cotton and bead-work apron, made fast to a cotton cord round the body above the

APRON.

hips. The apron, called a ' queyou,' is manufactured by the wearer in a most ingenious manner, each bead being slipped on the cotton thread in its proper place as it is being woven. The patterns of these dresses are marked out with red, blue, and white beads, and they generally have an ornamented border."

ARAS.—These magnificent birds are popularly known as Macaws. The Blue and Yellow Macaw is scientifically termed *Ara ararauna,* and the Scarlet and Blue Macaw is *Ara macao.* Both birds are tamed by the natives, and kept about their houses, in company with spider monkeys and other pets. Their long and splendid tail feathers are much used in the manufacture of head-dresses, some fine examples of which are in Waterton's museum.

ARMADILLO (*Dasypus sexcinctus*).—There are several species of Armadillo, but this is the one mentioned by Waterton. The Nine-banded Armadillo is called Cachicame.

ARROWS, Blow-gun.—These wonderful little Arrows are about nine or ten inches in length, and not thicker than a lady's steel knitting-needle.   Indeed, these Arrows (without

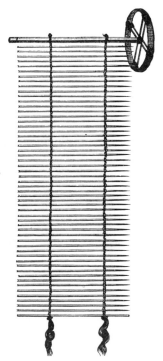

BLOW-GUN ARROWS STRUNG.

the poison) would answer very well for knitting.   The leaf-rib of the coucourite palm is, when dry, very hard and elastic, although like steel, it combines brittleness with hardness and elasticity.   It is also a heavy wood, for Arrows made of light woods never fly true. I have made imitations of these Arrows in many kinds of wood, and found yew to be the best. The end which is destined to receive the poison is beautifully tapered by means of the pirai-tooth sharpener, and can, in consequence of its hardness, be brought to a wonderfully fine point. Owing to their very small size, a hundred or more can be carried in the quiver, and they are arranged as shown in the illustration, taken from my own specimens.

The first illustration represents a few of these Arrows linked together as described.

I may mention that the strings at the ends of the central stick are double. The Arrows are laid one by one between the strings, a single turn being made between each Arrow, and they are kept in their places by a couple of sliding knots, which can be moved up and down the strings. The Arrows, when in their places, bear some resemblance to the peculiar mats used for cream cheeses, and perhaps a still greater resemblance to the parallel straws once employed by milliners in the operation of "gauffring" muslin, crape, and other fine textures.

BLOW-GUN ARROWS ROLLED AND TIED.

It will be seen that the Arrows can be rolled round the stick and tied together, and if one of the Arrows be wanted, it can easily be pushed between the spokes of the wheel without disturbing the roll.

By some tribes, the wheel is not employed, but the stick projects sufficiently to protect the hand, and is generally forked at the top.

Now for the Arrow as prepared for the blow-gun. The wild cotton, to which Waterton alludes, is soft, yellow in

colour, and fine in fibre, but the fibres are too short to fit it
for manufacture into thread, and for this purpose the native
has recourse to another plant belonging to the genus *Gossypium*,
or to the silk-grass.

The accompanying illustration shows the Arrow when complete.   In order to make the cotton adhere better to the
Arrow, the latter is slightly rubbed with Kurumanni wax,
and some of the cotton moulded round it in a sort of spindle

BLOW-GUN ARROW COMPLETE.

shape.   It is, in the thickest part, slightly wider than the
tube of the blow-gun, so as to leave no windage when propelled by the breath.

One of the chief difficulties in putting in the cotton is to
make it exactly symmetrical, for if one side be in the least
longer than the other, it cannot fly straight.   The cotton is
tied on in a sort of chequer patten, with a very fine fibre of
silk-grass, and some time is occupied in doing it properly.
But, a native cares nothing about time, especially when a
faulty Arrow may cost him a meal.

He generally prepares about ten or twelve for the blow-
gun, leisurely fitting and tying the cotton while lying in his
hammock.   These are kept in the quiver for present use, the
others forming a reserve.   Should he miss his aim while shooting, he does not search for his Arrow, but takes another.

The force with which these tiny weapons can be propelled
is really wonderful.   They can kill birds on the tops of lofty
trees where they are far beyond the reach of a shot gun.   I have
sent them a hundred yards, and have no doubt that a Macoushi
Indian could project them much farther.   They are perfectly
noiseless, and next to invisible, so that when one bird is shot,
another on the same tree will not take alarm.

ARROWS, Fish.—These are of considerable length, some of

them being six feet long. How they are made and used is shown by Mr. C. B. Brown in his work on Guiana.

" Our men frequently shot deep-bodied, silvery-scaled fish, called cartabac (*Tetragonopterus latus*), and another somewhat similar fish called pacu (*Myletes pacu*). The male of the latter has a large deep body of a dull goldfish colour, while the female is of a dull bluish brown. Their flesh is firm, and of a peculiarly pleasant nutty flavour. They have even rows of teeth shaped like the incisors of mammals. These fish browse upon the aquatic plants in the swift running water, and are easily shot, when feeding near the surface, by those skilled in the use of the bow and arrow.

" The bows that our men used for this purpose had been procured from the Indians of the interior. They were very long and straight, and made of hard red wood. The shafts

FISH-ARROW.

of the Arrows were made of long straight reeds—the flower-stalks of the wild cane—tightly bound to a short piece of extremely tough wood inserted at one end, called a ' shimara-sherie ' or ' wire-cash.' The end of the latter fits into an iron arrow-head, to which it is attached by a piece of cord in such a way, that when the point pierces the fish the barbed head comes off the arrow end, but still remains attached to it by the cord. This allows the shaft freer play, so that during the struggles of the fish it is not broken. Sometimes a light cotton cord of about fifteen feet in length is made fast to the wire-cash, one end being attached to the left hand of the fisherman. When the fish is within a short distance of the man the latter lets fly the Arrow, and aiming a few inches below the fish, to allow for refraction, strikes it in the body. The fish, pierced by the barbed point which remains in it, being now in direct communication with the man's hand by means of the cord, is easily landed."

The illustration of the head of one of these arrows is taken from a specimen in my collection. The ' shimara-sherie ' is made of letter-wood, *q.v.*, which is weighty as well as hard, so that, together with the iron head, the fore part of the arrow is heavy enough to enable the weapon to penetrate the water. Sometimes it is used for catching turtle, and then is shot high into the air so as to fall perpendicularly on the turtle's back.

ARROW, Hog.—This weapon is quite as large as the fish arrow which has just been described, and, with the exception of the head, is made in much the same manner. It is used for shooting wild hogs, capybara, tapirs, and the larger monkeys. One of the principal objects in putting the head loosely into a square, or rather, oblong hole, is, that the shaft falls to the ground, and can be picked up by the hunter and used again with a fresh point. Thus, he need not trouble himself to carry more than a couple of shafts, and, as a Guianan native never takes any trouble that he can avoid, this arrangement suits him admirably.

I once happened to say to Waterton that I supposed a native could easily sit down and make a fresh Arrow, and was

HOG-ARROW

immediately 'pulled up' as having shown ignorance of the native customs. For, as Waterton graphically put it, an Indian never runs if he can walk, never walks if he can sit, and never sits if he can lie down. All Arrow making is done while lying in the hammock.

The illustration represents the head of one of the Arrows in my collection, one figure showing it as ready to be placed on the bow, and the other as covered with its bamboo guard. The native is so cautious about the wourali, that he never uses any cutting instrument when the poison is uncovered, lest he might scratch himself, and some of the wourali find its way into the wound. He never carries the hog-arrow without its guard, and if an uncovered arrow be pointed at him, he is as much frightened as we should be if aimed at with a loaded rifle.

The feathers are only two in number.

ARROW, Rappu or Poison-wood.—I cannot find that this weapon is anywhere mentioned by Waterton, although he brought home many specimens, and gave me several of them, describing their properties, which are very nearly identical with those of wourali. Mr. C. B. Brown gives an amusing account of a controversy between three hunters. One named Parmu was well ahead of the others, shot a wild hog with a Rappu Arrow, and, knowing that it must fall, went after the rest of the herd, leaving the poisoned head in the wound. Presently, another hunter came up, fired at the hog, and as it did not run away, thought that he had inflicted a fatal wound. Hunter number three now came up, and also fired with the same result.

" On the return of the men, this hog was knocked on the head, the poisoned Arrow pulled out, and the animal brought to the boat, when Ben claimed it as the result of his prowess. Griffiths was astounded at this, declaring that he had slain it himself. When, however, it had been scalded and scraped, it was found that not a single shot had touched it, and the Arrow-head formed its only wound. The subject was a sore one for both men after their warm discussion, and it was frequently brought up by the rest of the party, when the topic of conversation turned on shooting."

The same traveller thus describes the manufacture of the Arrow.

"We arrived at a smooth open river beyond the Rappu Rapids. The islands in these rapids and a river near by are so called from the existence of a peculiar species of tall and graceful bamboo which flourishes there, not being found further north. Pieces of the stem of this bamboo are dried and used by the Indians as Arrow-heads, which are said to possess similar properties to the far-famed wourali poison. They split up the stem, and dry the pieces over a fire, and then shape them into lance-heads, which they fasten on the ends of Arrows. Wild animals wounded by these Arrows are at once completely paralyzed, and in that condition easily despatched. This bamboo is tall, growing singly, and not in clumps, from a mass of matted roots, like the common bamboo."

The heads are about six inches in length, and are shaped like willow leaves.

For the quivers employed for the blow-gun and hog-arrows, *see* "Quiver."

ARROW-REED (*Gynœcium saccharinum.*)—It is described on page 369.

ARROW-ROOT (*Maranta arundinacea.*)—This is a sort of cane, with broad, branching leaves and white flowers. Several species are cultivated for food.

AWNING, Canvas.—Later travellers have proved the value of Waterton's experience. Nothing is so certain to bring on the dreaded fever than the drenching rain which is so common in Guiana, especially when the rain-storm comes on at night. As the average temperature at night rarely varies more than from 73° to 85° Fahr. the traveller can sleep in the open air without inconvenience so far as regards heat and cold. Against rain, however, he must guard, and such a waterproofed canvas awning as Waterton describes is found to answer that purpose admirably.

B.

BAMBOO (*Bambusa arundinacea.*)—The many uses to which this gigantic grass is put are too well known to require notice.

BANANA (*Musa sapientium.*)—One of the strangest of plants. It scarcely ever grows wild, and has been so long propagated by cuttings that it has lost the power of seeding, except in the Andaman Islands, where it does produce seeds, some of which have been sent to England by the late C. Kingsley, who thus writes of it :—

" Most beautiful it is. The lush, fat, green stem; the crown of huge leaves falling over in curves like those of

BANANA.

human limbs ; and below the whorls of green or golden fruit, with the purple heart of flowers dangling behind them ; and all so full of life *that this splendid object is the product of a few months.*

" I am told that if you cut the stem off at certain seasons, you may *see* the young leaf actually move upwards from within, and grow before your eyes; and that each stem of plantain will bear from thirty to sixty pounds of rich food during the year of its short life."

Another plantain (*Musa paradisaica*) bears large fruits which require to be cooked, while the fruit of the banana is eaten raw.

BELL-BIRD.—*See* " Campanero."

BÊTE-ROUGE.—This horrible little pest much resembles our harvest bug in colour, size and habits. It is a minute species of tick belonging to the genus *Leptus*, and causes the most violent irritation when it attacks a human being. As its principal haunts are in grassy spots, the feet are generally exposed to its onslaught, but it will make its way between the collar and neck, or on the wrists, and, being so small, scarcely larger than the dot of the letter i, it is seldom discovered until the mischief is done.

Indeed there seems to be no mode of evading it. Mr. C. B. Brown mentions that he once thought that he had found a new species of Maam, both sides of the head being marked with a scarlet patch. But, on examining the bird closer, he found that the scarlet patches were nothing but clusters of the Bête-rouge.

BISA MONKEY (*Brachyurus satanas.*)—
Sometimes this monkey is called the Bearded Saki, or Cuxio. The male is a much deeper black than the female. It seems to be more solitary in its habits than the generality of its tribe, and to live rather in pairs than companies. It seems fearful of wetting its beard, and, when it drinks, scoops up the water in the hollow of its hand.

The name is sometimes spelled Beeshu.

BLOW-GUN.—Sometimes called Pucuna. The beautifully perfect specimen given to me by Waterton is exactly eleven feet in length, and is yet so light that it is only a little more than a pound and a half in weight. For the various materials from which it is made see "Wourali," "Ourah," "Samourah," "Silk-grass," "Acuero," &c.

The back-sight is made in a very ingenious manner. *See* "Acouri."

Slight as is the pucuna it is much stronger than it looks, and when held to the lips scarcely curves at all The mode

BISA MONKEY.

of holding it is rather curious, and was taught me by Waterton.

Artists generally represent it as held to the mouth with the right hand, and resting upon the left hand, the arm being stretched to its furthest extent. This is all wrong. When taking aim the native hunter places his left elbow against his side, with the palm of the hand turned upwards, just as if he were handling a violin, and grasps the tube about eight inches from the end. The right hand is next placed on it, with the palm downwards, so that when the tube is grasped, about two inches project from the hands.

It will then be found that merely by bending the body backwards the tube can be raised or lowered with scarcely

any exertion, the left elbow supporting its weight, and the muscles of the loins supplying the power. The Macoushies are very fastidious as to the straightness of the pucuna, which they never allow to lean against a tree, but always suspend by a loop just below the foresight. When on foot, they never carry the pucuna horizontally, as we 'trail' arms, but hold it perpendicularly, and keep it as upright as the vegetation will permit. In fact, the position of the holder is almost identical with that of a soldier when 'ordering arms.'

There is a shorter and much heavier Blow-gun used by some tribes. It has no ourah, and is made of a young palm, first split, then hollowed, then put together and bound spirally with vegetable fibre.

BOAT-BILL.—*See* "Crabier."

BOCLORA (*Trogon melanopterus*).—This species of Trogon seems to have a wider range than the generality of its kind. Mr. C. B. Brown was fortunate enough to have an opportunity of watching the bird and her young.

"Close to my tent at that place there was the nest of a common dark-coloured trogon, called Bowclora, which merely consisted of a hole scooped out of a large, round termite's nest, built on the stem of a tree. In it were two young ones which kept up a most doleful whistling all day, while the mother sat on a tree-bough near by, being afraid, from our near proximity, to approach them.

BLOW-GUN.

From examination of the stomach of the Boclora, its food seems to be of a rather mixed nature, portions of fruit and the remains of insects, chiefly the mantis, being found in it.

Bois Immortelle (*Erythrina umbrosa*).—The following description of this splendid tree is given by C. Kingsley :—

" Among the young cacao-trees, at some twenty yards apart, are the stems of a tree looking much like an ash, save that it is inclined to throw out broad spurs like a ceiba (cotton-tree). You look up, and see that they are Bois Immortelles, fifty or sixty feet high, one blaze of vermilion against the blue sky.

" Those who have stood under a Lombardy poplar in early spring, and looked up at its buds and twigs, showing like pink coral against the blue sky, and have felt the beauty of the sight, can imagine faintly—but only faintly—the beauty of this ' Madres de Cacao ' or Cacao-mothers, as they call them here, because their shade is supposed to shelter the cacao-trees, while the dew collected by their leaves keeps the ground below always damp."

Both scientific names of this gorgeous tree are appropriate. The first is derived from a Greek word, signifying red, and the second is Latin and means shady. The magnificent flowers are greatly frequented by humming birds.

Bonito (*Pelamys sarda*).—This well known fish seldom reaches a yard in length. Its flesh is eaten, but does not agree with many persons. One of my friends told me that he once had several attacks of virulent nettlerash, before he found out that he had been eating Bonito flesh. At the time, I was suffering from violent rash caused by handling the beautiful " canker-worm," *i.e.* the caterpillar of the gold-tailed moth, and on seeing my face and hands, my friend thought that I had been eating Bonito to find out what it was like, and was paying the price of curiosity. I never saw the flesh, but am told by those who have often eaten it, that it is very red and has much the look of fresh meat. The fish may be recognised by the longitudinal brown streaks on the belly.

Bouradi. *See* " Toucan."

Bulêtre (*Mimusops Balata*).—Sometimes called Burueh. One of the giant-trees of Guiana, with a reddish-brown trunk, and rising to the height of a hundred and fifty feet. From its bark, when cut, exudes a milky white sap, which, when congealed, produces a gum partaking of the properties of caoutchouc and gutta percha. This gum appears not to have reached the English market.

Once in every five years it bears an abundant store of excellent fruit, much like an English plum, and the tree is so gigantic that a single trunk will produce a log of a yard square and a hundred feet in length. The wood is superior to oak except for shipbuilding, sea-water injuring its otherwise incorruptible texture. Like the cotton-tree (*q.v.*), the trunk throws out spurs of great size.

The timber merchants call it Bullet, or Bully-tree, and as the wood is not injured by weather, it is used for house-frames, posts, and shingles. Another kind of Bullet-wood is procured from the Sapota Mulleri.

BUSHMASTER.—*See* " Couanacouchi."

BUSH-ROPE.—This is a general name applied to a vast number of climbing plants, which grow in the remarkable way described by Waterton. They are also known by the popular name of Liana. Schomburgk gives the following description of one species of Bush-Rope :—

" As we forced our way through the wood, we were greeted, from time to time, by the finest perfume, which we traced to a liana, or creeper, and one of the Bush-ropes of the colonists. Its sweet-smelling plant was *Schnella brachystachya*, with white flowers, of which the largest patch was spotted with pink, growing in voluminous clusters, its stem twisted and contorted in so remarkable a manner, as well to deserve the name of Bush-rope.

" To describe the various ways in which these twists and contortions take place would be difficult. Sometimes the stem is as delicate as a ribbon, while at others it presents a bundle of stems so closely twined together, as to make it no easy matter to separate them with an axe."

Some of these Bush-Ropes are very pliant, will bear any

amount of twisting, and are much used for housebuilding. They go by the name of Mamouril. Others are so brittle that they snap if tied in knots or twisted. Stedman compares the appearance of the tropical forest with its tall tree trunks and interlacing bush-ropes to that of a fleet at anchor, a comparison afterwards employed by Waterton.

CABBAGE, Mountain (*Oreodoxa oleracea*).—One of the most beautiful of the Palms. The topmost shoot is popularly called the "cabbage," and is a very excellent vegetable for the table. As the palm dies when the central shoot is destroyed, the usual plan is to cut it down, knowing that there are plenty of others ready to take the place of those which are destroyed.

Kingsley well described his first sight of the Cabbage Palm :—

"Grey pillars, which seemed taller than the tallest poplars, smooth and cylindrical as those of a Doric temple, each carrying a flat head of darkest green, were ranged along roadsides and round fields, or stood in groups or singly, near engine works, or towered above rich shrubberies which shrouded comfortable country houses. It was not easy, as I have said, to believe that these strange and noble things were trees ; but such they were. At last we beheld, with wonder and delight, the pride of the West Indies, the Cabbage-palm — Palmistes of the French settlers — which botanists have well named Oreodoxa, the 'glory of the mountain.'

"We saw them afterwards a hundred times in their own native forests, and when they rose through tangled masses of richest vegetation mixed with other and smaller species of palms, their form, fantastic though it was, harmonized well with hundreds of forms equally fantastic. But here they seemed, at first sight, out of place, incongruous, and artificial, standing amid no kindred forms, and towering over a cultivation and civilisation which might have been mistaken, seen from the sea, for wealthy farms along some English shore.

Gladly would we have gone on shore, were it but to have stood a while under those Palmistes."

It is the custom that when a spot has been cleared for the purpose of building a house, a few Cabbage-palms are left standing round it.

CAMOUDI (*Eunectes marinus*).—One of the giants among snakes, more generally known by the title of Anaconda. It is sometimes called Huillia. The snake is generally found near water, and is apt to be dangerous when large. Mr. C. B. Brown remarks that whenever a Camoudi is killed, two king vultures (*q.v.*) will come and take possession of it. Waterton noticed the same fact. When gorged, it is in the habit of lying coiled up near the water until it has digested its meal.

In this state it is so motionless that it might easily be mistaken for a log of wood. Indeed, Waterton mentions in one of his essays, that a negro committed the error of sitting down on one of these snakes, taking it for a fallen tree, and was only undeceived by the snake moving away.

Kingsley mentions a case where four young ladies were bathing in a lagoon, and one was seized by a Camoudi from behind. Thinking that one of her sisters had caught her dress in play, she felt no alarm until she saw her three sisters on the bank, and found that she had been seized by a snake. The three girls courageously dashed into the water and tried to drag her away from the snake. Fortunately the reptile had only caught her bathing-dress, which, being made of thin cotton, gave way, and she escaped safely to land.

CAMPANERO (*Chasmorhynchus niveus*).—No one has described the singular cry of this bird as Waterton has done.

It is one of the great tribe of the Chatterers. The horn-like projection from the base of its beak has in all probability much to do with the resonance of the cry. The accompanying illustrations show the two positions of the 'horn.' The head of the bird gives the horn as it appears while the bird is tolling its wonderful bell, and the full figure depicts the flaccid state of the horn while the bird is at rest.

Capivi, or Copaiba Gum.—This important gum is produced from several species of *Copaifera* (*see* " Purple-heart "), and is obtained by making incisions in the branches.

CAMPANERO TOLLING.

Caprimulgus.—The Latin term for Goatsucker. This is an example of Waterton's lax nomenclature, the Whip-poor-Will (*q. v.*) mentioned in the same sentence being also a Goatsucker.

CAMPANERO SILENT.

Caracara.—Evidently a Liantasse, probably belonging to the genus *Schnella*.

Cassava (*Jatropha manihot*).—This most useful plant is sometimes called Manioc, and is to the Guianan natives what

corn is to us. It is a tall, unbranched plant, growing irregularly and knotted at intervals, and having
leaves with a purple gloss.

The root is the portion that is eaten, and it is
scraped down on a board stuck full of sharp flint or
other stones, and called by the name of Tumarrie.
It then looks just like horseradish as brought to
our tables, but is filled with a poisonous juice. In
order to extract this juice, the scraped cassava is
forced into a long, narrow basket called a matappi,
and made exactly on the principle of the 'Siamese-
links' which were once popular as toys. The material of which it is made is a species of Calathea.

When the matappi is full, it is scarcely half its
length when empty, but is more than double its
thickness. It is then hung to a branch of a tree or
to a beam of a house, an earthen pot is placed under
it, and a heavy weight is tied to the lower end. The
weight of the stone causes the matappi to increase
in length, but to diminish in thickness, thus exerting a powerful pressure on the cassava, and squeez-
ing out the juice, which runs through the interstices,
and so down the matappi into the pot.

The dry Cassava is then removed from the matappi,
rubbed through a basket-work sieve, formed into
flat circular cakes about two feet in diameter, and a
quarter of an inch in thickness, and baked upon a

flat, heated stone or
plate of iron.

Meanwhile, the poi-
sonous juice has been
kept out of reach of
children, poultry, &c.,
and, on being boiled,
and flavoured with

CASSAVA PRESS.   CASSAVA BOWL.

red-pepper or capsicum, becomes the well-known cassareep or pepper-pot of the West Indies. The pot is never cleaned, so that, as it is very thick, very soft, and very porous, it absorbs the juices. When Cassava bread is eaten, it is generally dipped in the cassareep, which often contains pieces of meat, &c., and which, when the palate has become accustomed to the inordinate amount of red pepper, is not only nourishing, but appetizing. A newcomer, however, will run the risk of starving altogether, for the native cook is so very heavy-handed with her red pepper, that the lips and tongue of a novice are scorched as if with red-hot iron.

The illustration of the matappi and cassareep pot is taken from specimens in my collection. A considerable amount of Cassava is consumed in this country under the names of tapioca and semolina.

CASSIQUES.—These birds, of which there are several species, all belonging to the genus *Cassicus*, are popularly called Merles in Jamaica. The word is evidently the same as our Merle (Lat. *Merula*), which distinguishes the common blackbird.

According to C. Kingsley, the Merles are "birds the size of a jackdaw, brown and yellow, and mocking-birds, too, of no mean ability. The pouches (nests) two feet long and more, swayed in the breeze, fastened to the end of the boughs with a few small threads. Each had, about half-way down, an opening into the round sac below, in and out of which the merles crept and fluttered, talking all the while in twenty different notes.

" Most tropic birds hide their nests carefully in the bush : the merles hang theirs fearlessly in the most exposed situations. They find, I presume, that they are protected enough from monkeys, wild cats, and gato-melaos (a sort of ferret), by being hung at the extremity of the bough. So thinks M. Léstaud, the accomplished describer of the birds of Trinidad."

Some writers call the Merles by the name of mocking-birds.

CASTOR-OIL (*Ricinus communis*).—Another of the plants

imported from the Old World   It belongs to the great tribe of the Euphorbiæ or Spurges, of which our common milky-weed is a familiar example.

From its seeds is obtained the Castor-oil of commerce.   The best, called ' cold-drawn ' oil, is procured by simple pressure. The plant is sometimes called Palma Christi, because its leaves look something like widely-spread fingers.

The Romans gave it the name of Ricinus, because the seeds bear some resemblance in shape to sheep-ticks or ' ricini.' They procured it originally from Egypt, where seeds may still be found in the tombs.

CAYMAN (*Alligator nigrer*).—This is the animal which Waterton so brilliantly captured.   There are many of the crocodiles and alligators in North and South America, and in habits they seem to be much alike.

All have the peculiar way of attacking animals on land by knocking them into the water with a blow of the tail, and

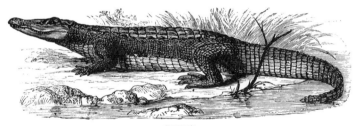

CAYMAN.

carrying them off before they can recover from the effects of the blow.   Sometimes they have been known to attack canoes in this manner.

They all possess a most abominable musky smell, " floating," as Mr. C. B. Brown says, " like a deadly miasma round our camp, and finding its way even to our palates."   Then, all of them are in the habit of emitting loud, bellowing noises, especially at night, so that they make themselves as objection-able to the ears as to the nostrils.

The hook which was used by Waterton was engraved in the original edition of the *Wanderings*, but I am sure that the

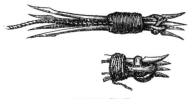

CAYMAN HOOK.

draughtsman who drew it could not have seen it. The instrument itself is in Waterton's museum, and I have here substituted my own sketch of it.

The four prongs are not barbed, but are sharply pointed, as seen in the illustration. They are flattish, and very tough, as they need be, for they are bitten and cracked all over by the teeth of the cayman. The prongs are kept in their diverging position by wooden pegs driven between them, and the whole instrument is thus made so elastic that it can be compressed by a strong grasp of the hand, and then springs back again to its original form. So, when compressed by the entrails of the acouri, which were wrapped round them, the instrument would slip easily down the cayman's throat, and then expand on being swallowed.

CHAMELEON.—One of the Anolis Lizards, probably the Red-throated Anolis (*Anolius bullaris*), which are active, chase flies upon trees, and are changeable in colour when excited. The true Chameleons exclusively inhabit the Old World, and are much too sluggish to chase insects. There are several species of Anolis in Guiana.

CHIGOE, sometimes spelled JIGGER, or TSCHIKO (*Pulex penetrans*.)—Tiny as it may be, the little Chigoe is one of the most detested plagues of the West Indies. To all appearances it resembles our common domestic flea, but it has fortunately not yet become acclimatised in any part of Europe. There is scarcely a traveller in the West Indies who writes with the least patience about this more than troublesome insect. There is some credit in facing a rattlesnake, killing a jaguar, or in braving the many dangers of tropical travel, but there is none in becoming the victim of a flea, though the apparently insignificant enemy may, unless its attacks be properly repelled, cause the loss of a limb, or even of life.

In one of his essays Waterton has extended the information given in his *Wanderings*.

" In the plantations of Guiana there is generally an old negress known by the name of Granny, a kind of *Junonis anus*, who loiters about the negro yard, and is supposed to take charge of the little negroes who are too young to work. Towards the close of day you will sometimes hear the most dismal cries of woe coming from that quarter. Old Granny is then at work grubbing the Chigoe nests out of the feet of the sable urchins, and filling the holes with lime-juice and cayenne pepper. This searching compound has two duties to perform ; firstly, it causes death to any remaining Chigoe in the hole ; and secondly, it acts as a kind of a birch rod to the unruly brats, by which they are warned, to their cost, not to conceal their Chigoes in future ; for, afraid of encountering old Granny's tomahawk, many of them prefer to let the Chigoes riot in their flesh, rather than come under her dissecting hand.

" A knowing eye may always perceive when the feet of negroes are the abode of the Chigoe. They dare not place their feet firmly on the ground, on account of the pain which such a position would give them ; but they hobble along with their toes turned up ; and by this you know that they are not suffering from tubboes (a remnant of the yaws), but from the actual depredations of the Chigoes, which have penetrated under the nails of the toes, and then formed sores, which, if not attended to, would, ere long, become foul and corroding ulcers. As I seldom had a shoe or stocking on my foot from the time that I finally left the sea-coast in 1812, the Chigoe

was a source of perpetual disquietude to me. I found it
necessary to examine my feet every evening, in order to
counteract the career of this extraordinary insect. Occasionally, at one overhauling, I have broken up no less than four
of its establishments under the toe-nails.

" In 1825, a day or two before I left Guiana, wishful to try
how this puny creature and myself would agree during a sea
voyage, I purposely went to a place where it abounded, not
doubting but that some needy individual of its tribe would
attempt to better its condition. Ere long a pleasant and
agreeable kind of itching under the bend of the great toe
informed me that a Chigoe had bored for a settlement. In
three days after we had sailed a change of colour took
place in the skin, just at the spot where the Chigoe had
entered, appearing somewhat like a blue pea. By the time
we were in the latitude of Antigua my guest had become
insupportable, and I saw there was an immediate necessity
for his discharge. Wherefore, I turned him and his numerous
family adrift, and poured spirits of turpentine into the cavity
which they had occupied, in order to prevent the remotest
chance of a regeneration.

" The Indian and negro wenches perform the operation of
extracting Chigoes with surprising skill. They take a pin,
and, by a very slow process, they lay the part bare, and contrive to work quite round the bag which contains the Chigoe
and its offspring. As soon as this has been effected, they
turn the bag out, whole and uninjured, by which means none
are left in the hole to form a new colony. For my own part,
I never trouble these gentle operators, although I have looked
on many a time, and admired their exquisite skill, while they
were fingering the toes of my acquaintance.

" Once, however, I had it not in my power to be my own
surgeon, and on that occasion a faithful old negro performed
the friendly office. I was descending the Demerara, with an
inveterate tertian ague ; and I was so much exhausted by
sitting upright in the canoe that I had no sooner got ashore

at the Indian hut than I lay down on the ground at full length. Sickness had pressed so heavily on me that I was callous to the well-known feeling which the Chigoe causes. I was quite unconscious that there were nine thriving nests of Chigoes in my back, until one was accidentally observed by the old negro ; and this led to the discovery of the rest. I handed him my penknife, and told him to start the intruders. Sick as I was, I wished an artist were present at the operation. The Indian's hut, with its scanty furniture, and bows and arrows hanging round ; the deep verdure of the adjoining forest ; the river flowing rapidly by ; myself wasted to a shadow ; and the negro grinning with exultation as he showed me the Chigoes' nests which he had grubbed out, would have formed a scene of no ordinary variety.

" Dogs are often sorely tormented by the Chigoe ; and they get rid of them by an extremely painful operation. They gradually gnaw into their own toes, whining piteously as they do it, until they get at the Chigoe's nest. Were it not for this singular mode of freeing themselves from the latent enemy, dogs would absolutely be cripples in Guiana."

In Mr. Brown's *Camp and Canoe Life in Guiana* there is an anecdote which well expresses the terrors which this tiny plague can inspire into Europeans as well as natives.

" Just then Ben returned from a voyage of discovery along the path leading away from our camp, with a joyful expression of countenance betokening good news. ' Why, sir,' he said, ' there is a good house not far off, and it ain't got no one in it.' I immediately went with him to see it, and, plodding through mud and water, climbed a slight eminence to a large open shed, situated in the midst of a clearing. I halted close to it, and proposed that he should take a look at the floor for insects. He walked boldly in, hesitated, looked down at his bare feet, and, exclaiming ' Jiggers and dog fleas full da here ! ' fled precipitately. I may here mention that the jigger or Chigoe is a small flea that burrows under the toe-nails, where it forms an egg-bag almost the size of a small pea, which has to be extracted with a needle, an operation giving a considerable amount of pain.

" I remarked to Ben in a casual way, ' Surely the natives have some way of getting rid of these insects ? just think the matter over in your mind, and don't lose sight of the fact that it depends upon you whether we sleep in the moist swamp to-night, or under this good roof.

" He proposed two ways of performing the operation, one was to ' bun them,' as he called it, and the other was to sweep them out. I seized upon both ideas ; we would burn them first, and sweep out their roasted carcases afterwards.

" Fortunately there was a heap of dry palm-leaves in the house, of which a few bunches were made into brooms, and the rest scattered over the floor. If any one had been looking at us from a short distance when performing this operation, he would have come to the conclusion that we were both demented, from the way in which we skipped about, darting out every now and then to brush off our enemies from our clothes. Then we set fire to the leaves, and had the whole place covered with flames a foot in height—a grand and satisfactory though short-lived flare-up. At this stage of the proceedings we were reinforced by Pedro and Vincente, who, on the subsiding of the flames, swept out the residuary matter, composed of carcases, ashes, and dust. After the crusade was over, a few hundreds of the enemy were left, but these we did not mind.

" It is a curious and sad fact, as I have always found to my cost, than when Indians leave their houses for a time the dust on the floors becomes infested with jiggers and fleas. The former come from the eggs dropped from the jigger egg-bags in the toes of both Indians and their dogs, and the latter from eggs dropped by the fleas of the dogs."

The " nest " of the Chigoe is in reality the swollen body of the female, which contains the eggs, and becomes as large in proportion to the head, thorax, and limbs, as does that of the queen termite. In common with most noxious insects, such, for example, as the mosquito and the wasp, the females are the only aggressors. The male mosquito cannot bite, nor the male wasp sting, nor the male Chigoe form its irritating nest.

There is now before me one of these female Chigoes, with the abdomen fully swollen and full of eggs. It was sent to me by a resident in the West Indies, who was kind enough to allow it to inhabit his toe until it was sufficiently developed, and then removed it and preserved it for me. The skin of the swollen abdomen is very tough, so that it can easily be turned out of the hollow which it has formed. The size of my specimen is as nearly as possible equal to that of an ordinary sweet-pea. In some places the Chigoe is called Chicorine.

CINNAMON (*Cinnamomum Zeylanicum*).—Only the bark of the young shoots is used. Ceylon is the chief country of the cinnamon. It is allied to the common laurel.

CLOVE.—The cloves of commerce are the unexpanded flowers of a plant, known scientifically as *Caryophyllus aromaticus*. It is one of the myrtle tribe. The name clove is a corruption of the French name *clou*, the dried flowers bearing some resemblance to a nail.

COCOA-NUT PALM (*Cocos nucifera*).—Essentially a sea-side tree, and apparently not a native of the West Indies, but imported, either by man or by the wind and waves. It grows freely in India and the South Sea Islands, as well as in the West Indies, and reaches a height of a hundred feet.

The nut grows in a very curious manner. When it has fallen, one of the three holes gives way to a shoot, which strikes out a root, piercing into the ground, while it still retains its connection by a sort of cord, with the nut from which it draws its nourishment, until it is strong enough to obtain the whole of its sustenance from the ground. See the fallen nuts in the foreground of the illustration.

It has a "cabbage" like that of the cabbage palm, and is sometimes cut down for the sake of obtaining this vegetable.

COCOA PALM AND COCAL.

Toddy is simply the fermented juice of the tree ; coir is made from the husk, which is also cut up into scrubbing-brushes for household use ; and the "porcupine wood" of the cabinet-maker is obtained from the dense and heavy wood near the root.

The long groves of Cocoa palms are called cocals, and some-times extend for several miles along the shore.   The Cocoa palm should not be confounded with the cacao, of which chocolate and cocoa are made, and which is a totally different plant, belonging to the genus *Theobroma*.

COCK OF THE ROCK (*Rupicola crocea*).—This fine bird is the largest of the Manakins, *q.v.*, and on account of the beauty

COCK OF THE ROCK.

of its plumage is in great request with bird stuffers.   Un-fortunately, the brilliant orange of its feathers is very fugitive, and a stuffed bird is sure to fade unless protected from the light.

I have before me a specimen of a stuffed Cock of the Rock which has been exposed to daylight for several years, and the colour of which has so completely faded, that the bird can only be recognized by its shape, the feathers having changed from brilliant orange to a dull yellowish brown.

The following account of this bird is taken from Mr. C. B. Brown's work on Guiana :—

" Cocks of the Rock were numerous in the surrounding thickets, where their sharp disagreeable cry was frequently heard.

" They are so restless, jumping and flying from bough to bough, and tree to tree, that Paulie, who was trying to shoot them, started five, but only succeeded in obtaining one specimen. He found a dancing place of these birds in a thicket, the ground being beaten down quite smooth by their feet ; and on visiting it early in the morning with Ben, the two together succeeded in shooting two cocks and a hen bird. They told me that there were numbers around the dancing place, and that the two cocks they shot were strutting about with their feathers distended, showing themselves off before the rest."

Only the adult males possess the rich orange plumage, the females and immature males being of a dull yellow-green, and having but a small crest. The bird, though the largest of the Manakins, is but a small one, being scarcely equal in size to a Tumbler pigeon.

COFFEE.—It is rather remarkable that the two chief pro-ducts of the West Indies, namely Coffee and ugar, are both natives of the Old World, and have been acclimatized in the New.

Coffee, as its name imparts, *Coffœa Arabica*, is indigenous to Northern Africa, and was imported into Europe as a curiosity. Not much more than a hundred and fifty years ago a single layer of two slips was taken from Holland to Martinique, and it throve so well that it furnished a supply for the whole of the West Indies.

There is a romantic story connected with its introduction: A Frenchman, named Desclieux, had charge of the plant. On the voyage the vessel fell in with a series of storms, and all on board were put on short allowance of water. The heroic Frenchman divided his share of water with the Coffee-plant,

> " And Martinico loads her ships
> With produce from those dear-saved slips."

It belongs to the useful group of Cinchonaceæ. Even the leaves possess many of the qualities which make the seeds so useful.

COPAL. *See* " Locust Tree."

CORAL SNAKE (*Elaps corallinus*).—In some parts of the country this snake is made a pet, being twisted round the neck like a gold and black " torque." It is but a small snake, averaging twenty-six inches in length.

COTINGAS.—These all belong to the group of the Ampelinæ, or Chatterers.

The Pompadour Cotinga (*Cotinga pompadoura*) is a singularly beautiful bird, its plumage being mostly of the beautiful hue which is known as pompadour, and which used to be very fashionable at the beginning of the present century. The feathers are splashed and streaked with white, and the wings are tipped with black. In size it rather surpasses our starling.

The Purple-throated Cotinga is known to science as *Cotinga cayenna*. The Purple-breasted Cotinga is *Cotinga cærulea*, and the Scarlet Cotinga is *Rhænicocercus carnifex*.

COTTON.—The cotton which is used for thread and string, is procured from several species of *Gossypium*, one of which produces the cotton so largely used by ourselves. The natives always have some of these bushes planted near their houses, and cotton spinning goes on almost as interminably as knitting or crochet among English ladies.

The mode of spinning is that which is prevalent all over the world, and even in England has only lately been super-seded by machinery. A wooden spindle is passed through a whorl of a heavy wood, bone, or sometimes stone, and the fibres attached to it. The spindle is then made to revolve, thus spinning the fibres into thread. In savage countries, the invariable practice is, to roll the thread on the bare thigh, and sometimes this labour is carried on so unceasingly as to cause sores.

Spindles such as have been described were found in the tombs of the Incas, and several of them came into my possession, together with pieces of the fabrics made from the threads spun by them.

The species which is so largely cultivated for commerce is *Gossypium tricuspidatum*.

COTTON-TREE, (*Bombax ceiba*).—This magnificent tree, sometimes called the Silk-Cotton, is among the many wonders of the West Indies, and is admirably described by C. Kingsley in his joyous book *At Last :*—

"These latter (the Ceibas) are useless as timber ; and their roots are, of course, hurtful to the sugar-canes. But the negro is shy of felling the Ceiba. It is a magic tree, haunted by spirits. There are 'too much jumbies in him,' the negro says ; and of those who dare to cut him down some one will die, or come to harm, within the year.

"'In Jamaica,' says my friend Mr. Gosse, 'they believe that if a person throws a stone at the trunk, he will be visited with sickness, or other misfortune. When they intend to cut one down, they first pour rum at the root as a propitiatory offering.' The Jamaica negro, however, fells them for canoes, the wood being soft, and easily hollowed.

"But here, as in Demerara, the trees are left standing about in cane-pieces and pastures to decay into awful and fantastic shapes, with prickly spurs and board-walls of roots, high enough to make a house among them simply by roofing them in ; and a flat crown of boughs, some seventy or eighty feet above the ground, each bough as big as an average English tree, from which dangles a whole world of lianas, matapolos, orchids, wild pines with long air-roots or grey beards ; and last, but not least, that strange and lovely parasite the *Rhipsalis cassytha*, which you mistake first for a plume of green sea-weed, or a tress of mermaid's hair which has got up

there by mischance, and then for some delicate kind of pendent mistletoe ; till you are told, to your astonishment, that it
is an abnormal form of cactus—a family which it resembles,
save in its tiny flowers and fruit, no more than it resembles
the Ceiba-tree on which it grows ; and told, too, that, strangely
enough, it has been discovered in Angola—the only species of
the cactus tribe in the Old World."

SILK-COTTON-TREE.

The Cotton-tree was a never-failing wonder to Kingsley,
who again writes of it in the same work :—

"If you are all safe, your next steps probably, as you
struggle through the bush, between tree-trunks of every
possible size, will bring you face to face with huge upright
walls of seeming boards, whose rounded edges slope upward,
till, as your eye follows them, you find them enter an enormous
stem, perhaps round, like one of the Norman pillars of

Durham nave, and just as huge; perhaps fluted, like one of William of Wykeham's columns at Winchester.

"There is the stem, but where is the tree? Above the green cloud. You struggle up to it, between two of the board walls, but find it not so easy to reach. Between you and it, are half a dozen tough strings which you had not noticed at first—the eye cannot focus itself rapidly enough in the confusion of distances—which have to be cut through ere you can pass. Some of them are rooted in the ground, straight and tense; some of them dangle and wave in the wind at every height.

"What are they? Air-roots of wild pines (*tillandsia*), or of matapolos, or of figs, or of seguines (*philodendron, anthurium*, &c.) or of some other parasite? Probably: but you cannot see. All you can see is, as you put your chin close against the trunk of the tree and look up, as if you were looking up against the side of a great ship set on end; that some sixty or eighty feet up in the green cloud, arms as big as English forest trees branch off; and that out of their forks a whole green garden of vegetation has tumbled down twenty or thirty feet, and half climbed up again. You scramble round the tree to find whence the aerial garden has sprung: you cannot tell. The tree-trunk is smooth and free from climbers; and that mass of verdure may belong possibly to the very cables which you met ascending into the green cloud twenty or thirty yards back, or to that impenetrable tangle, a dozen yards on, which has climbed a small tree, and then a taller one again, and then a taller still, till it has climbed out of sight, and possibly into the lower branches of the big tree. And what are their species? What are their families? Who knows? Not even the most experienced woodman or botanist can tell you the names of plants of which he sees only the stems."

From this tree is procured the Wild Cotton which has already been mentioned on page 134. I believe that yet no use has been found for this delicate and short yellow fibre, except as stuffing for pillows and couches. The native never troubles himself to remove the seeds, which are hard, spherical, nearly black, and about as large as peas.

COUANACOUCHI (*Lachesis mutus*).—Popularly called Bushmaster, a name originally given to it by the Dutch. Sometimes it is called Curucuru. When living, it is as beautiful as it is deadly, but the lovely prismatic colours which play over the body during life are extinguished in death, and not even Waterton could restore to the skin the beauty of the living serpent. It is found both in trees and on the ground.

COUCOURITE-PALM.—There are several species of this palm, all belonging to the genus Maximiliana. The most beautiful

COUCOURITE.

of them is the species mentioned by Waterton, and appropriately named *Maximiliana regia*. "In this plant," writes Kingsley, "the pinnæ are set on all at the same distance apart, and all in the same planes in opposite sides of the stalk, giving to the whole foliage a grand simplicity; and producing, when the curving leaf-points toss in the breeze, that curious appearance which I mentioned in an earlier chapter, of green glass wheels with rapidly revolving spokes."

The leaves are sometimes twenty-five feet or more in length, and their stems are triangular. When dried, they are wonderfully light, strong and elastic, and are often cut into lengths and imported to England as walking-sticks. When young, the tree has scarcely any stem, the leaves springing almost directly from the ground. These trees flourish best on sand or gravel.

Stedman describes the young leaves as diverging from each other like the flaming fuse of a shell.

COUGUAR (*Leopardus concolor*).—It is sometimes misnamed the American lion, and sometimes the panther, just as the jaguar goes by the name of tiger. In some places it is called the deer-tiger. Mr. C. B. Brown had a curious adventure with one of these animals :—

" One morning, whilst returning to camp along the portage path that we were cutting at Wonobobo falls, I walked faster than the men, and got some two hundred yards in advance. As I rose the slope of an uneven piece of ground, I saw a large puma (*Felis concolor*) advancing along the other side of the rise towards me, with its nose down on the ground. The moment I saw it I stopped ; and at the same instant it tossed up its head and seeing me also came to a stand. With its body half crouched, its head erect, and its eyes round and black, from its pupils having expanded in the dusky light, it looked at once a noble and an appalling sight. I glanced back along our wide path to see if any of my men were coming, as at the moment I felt that it was not well to be alone without some weapon of defence, and I knew that one of them had a gun ; but nothing could I see. As long as I did not move the puma remained motionless also, and thus we stood, some fifteen yards apart, eying one another curiously. I had heard that the human voice is potent in scaring most wild beasts, and feeling that the time had arrived to do something desperate, I waved my arms in the air and shouted loudly. The effect on the tiger was electrical; it turned quickly on one side, and in two bounds was lost in the forest. I waited until my men came up, however, before passing the place at which it disappeared, in case it might only be lying in ambush there; but we saw nothing more of it.

" When returning down the portage and dragging our boats over, we saw a jaguar sitting on a log near the same spot, watching our movements with evident curiosity, and although the men were singing as they hauled the boats along, it did not seem to mind the noise. As soon as it saw that it was observed, it jumped off the log, and with a low growl made off. From this I infer that the flight of my puma must have been owing more to the windmill-like motion of my arms than to my voice."

COULACANARA.—Waterton does not give sufficient description of this snake for identification. It is almost certainly *Boa imperator.*

It is characteristic of Waterton that he should have sat down immediately after his battle with the snake to send an account of it in Latin hexameters to his old friends at Stony-hurst. Mr. Edmund Waterton only lately discovered the document in pencil among his father's papers.

COURADA (*Avicennia nitida*).—Sometimes spelled Courida. The White Mangrove of the Colonists.

The trees grow in profusion on the shore, reaching a height of fifty or sixty feet, and from their upper branches dangle innumerable air-roots, which, when they reach the ground, will strike into it, and become the stems of future trees. The manatee is fond of browsing on the leaves of the Courada.

CRABWOOD (*Carapa Guianensis*).—The tree is very useful on account of an oil, called 'crab-oil,' which is expressed from its seeds. It serves various purposes, and gives a good light when burned in a lamp. The timber of the Crabwood is in great request for masts and spars.

CUIA.—A species of Trogon, similar in size to the boclora, but brighter in colours, as mentioned by Waterton.

CRABIER.—-The Boat-bill (*Cancroma cochlearia*).—It is a small heron, having an oddly-shaped beak, much resembling a boat turned upside down.   It frequents the shores, and feeds chiefly on the smaller crustacea.   Sometimes it is called the Wallaba Bird.

CRICKET.—Waterton uses the colloquial term.   The so-called Crickets are in fact Cicadas, several species of which are common in the southern· parts of Europe.   Only one British species is known, and may be found in the New Forest.   In Guiana, the Cicadas attain a very large size, and their cry has been compared to the whistle of a railway engine.

CUCKOO, METALLIC (*Coccygus Americanus*).

CURLEW, SCARLET.—Waterton here employs the colloquial name for the Scarlet Ibis ([*Tantalus*] *Ibis rubra*).

There are several species of Ibis, the most familiar being the sacred Ibis of Egypt, which figures so largely in the ancient Egyptian sculptures and paintings.   This is but a dull bird in colour, being only white and black, and with a neck quite bare of feathers, and looking as if made of a very old and very crumpled black kid glove.

The Scarlet Ibis, however, is far more beautiful than any of its congeners, being of a most brilliant scarlet, with a few patches of jet black.

SCARLET CURLEW.

The accompanying illustration represents one of these birds at it appeared when sunning itself in the Zoological Gardens. It bowed its head until the tip of the curved beak nearly touched the ground, half opened its wings, thrust them forward, and kept up a tremulous movement of the feathers over the whole body. The bird is mostly found along the coasts.

Another species, the River Ibis (*Ibis infuscatus*), is found, as its name imports, on the rivers of Guiana. It is larger than its scarlet relative, but is not nearly so handsome, being dull olive-green, with light green legs and beak. It goes by the popular name of Curi-curi, in consequence of its cry, which is said to resemble these words.

D.

DEER.—Several species of Deer inhabit Guiana, but that mentioned by Waterton is probably the Forest Deer (*Cervus humilis*). It is a small animal, reddish fawn in colour, spotted with white on the flanks, and with little straight horns. The native name is Wiriebiserie.

DIAMOND ROCK.—This is a very singularly-shaped rock, close to Pointe du Diamante, and having only a narrow channel between itself and Martinique. The shape is roughly conical, and is said to resemble the great Pyramids of Egypt, but to be twice as large as the largest of them.

"In the end of 1803," writes the late C. Kingsley, "Sir Samuel Hood saw that French ships passing to Fort Royal harbour in Martinique escaped him by running through the deep channel between Pointe du Diamante and this same rock, which rises sheer out of the water 600 feet, and is about a mile round, and only accessible at a point to the leeward, and even then only when there is no surf. He who lands, it is said, has then to creep through crannies and dangerous steeps, round to the windward side, when the eye is suddenly relieved by a sloping grove of wild fig-trees, clinging by innumerable air roots to the cracks of the stone.

"So Hood, with that inspiration of genius so common then among sailors, laid his seventy-four, the *Centaur*, close along-

side the Diamond; made a hawser, with a traveller on it, fast
to the ship and to the top of the rock; and in January, 1804,
got three long 24's and two 18's hauled up far above his mast-
head by sailors who, as they 'hung like clusters,' appeared
'like mice hauling a little sausage. Scarcely could we hear
the governor on the top directing them with his trumpet; the
Centaur lying, close under, like a cocoa-nut shell, to which
the hawsers are affixed' (*Naval Chronicles*).

"In this strange fortress Lieutenant James Wilkie Maurice
(let his name be recollected as one of England's forgotten
worthies) was established with 120 men and boys, and ammunition, provisions, and water for four months; and the
rock was borne on the books of the Admiralty as his Majesty's ship Diamond Rock, and swept the seas with her guns
till the 1st of June, 1805, when she had to surrender, for
want of powder, to a French squadron of two 74's, a frigate,
a corvette, a schooner, and eleven gunboats, after killing and
wounding some seventy men on the rock alone, and destroying three gunboats, with a loss to herself of two men killed
and one wounded.

"Remembering which story, who will blame the traveller
if he takes off his hat to his Majesty's quondam corvette, as
he sees for the first time its pink and yellow sides shining in
the sun above the sparkling seas over which it domineered of
old?"

I may add that the sailors were greatly amused at their
very remarkable sloop, and invariably used nautical terms
when speaking of it, or "her." For example, when they had
by extreme ingenuity "parbuckled" a couple of guns nearly
to the summit of the rock, they named them the "topgallant
battery." Everything went on exactly as on board a man-of-
war. Watches were set and relieved according to naval discipline, observations were daily taken, and, except that there
was no man at the wheel, and no sails had to be looked after,
the crew had just the same duties as if the rock had been a
ship afloat.

When at last they did surrender, they were allowed to leave their "sloop" with all the honours of war, and to row themselves in their own boats to the French ships.

DOLPHIN.—The creature which Waterton here describes is not the true dolphin, which is one of the mammalia, and not a fish; but is the Coryphene (*Coryphene hippuris*), a splendid fish, which sailors will insist on calling by the name of dolphin. The weapon which is thrown at, or rather dropped upon the fish is called by the name of "grains," and much resembles Neptune's trident, except that it has five points instead of three. The colours of the dying Coryphene are singularly beautiful; but it is evident that the thick, tough, blubber-lined hide of the true dolphin could undergo no change.

DUCALABALI.—One of the many useful species of West Indian Laurus, the value of which is not sufficiently recognised in this country. The wood is very hard, close-grained, heavy, durable, and deep-red in colour. Only the heart-wood is used. As it is spotted with blackish-brown, like the jaguar's skin, it is often called Tiger-wood. The tree is rare, and is mostly found near the Essequibo. It grows chiefly in clay and sandy soils, and reaches about one hundred and twenty feet in height. The heart-wood, however, is seldom more than two feet in diameter.

DURAQUAURA (*Odontophorus Guianiensis*).—This bird, like the English partridge, builds a nest on the ground, but is a better architect. The nest is made of leaves and twigs, and is placed under the shelter of a bush. It is roofed, and has a small entrance in front. The eggs are eight or nine in number, white in colour, and are about as large as those of the bantam.

E.

EAGLE, White Headed (*Haliaëtus leucocephalus.*)

EBONY TREE.—There are several trees which furnish the well-known ebony of commerce, but the best kind is obtained from the heart-wood of *Diospyros ebenum.*

EGRET.— This beautiful little heron (*Ardea egretta*), is pure white in colour except the delicate train feathers, which have a slight creamy tinge. They are long enough to hang over the tail, which they conceal when the bird is in repose.

EGRET

Owing to their beauty, these plumes are in great request for the ornamentation of head-dresses, not only for the natives, but for ladies in Europe. The natives, who take great pride in their head-dresses of ceremony, and arrange the feathers with marvellous taste, make much use of the plumes, which they mingle with the feathers of macaws and parrots.

The second sketch was taken from a fine specimen in the possession of J. F. Jackson, Esq., of Bexley. As evening had come on the bird had retired to a sort of small grotto on the edge of a pond, and had sunk to sleep, as represented (p. 406). Owing to the darkness of the evening I had nearly passed the bird without seeing it, and but for the snowy whiteness of its plumage, it would have escaped unnoticed.

In many parts of Guiana the Egret is called by the name of White Gauldin.

F.

FIG, WILD (*Clusia alba*).

FINCH, RED-HEADED (Probably *Passerina gularis*).

FIREFLY.—In Tropical America there are so many luminous insects which go by the popular name of firefly that no particular species can be here designated. Most of these, however, are beetles belonging to the group of elaters. Many species exist in England, and are well-known as skip-jack beetles, spring-beetles, or click-beetles, because if laid on their backs, they spring up in the air with a smart click, and take

EGRET ASLEEP.

their chance of falling on their legs. The terrible wire-worm is the larva of one of these beetles.

The species which is most common is the Cucujo (*Pyrophorus luminosus.*) As is the case with our glow-worm, the light disappears after death, and, indeed, how it is produced in life is an unsolved mystery. Even the spectroscope yields no information, giving only a ' continuous ' spectrum, *i.e.* one which is not crossed by lines, either dark or luminous.

Still, the light which the insect emits is so powerful that, as Waterton mentions, it will, if held over a paper at night, permit the holder to read or write by its natural lantern. It is seen at its best when on the wing, as it then discloses four luminous spots, of which only the upper pair are visible when the insect is at rest.

The upper pair are oval in shape, and are seen at the base of the thorax, one on either side, and after death fade into a brownish yellow. When the beetle expands its wings for flight, two more spots are seen, which had been concealed by the wing-cases, so that the appearance of a single Firefly on the wing is gorgeous in the extreme, and, considering that they fly in countless thousands, their coruscating lights can be compared to nothing but starry showers of fireworks. Even in the warmer countries of Europe the Fireflies are very beautiful, but they are completely surpassed in splendour by those of the tropics.

In one of his essays, Waterton mentions an absurd statement, that there are certain birds which fasten Fireflies on their nests in order to keep off the bats which might devour their young. He very curtly disposes of the matter by saying that bats do not eat young birds, but that they do eat Fireflies, and would in consequence rather be attracted than frightened by them.

FLAMINGO (*Phœnicopterus ruber*).—Waterton devotes part of one essay to a congenial task, that of demolishing an error in natural history. This particular error concerns the nesting of this bird, which is said to raise conical mounds of mud in order to keep its nest out of the water, to lay its eggs on the top of the heap, and to sit upon them with its legs hanging down into the water.

This attitude, as Waterton showed, by reference to his own herons, is not necessary, the long legs of the Flamingo and the heron being as easily bent under the body as those of the short-legged birds. In consequence of a conversation with Waterton on the subject, I went to the Zoological Gardens in order to watch the attitudes of the Flamingo, and was greatly struck with the lithe activity of the bird. I made a number of sketches from them, some of which are here given to the reader.

Judging from stuffed specimens, the Flamingo seems to be rather an awkward bird, but in reality, it is peculiarly easy and graceful in its movements. The long neck can be twined and turned in all directions, very much like the coils of a serpent,

or the lithe proboscis of the elephant. Some of the curious attitudes which it assumes are shown in the illustrations.

As may be seen by them, the legs, awkward as they may seem, are as much under command as the neck, and I have seen the Flamingo scratch its head with its claws as easily as if it were a parrot or a canary. Any one who had not studied the living bird, would have thought that when it required

SLEEPING

PREPARING FOR SLEEP.

repose, it would squat on the ground, so as to rest its stilt-like legs. But, in common with many other birds, it sleeps while

standing on one leg, which is kept perfectly straight, while
the neck lies in folds upon the shoulder, with the head nestling
among the feathers.

This position of the head during sleep or illness is universal
among birds, and is popularly called "putting the head under
the wing." How such a phrase could have been invented or
perpetuated is really wonderful, as any one who has kept
poultry or pet birds of any kind must have noticed that the

head is not hidden under the wing, but rests among the
plumage of the shoulders. So, we must bid farewell to our
pretty nursery rhyme :—

> "The north wind doth blow,
> And we shall have snow,
> And what will poor Robin do then,
>   Poor thing ?
>
> He will sit in a barn
> To keep himself warm,
> And hide his head under his wing,
>   Poor thing !"

During life the beak of the Flamingo is pinkish yellow at
the base, becoming black at the tip. After death, however,
although the tip retains its blackness, it loses its polish,
and fades into dingy yellowish brown. Similarly, the legs,
which are red in life, become brown at death, and the only
mode of restoring these colours has been by employing paint,
which has really a ghastly appearance. I have not had the
opportunity of treating the beak of a Flamingo as Waterton
managed to colour the beak of a toucan, but I have little
doubt that the process would be as effectual with one bird as
it has been with the other.

The feathers are mostly white with a slight pink tinge, but the wing-feathers are mostly brilliant scarlet, and have earned for the bird the generic title of Phœnicopterus, *i.e.* ' scarlet-winged.'

The curving bend, or angle in the beak of the Flamingo, is given to the bird in order to enable it to feed after its own peculiar fashion. Like the duck, the Flamingo feeds by dabbling with its beak in muddy water, and filtering out the nutritive matter by means of an arrangement which much resembles a pair of very fine, soft, and flexible combs, fitting

into each other in strainer fashion. The duck, having short legs, can push its bill into the water without difficulty, but owing to its very long neck and legs, the Flamingo could not do so, except for the peculiar curve in its bill, which enables it to place its head upside down when it feeds, and in this rather odd position to extract nourishment from the water.

Any one who wishes to see the mechanism by which a Flamingo separates the nutritive substances from the water, has only to take the head of a duck and examine the beak and tongue. In order that the structure should be seen in perfection, the head ought to be held under water during examination, the beak widely opened and closed, and the finger be used as well as the eyes.

The accompanying illustrations are taken from sketches made at the Zoological Gardens, in order to show the extraordinary attitudes into which this bird throws itself, and especially the power of balance on one leg when sleeping, and the extraordinary contortions into which the bird can twist its neck while the body is resting on the ground.

FLYING-FISH (*Exocœtus volitans*).—Waterton, while mentioning the flight of this curious fish, does not touch on the disputed point of its capacity to alter its course in the air, or to extend its flight by flapping its wing-like fins. C. Kingsley, however, believes from personal observations, that it can do both.

" The flying-fish now began to be a source of continual amusement, as they scuttled away from under the bows of the ship, mistaking her, probably, for some huge devouring whale. So strange are they when first seen, though long read of and long looked for, that it is difficult to recollect that they are actually fish. The first little one was mistaken for a dragon-fly, the first big one for a grey plover.

" The flight is almost exactly like that of a quail or partridge-flight, I must say ; for, in spite of all that has been learnedly written to the contrary, it was too difficult as yet for the English sportsmen on board to believe that their motion was not a true flight, aided by the vibration of the wings, and not a mere impulse given (as in the leap of the salmon) by a rush under water.

" That they can change their course at will is plain to one who looks down on them from the lofty deck, and still more from the paddle-box. The length of the flight seems too great to be attributed to a few strokes of the tail ; while the plain fact that they renew their flight after touching, and only touching, the surface, would seem to show that it was not due only to the original impetus, for that would be retarded, instead of being quickened, every time they touched. Such were our first impressions ; and they were confirmed by what we saw on the voyage home."

I think that this statement from a good naturalist and keen sportsman, such as was Kingsley, settles the question of flight. I doubt, however, whether the fish dip into the sea for the purpose of wetting their wings, as suggested by Waterton. Perhaps their flight may be like that of the short-winged birds, and consist of alternate dippings and risings.

FRIGATE BIRD (*Attagen aquila*).—This really wonderful bird seems mostly to be composed of feathers, the body being quite small, and the expanded wings measuring about eight feet from tip to tip. The total length of the bird, including the long tail, is about three feet. The muscles of the breast, by which the wings are moved, are themselves one quarter the weight of the entire body. Thus, like the albatross, it can pass the greater part of its time on the wing,

FRIGATE BIRD.

not seeming to feel fatigue. As it wheels its flight over ships, the scarlet throat pouch is very conspicuous, the light shining through its skin when expanded.

It is a **very** voracious bird, and Dr. Bennett remarks that he has repeatedly seen it sweep upon the top of the mast and carry away the coloured vane.

Being no diver, and a very poor swimmer, it is apt to pounce upon gannets and other diving birds, and rob them of their prey. Should the gannet pluck up sufficient spirit to resist, the Frigate bird is sure to be worsted. Both birds necessarily fall into the sea, where the gannet is quite at home, and escapes by diving, while the Frigate bird is helplessly flapping about in the water.

The colour of the adult male Frigate bird is black, with a gloss of green, the female being of much duller black above without any green gloss, and having the under surface nearly white, with splashes of reddish brown.

Fox (*Vulpes cancrivora*).—This animal is generally called Savannah Fox by the colonists, and Mikang by the natives. It is very swift, and in fair chase can outrun most dogs. It is very small, grey in colour, and has a large bushy tail.

G.

GOATSUCKERS.—All these birds, of which there are many in Guiana, belong to the Caprimulgidæ, and some, from the singular cry which they utter, are objects of superstitious dread, both to natives and negroes. Kingsley gives an amusing and graphic description of the alarm caused by one of these birds. After narrating how he tried to sleep, and was kept awake, first by the romping of his companions, who broke down a four-post bedstead in their play, and then by the wind, which blew all the clothes off the bed, he proceeds as follows :—

" Then the dogs exploded outside, probably at some hen-roost robbing opossum, and had a chevy through the cocos till they treed their game, and bayed it to their hearts' content. Then something else exploded—and I do not deny it set me more aghast than I had been for many a day—exploded, I say, under the window, with a shriek of hut-tut-tut-tut, hut tut, such as I hope never to hear again. After which, dead silence ; save of the surf to the east and the toads to the west. I fell asleep, wondering what animal could own so detestable a voice ; and in half an hour was awoke again by another explosion ; after which, happily, the thing, I suppose, went its wicked way, for I heard it no more.

" I found out the next morning that the obnoxious bird was not an owl, but a large Goatsucker, a Nyctibius, I believe, who goes by the name of jumby-bird among the English negroes ; and no wonder ; for most ghostly and horrible is his cry. But worse ; he has but one eye, and a glance from that glaring eye, as from the basilisk of old, is certain death ; and worse still, he can turn off its light as a policeman does his lantern, and become instantly invisible ; opinions which, if verified by experiment, are not always found to be in accordance with facts. But that is no reason why they should not be believed.

" In St. Vincent, for instance, the negroes one evening

rushed shrieking out of a boiling-house. ' Oh ! Massa Robert, we all killed. Dar one great jumby-bird come in a hole a-top a roof. Oh ! Massa Robert, you no go in ; you killed, we killed,' &c. &c. Massa Robert went in, and could see no bird. ' Ah ! Massa Robert, him darky him eye, but him see you all da same. You killed, we killed,' &c., *da capo.*"

Not being able to identify any of Waterton's Goatsuckers, I asked the opinion of Dr. P. L. Sclater, who kindly sent me the following answer :—"As you say, the largest species must be *Nyctibius grandis.* The other Caprimulgidæ of which I have seen examples from Guiana, are—1. *Nyctibius bracteatus.* 2. *Lurocalis semitorquatus.* 3. *Antrostomus nigrescens.* 4. *Chordeiles acutipennis.* 5. *Stempsis cayennensis.* 6. *Hydropsalis schomburgki.* 7. *Nyctidromus albicollis.* But, I regret to say, there is nothing in Waterton's words to assist you in identifying them with this species."

GOBE-MOUCHE, GRAND.—*Querula rubricollis.*

GREENHEART (*Nectandra rodœi*), called by the natives Bibiri.—Here we have another of the neglected products of Guiana. Kingsley thus mentions it in his *At Last :*—

" The carapo is not the only tree of South America whose bark may be used as a substitute for quinine. They may be counted possibly by dozens. A glance at the excellent enumerations of the uses of vegetable products to be found in Lindley's *Vegetable Kingdom* (a monument of learning), will show how God provides, and how man neglects and wastes.

" As a single instance, the laurels alone are known already to contain several valuable febrifuges, among which the Demerara Greenheart, or Bibiri, claims perhaps the highest rank. ' Dr. Maclagan has shown,' says Dr. Lindley, that ' sulphate of Bibiri acts with rapid and complete success in averting ague.' This tree spreads from Jamaica to the Spanish Main. It is plentiful in Trinidad, still more plentiful in Guiana ; yet all of it that reaches Europe is a little of its hard, beautiful wood for the use of cabinet-makers ; while in Demerara, I am assured by an eye-witness, many tons of the precious

Greenheart bark are thrown away year by year. So goes the world, and man meanwhile at once boasts of his civilization and complains of the niggardliness of nature."

This is just the complaint made by Waterton in more than one passage of the *Wanderings*. He had some furniture at Walton Hall made of the Greenheart, and very excellent furniture it was, and probably is still.

Greenheart is one of the eight A 1 timbers at Lloyds'. It is employed for kelsons, planking, and ' knees,' when these are not made of wrought iron. It is time that legal protection should be given to this tree, for the timber-merchants and charcoal-burners have made great havoc with it. There are three varieties, called respectively, the Yellow, Black, and Mainop Greenheart. Logs are sometimes seventy feet long and two feet square.

Every part of the Greenheart is useful, bark, juice, and timber being equally valuable in the service of man.

GROSBEAK, SCARLET.—Several birds are so called, the best known being *Cardinalis Virginianus*, figured on page 468. Waterton's bird, however, is evidently not a Grosbeak at all, but one of the Tanagers, *Pitylus erythromelas*. The Tanagers and the Finches are closely allied, and as the beak is very large at the base in the genus *Pitylus*, the name of Grosbeak is not inappropriate. The bird is a small one, and the colour is crimson rather than scarlet.

GUANA or IGUANA (*Iguana tuberculata*).—This is a very odd-looking, and not very handsome lizard, which inhabits the West Indies, and is mostly found on the branches of trees which overhang the water. It is rather large, an average sized adult being about four feet long, while some attain a length of six feet. The body however, is not very large, but the tail is very long, and can be lashed from side to side so sharply, that a stroke will cause much pain.

In Mr. Brown's work on Guiana are some interesting remarks on this lizard, of which, by the way, there are several species :—

"We were frequently amused with the manner in which the Iguanas, alarmed by the noise produced by the boat's paddles, threw themselves from the overhanging branches of trees into the river, many coming down broadside on the water. Their flesh resembles that of a chicken in flavour and quality, and is very good when properly cooked.

"They are exceedingly numerous on the river (the Cuyuni), where they dig long underground chambers in the sandbanks at the ends of islands, in which they deposit their eggs. Near the foot of a cataract, where there was a high beach, our men dug up the sand in order to trace out some of these chambers for eggs, and succeeded in capturing four Iguanas, which they dragged out by their tails and then seized by the back of the neck and secured. They had to be pretty quick, for the Iguana can turn round suddenly and give a fearful bite. An Iguana must be drawn from its hole with rapidity, for, if it has time to think, it lets go its tail at the base, leaving it in the hands of the would-be capturer, and thus escapes.

"One of these reptiles, captured at its burrow, when killed and cut up for cooking, was found to contain ten eggs of an ellipsoidal form, shell-less, and midway in size between a pigeon's and a hen's egg. These are good eating when boiled for about five minutes and then allowed to get quite cold. They then require some manipulation. A hole is made in one end of the skin, and the albuminous part, which never coagulates, is squeezed out; then the skin is stripped off, and the semi-hardened yelk, of the consistency of butter, is eaten with salt.

"Our men and the Indians had a most cruel way of preventing captured Iguanas from escaping, by slitting down the sides of two fore and two hind toes, on opposite feet, and passing the toes between the bone and sinew in such a manner that they could not be disengaged by the struggles of the poor animal. The manner in which they were slaughtered, viz., by inserting a hard-pointed stick up one nostril into the brain, was also a very cruel proceeding."

Perhaps this may be a cruel way of killing the Guana, but, like nearly all reptiles, it is little sensitive to pain, and wonderfully tenacious of life, and, as it must be destroyed for food, perhaps the pointed stick is the quickest mode of killing it. Not that the natives trouble themselves about the infliction of pain, for, besides the mode of securing the Guana as above mentioned, they sew its lips together, in order to prevent it from biting, and keep it without food until they want it. Here, again, they are not more cruel than our rat-catchers, who used to sew together the lips of their ferrets, or our fishermen, who used to disable their lobsters by "pegging" their claws as soon as caught.

Guava (*Psidium pomiferum*).—The tree which bears this well-known fruit, is quite a little one, scarcely larger than a

GUAVA.

privet bush, and the fruit is small, round and green. It can be eaten without any preparation, but is mostly made into jelly.   It is remarkable, however, that few tropical fruits, except the orange, the cocoa-nut, the pine apple, and the durian, can be compared with our plums, peaches, strawberries, &c.   The durian indeed, which is said by its lovers to be the king of fruits, requires an education before it can be appreciated; but when it is once tasted, the eater feels as if he can never have enough of it.

There are several species of Guava, among which is the little, stunted-looking Water Guava (*Psidium fluviatile*).   The most valued of them is the Perfumed Guava (*P. pomiferum*), which grows abundantly on the banks of the Cuyuni river, its roots insinuating themselves into the cracks among the stones.

At least seven species or varieties are cultivated.

H.

HACKEA (*Siderodendron triflorum*).—A tree growing in sandy soil, and flowering in November.   The flowers are bright yellow, and when the trees are seen against the dark foliage of the forest, they look like masses of gold.   Hence the name Siderodendron, or Star-tree.

The wood is not used for general purposes, on account of its extreme hardness, but is exceedingly valuable for cogs, shafts, &c.   The tree is about sixty feet in height, and the wood is brown in colour.   It squares about fourteen inches.

HAIARRIE.—*See* "Wourali."

HAMMOCK.—These ingenious contrivances are now so well known in England that little description is needed.   Here they are a luxury, and a very great one; there, they are an absolute necessity.

They are sometimes formed of silk-grass fibre, and sometimes of cotton, the latter being the more pliant, and the former the more lasting.   The best hammocks are not formed like nets, and knotted, but the strings are intertwined so that they adapt themselves to every movement of the body.   A native never goes on a journey without his hammock, which he rolls into a sort of rope, and passes it over one shoulder and under the other, just as officers in the army wear their overcoats on the march.

In such a moist country as Guiana, where to sleep wet means to ensure a fever, and where a traveller will sometimes have to walk day after day up to his knees in water, the hammock is a necessary of life. When a traveller wishes to rest, he has only to hang his hammock between a couple of trees, and he can then clamber into it, rub his wet legs dry, and lie down in comfort and security.

Hammocks are of various sizes, some being very small and made for children, while others are large enough to hold two or more people. As a rule, however, each person has a hammock to himself.

HANNAQUOI (*Ortalida motmot*).—If the reader will refer to the Powise, page 461, he will see a typical example of a large family of birds, called popularly the Curassows.

There is a group or sub-family of them called Guans, and distinguishable by the naked and dilatable skin of the throat. To these belongs the Hannaquoi, which is also called the Motmot Guan. In size it is about equal to a small gamecock, though it looks larger in consequence of its long tail, which, as Waterton remarks, has caused it to be wrongly ranked among the pheasants. The tail, however, even when closed, resembles that of the pheasant in nothing but its length; and when it is opened, is shaped almost exactly like that of the Powise, but much longer in proportion to the size of the body.

As is the case with the Curassows, the flesh of the Guans is peculiarly delicate.

It is not at all a showy bird, the colours being chiefly brown and grey, darker above than below. There is, however, a tinge of a warm character in the head and upper part of the neck.

In a wild state they are not so gregarious as the Curassows, which are fond of assembling in large groups upon the branches of trees. The Guans, however, although so closely allied to the Curassows, are quite distinct in their habits, leading comparatively solitary lives in the forest. They feed mostly on fruits.

Mr. C. B. Brown found a nest of the Hannaquoi situated in a low tree. It was made of sticks, and contained four speckled eggs, about equal in size to those of the common fowl.

The bird is easily tamed, and soon becomes domesticated with the poultry. It will even breed with them, and the hybrid is said to be exceedingly quarrelsome and pugnacious.

HAYAWA TREE.—*See* "Acaiari."

HERON, BLUE (*Ardea leucogaster.*)

——— BROWN (*Ardea virescens.*) Popularly called the Grey Gauldin.

HIA-HIA.—*See* "Parrot, Sun."

HITIA.—As this tree is mentioned in conjunction with the siboalalis, it is probably an Eperna.

HOCCO.—*See* "Powise."

HOG, WILD.—*See* "Peccary."

HOUTOU (*Momotus Braziliensis*).—This is a very remarkable bird, if only for the peculiarity in the central tail-feathers, attributed by Waterton to art, but really due to Nature alone. As may be seen by the illustration, a portion of the web in the two central feathers is wanting, and the bird really does strip the vanes from the stem, as mentioned by Waterton. There are, however, several birds, notably the Variegated Bee-eater of Australia, which have similarly-shaped tail-feathers, but in which the peculiar formation is due to Nature, and not to art. It is a fly-catching bird, sitting quietly on a branch until an insect flies near, when it darts from its perch, catches the insect, re-seats itself, and then swallows its prey.

The plumage of a fresh specimen is bright blue and green

glossed with crimson, and there is a black velvety spot on the breast and head. But the colours soon fade in a stuffed specimen when exposed to light.

HOUTOU.

HOWLER, RED (*Mycetes ursinus*).—This fine monkey, of which so many strange stories are told, is sometimes mentioned under the title of Araguato. It sometimes attains a total length exceeding six feet, the tail occupying more than half of that measurement. The following account of the Red Howler is taken from Mr. C. B. Brown's work on Guiana :—

"At early morning, at dusk, and through the night, at all our camping places, we were accustomed to hear the Howlers serenading. To my mind the sounds produced by these monkeys more nearly resembled a roar than a howl, and when sufficiently far off are not unpleasant to the ear. When heard from a distance of half a mile or so, they seem to begin with low notes, swelling gradually into louder and longer

ones till they merge into a prolonged roar, which dies gradually away with a mournful cadence.

"When not more than one or two hundred yards away,
and consequently plainly heard, they commence with a series
of short howls, which break off into grunts, and, at every
repetition, become longer and longer till their voices have got
fairly in tune, when they give their final roar, which dies as
gradually away. Then, after an instant's silence, a few deep
grunts are given, as if the remains of the compressed air in
their throat drums were being got rid of. Listening carefully

HOWLER.

to the performance, one can detect a voice at a much higher
key than the others, especially in the dying-away portion.
The Indians say this is made by a dwarf monkey of the same
family which accompanies every troop. I was of the opinion
that it was the voice of a female Howler, but the Indians,
who are very careful observers, said it was not. With their
black negro-like faces, and long red beards covering the bony
howling apparatus below their throats, they are curious-
looking creatures."

Some specimens of the Red Howler which were brought to

England, exhibited the peculiar structure of the throat most admirably. When the monkey opens its mouth, the development of the 'hyoid' bone is easily seen. It forms a kind of bony drum communicating with the wind-pipe, and enabling the animal to emit those horrid yells which have earned for it the popular name of Howler.

The reader is here requested to look at the note upon the "Nondescript."

KARABIMITI.

HUMMING-BIRD, ARA, or KARABIMITI (*Topaza pella*), sometimes called the Crimson Topaz.—This is one of two humming-birds which are distinguishable by the length of two tail-feathers, which are supposed to resemble the elongated tails of the aras or macaws. The other species is the fiery topaz (*Topaza pyra*), so called because the general colour of the bird is flaming scarlet instead of the rich crimson which distinguishes the Karabimiti.

The food of the humming-birds was long a matter of

uncertainty, but has been definitively settled by Waterton and other practical naturalists who came after him.

" Neither the monkey nor the humming-bird, on account of the formation of the feet in this, and of the hands in that, can labour on the ground for their food. Yet, when they are in the right region to acquire it, there is a visible difference in their mode of proceeding. Thus, the monkey sits on the branch, and in that position supplies its wants with what the tree produces. But the humming-bird must be on the wing whilst it extracts food from the flowers, and never can it possibly be seen to take nourishment whilst perching on a twig.

" This rule is absolute for the humming-bird.

" The vault of heaven offers a large supply of food to these birds. It is interesting to see how they satisfy the calls of hunger, by invading the columns of insects which frequent the circumambient atmosphere. Darting from the shade with the rapidity of a meteor, the humming-bird stops short at the column, and then, apparently motionless, it regales itself, and then departs as swiftly as it had approached.

"Authors are divided as to the exact kind of food which humming-birds require. In all the species which I have inspected (and I have inspected not a few) I have found insects, or fragments of insects, in the œsophagus ; and occasionally, by applying my tongue to the contents of the stomach, I have experienced a sweet taste, as though of sugar and water. Still, were I asked if I considered that the nectar in flowers constituted the principal food of humming-birds, I should answer in the negative. Insects form their principal food. The robust frames of these birds seem to require something more solid to support life than the nectareous dew abstracted from flowers ; and I don't exactly see, if these birds do principally exist on this kind of nutriment, how it is that they continue to keep it pure in their own hot stomachs ; and then, by a process unknown to us, convey it to the stomachs of their gaping little ones."

Waterton was, as usual, perfectly right in his surmises. Several experiments have been made since he was in Guiana, and they have proved the soundness of his reasoning.

Mr. Webber succeeded in taming a ruby-throated humming-bird, which would come from any part of the room, and eagerly drink sugar and water and honey from a china-cup, perching on the brim, and thrusting its long beak into the sweet mixture as far as the very base.

The same naturalist afterwards reared a pair of ruby-throats, which were so completely domesticated that, although they went away with their comrades at the usual time of migration, they returned to the house in the following season and brought their mates with them, so that in time there was quite a family of humming-birds perched upon the cups and drinking.

He found, however, that they required other food besides nectar, and discovered that they were in the habit of poising themselves before spider-webs, and delicately picking out the spider from the centre of its web. Mr. Gosse, who tamed several humming-birds during his stay in Jamaica, found that they required insects as well as syrup, and were especially fond of small ants, that used to crawl into the syrup, and nearly cover its surface with their bodies.

I may here mention that Bimiti is the native name for Humming-birds in general. Thus K'Ara-Bimiti is 'The Ara Humming-bird,' as stated by Waterton.

I.

IBIBOUROU (*Cyanocorax cayanus*). — More than twenty species belong to this genus and are all very similar in their habits. They are noisy, sociable birds, loving forests more than the open country. The familiar Blue Jay of North America (*Cyanocorax crystatus*), belongs to them.

IGUANA.—*See* " Guana."

INDIA RUBBER TREE (*Ficus elastica*).—Sometimes called the Caoutchouc Tree.

J.

JABIRU (*Mycteria Americana*).—The Jabirus, of which there
are several species, are closely related to the well-known
adjutant birds of India, and belong to the family of storks.
Large as are several of the storks, the Jabirus are still larger,
and come next to the ostriches in point of size. They may be
easily distinguished from other storks by the shape of their
very large beaks, which turn slightly upward at the point.

One species inhabits Australia, and from the account of
Dr. Bennett, who kept one in confinement for a long time, it
almost exactly resembles the South American species, especially in its extreme wariness. It is so cautious that even the
natives find great difficulty in procuring a specimen.

The bird became very tame, and was allowed to wander
about the house and yard. It made friends with the cook,
and when hungry, used to search for her. It never tried to
steal the meat, but waited patiently until it was cut up. Dr.
Bennett mentions that it would catch flies on the wing, and
that he has seen it, while squatting on the ground, with its

long legs doubled up beneath its body, dart its
bill into the ground, and drag out the larvæ of
insects, mostly those of the great cicada.

On account of the black, bare head, the Dutch
of Surinam call it negro-cope, or black-head.

Both illustrations here given were sketched in
the Zoological Gardens from the same bird, in
order to show how completely the attitude alters
the aspect. The first shows it as it was viewed
from behind. The bird was then standing
quietly, resting the whole weight of its body on
one leg, and having the other slightly raised.

JABIRU
CONTEMPLATIVE.

Its attention was roused by my movements as
I shifted about to procure a favourable view, and it kept a
watchful eye upon me the while.

The second view was taken from the front, when the Jabiru was enjoying itself in the sun. While thus employed, it kept up a continual shivering movement of the feathers, just as has been related of the ibis. In its native state it is to be

JABIRU SUNNING ITSELF.

found on the banks of lakes, marshes, and rivers, and feeds upon the aquatic reptiles, fish, &c., which it finds in such localities.

Every traveller in Guiana is sure to see this splendid bird, and Mr. C. B. Brown often met with it. He gives the following description of the nestling :—

"I was greatly amused with the appearance of two young but fully fledged Jabirus, which stood on their large, flat nest, composed of sticks entwined together, on the branch of a large isolated tree, growing on the river's bank. They looked like two shipwrecked mariners on a rock in mid-ocean, waiting to be delivered from their lonely watch by a passing ship. They stood there as if scanning the horizon, apparently deep in thought, shifting their position now and then from one leg to the other, or taking a solemn or stately stroll round the confines of their nest. Thus we left them, to await the time when their powers of flight would be sufficiently developed to enable them to go forth into the world and forage for themselves. They were fully feathered with a grey plumage, which on moulting would change to pure white."

The same author mentions, on another page, the habits of

a domesticated Jabiru, which behaved very much after the fashion of the bird described by Dr. Bennett.

"The people had a tame Jabiru, which stalked about in a most deliberate and stately way, as if every step it took was a matter of deep deliberation. In spite of its sage looks there was some fun in it, as it seemed to enjoy playing a practical joke now and then on the village dogs; for whenever it had a chance it stalked stealthily behind one and delivered a well directed prod with its pointed beak, full on the dog's back, which caused the dog to fly and the old Jabiru to 'smile inwardly.'"

If the Jabiru can find a tall, pillar-like rock, it is sure to build its nest on it just as does the stork.

Schomburgk gives a touching account of a Jabiru which had built its nest on the top of a tall basaltic pillar named Pieré-piapa, about fifty feet in height. One young bird was in the nest, and the mother, on seeing the travellers, flew to its help, and stood guard over it. One of Schomburgk's men saw the bird standing over its young, and shot it before he could be checked.

The Jabiru is called by the natives Tararama. Its flesh is eatable, and is said to resemble beef.

JACAMARS.—The species here described is the Great Jacamar —(*Jacamerops grandis*).

The mode of feeding employed by this bird, and described by C. Kingsley in *At Last*, exactly corroborates Waterton's account. He had been startled by seeing a bat fly past at mid-day, the shade of the tropical forest being so deep and dark.

"And there is another! No; as it turns, a blaze of metallic azure off the upper side of the wings proves this one to be no bat, but a morpho, a moth as big as a bat. And what was that second large flash of golden green, which dashed at the moths, and back to yonder branch not ten feet off? A Jacamar—kingfisher, as they miscall her here, sitting fearless of man, with the moth in her long beak. Her throat

is snowy white, her under parts a rich brown. Her breast
and all her upper plumage and long tail, glitter with golden
green. There is light enough it seems, in the forest."

The morpho, by the way, is a butterfly, and not a moth.

GREAT JACAMAR.

JAGUAR (*Leopardus onca*).—Waterton did not see much of
the jaguars (which he sometimes calls tigers), and certainly
was not afraid of them. Mr. Brown gives the following
account of the mode in which the jaguar is successfully
hunted :—

" On returning to the head of the New River for provisions,
we were followed for many miles by a Tiger, for on going
back we saw its huge tracks in the swampy places on our
path.

" With good hunting-dogs fine Jaguar and Puma hunting
might be obtained on the banks of this river, where without
doubt they are exceedingly numerous.

" Many of the Indian hunting-dogs, trained for deer or
tapir, will hunt Tigers. When on the track of either of those
animals. should they come across the scent of a Tiger, their

eager and confident manner of pressing on after the game is immediately changed, and with the hair on their backs erect they become cautious and nervous to a degree, jumping at even the snapping of a twig. Abandoning the hunt they take up the Tiger's track and follow it. But should the huntsman call them from it, or not cheer them on with his voice from time to time, they exhibit great fear, and keeping close to his heels cannot be induced to hunt any more in that district for that day.

" On the contrary, if allowed to follow the Tiger, they track it up with caution, being fully aware of the cunning dodge practised by that animal ; which is, when the dog is close at hand, to spring to one side and lie in ambush until it passes, when with one spring the dog is seized.

"Ordinary dogs would fall a prey to this trap, but not the self-taught Tiger-dogs. Their fine powers of scent warn them of their near approach to the quarry, when they advance with great caution, never failing to detect the Tiger in time, and when once their eye is upon their enemy it has no chance of escape.

" In its pride of strength, the Jaguar scorns the dogs, and with a rush like a ball from a cannon springs madly at one of them, feeling sure that it cannot escape. It has reckoned, however, without its host, for the dog eludes the spring with ease, and with great quickness flies on the Tiger's flank, giving it a severe nip. As the Tiger turns with a growl of pain and disappointment, the dog is off to a little distance, yelping lustily, and never remaining still an instant, but darting first on one side and then on the other. After one or two in effectual charges the Tiger gives it up, and on the approach of the hunter springs into the nearest suitable tree, which it seldom leaves alive."

It is to be wished that Waterton had secured an uninjured specimen of a Jaguar skin, on which he might have exercised his unrivalled powers of taxidermy.

JUMBO.—The negroes still retain this term for their chief

deity, which, of course, is a malignant one. They crouch in abject terror before Jumbo, who, according to them, takes possession of birds (*see* Goatsucker), desolate swamps, and so forth.

The really terrible Obeah or Fetish-worship of the negroes is connected with Jumbies and Duppies (the spirits of the dead), and the negroes are absolutely subservient to the Obeah men and women, who can put Obeah into anything they choose. Even the whites are not free from the fear of them, and with reason, for they have an intimate knowledge of many poisons, and will use them on either black or white. Stedman mentions several instances of such crimes, and it was nearly certain that his faithful Joanna fell a victim to the insidious poisons of Obeah.

K.

KARABIMITI.—*See* "Humming Bird. Ara."

KESSI-KESSI.—A vast number of parrots are called Kessi-kessis, and are very plentiful. They all may be referred to the genus *Conurus*, and between forty or fifty species are known.

They are always to be found among the forests bordering on rivers, and are very noisy among the upper branches, the more so as they are sociable in their habits. Some species make their nests in the hollows of trees, upon the decaying wood, and several pairs of birds may be found in the same cavity. Others build in trees. Their nests are large, tolerably globular in shape, made of thorny branches, and have the entrance by an aperture at the side.

The best-known species of kessi-kessi parrots is known scientifically as *Conurus solstitialis*, and is one of the most plentiful of the parrakeets. It is a very pretty creature, its plumage being a mixture of orange, red, and green.

KING of the VULTURES.—*See* "Vulture, King."

KURUMANNI WAX.—This is chiefly obtained from the *Ceroxylon andicola*, mixed with a pitch-like substance obtained from several other trees, chiefly the Maam. It is pitchy black in colour, and when exposed to heat, looks almost exactly like pitch. It is used for many purposes, and is equally useful as a waterproof material or a cement. The seams of canoes are always " payed " with Kurumanni wax.

L.

LABARRI.—This snake, which is mentioned by Waterton in his Autobiography, as well as in the *Wanderings,* is evidently a *Craspedocephalus,* and allied to the Rattlesnake and Fa-de-Lance. In a letter to me, Waterton states that it often climbs trees.

LABBA, sometimes spelled LAPO (*Cœlogenys paca*).—Allied to the Cavies, of which the common Guinea-pig is so familiar an example. The name Cœlogenys, or Hollow-cheek, is given to it on account of its enormously developed cheek-bones, and large cheek-pouches. Its flesh is very delicate, being as rich in fat as that of the Acouri is destitute of it. The mode of hunting the Labba is described by Mr. C. B. Brown in his work on Guiana.

" The flesh of the Labba is considered the most delicate of all bush animals, and is therefore much sought after. This animal is a rodent about the size of a hare, but with a stouter body, and more rat-like head. It is nocturnal in its habits, spending the day in its burrow under tree-roots near the edges of rivers. These sleeping-chambers are not very long, and have two entrances. The huntsman rams a thin pole in at one end, which startles the occupant, causing it to fly precipitately from the other, like a ball from a cannon, closely followed by the dog.

" The Labba, when close pressed, takes to the water, and while swimming is hunted down by the Indian sportsman in his wood-skin. Sometimes the animal escapes by diving, and hiding amongst fallen brushwood on the river's edge, but more frequently falls a victim to the arrow of the Indian."

Its colour is dark brown, with four rows of white spots on each side. The fur is considered useless.

LEMON (*Citrus limonum.*)—This tree belongs to the same genus as the orange, and there are nearly as many varieties of Lemons as there are of oranges.

LETTER-WOOD (*Brosimum aubletii*).—The wood of this small tree is intensely hard and very heavy. It derives its popular name from the colour of the wood, which is deep brown scribbled over with reddish marks looking something like Persian or Arabic letters. In consequence of its weight and hardness it is much used for the "shimara-sherie" of the long fish and hog arrows, *q. v.*

In this tree, only the heart-wood produces the beautiful markings, and in a tree of twenty inches in diameter the heart-wood measures barely seven inches. It runs to about eighty feet in height, and is rather scarce. The natives call it by the name of Buro-koro, or Paira. It may be here mentioned that the native name for all heart-wood is Tacouba.

LOCUST-TREE (*Hymenœa courbaril*).—For its use in canoe making *see* PURPLE-HEART.

The bark of this tree has but one defect. It is rarely more than a quarter of an inch in thickness, and so is easily bent to the required form. But it is heavier than water, so that if the canoe be upset, it immediately sinks, and cannot be raised without difficulty.

It is from the Locust-tree that the gum animi of commerce is obtained. Very often, when the tree is dead and decayed, enormous quantities of the gum may be found on the spot which it had occupied. The wood makes excellent furniture-being hard, heavy, brown streaked with veins, and taking a fine polish. The tree is also known by the names of Simiri and K'wanarri.

M

MAAM. *See* " Tinamou."

MAHOGANY (*Swietonia mahagoni.*)—The tree which furnishes the well-known mahogany wood is a very fine one, some specimens being nearly a hundred feet in height. It belongs to the group of Cedraceæ. The timber is especially valuable, because, no matter how large or long it may be, it is almost invariably sound throughout, and free from ' shakes.' A single log has been sold for a thousand pounds. Its uses were discovered by Sir W. Raleigh.

Rosewood, which comes from the same country is a Mimosa, several species of which furnish the wood. It derives its name from the rose-like smell of the freshly-cut timber.

MANAKINS.—These are nearly all small birds, the Cock of the Rock, *q.v.*, being the largest of them. Waterton's first Manakin seems to be the White-throated Manakin (*Pipra gutturalis*) ; the second is the Red and Black Manakin (*Pipra aureola*) ; the third is the White-headed Manakin (*Pipra leucosilla*) ; and the fourth is the Gold-headed Manakin (*Pipra erythrocephalus*).

MARIBUNTA.—This is merely a Portuguese word signifying a Wasp, and is applied to all wasps indiscriminately.

MAROUDI.—There are several species of Maroudis, those which are best known being the common maroudi (*Penelope cristata*), and the white-headed maroudi (*Penelope pipile*). Of these birds, Mr. C. B. Brown writes as follows :—

" The white-headed maroudi makes an extraordinary rattling noise with its wings in early morning and late in the evening, evidently amusing itself, or following a custom of its kind, for when it likes, it can fly noiselessly enough.

" I examined their wings, and found that the males have four curiously shaped feathers at the tip of the wing, with which they make this noise. The end portion of these feathers is stiff, with very short pennules. The white-headed females have only three of these feathers in each wing, which are not so intensely modified as in the male; while the male of the common kind has only two of those feathers in each wing, which are modified in a less degree than those in the females of the white-headed species."

WHITE-HEADED MAROUDI.

If the reader will refer to the note on Pee-ay-man, he will see that the Maroudi is thought to be a bird of good spiritual influence. This is the Jacatinga of Spix.

Moco-moco Tree (*Calladium arborescens*).

Monkey, Brown (*Cebus Apella*).—This monkey is well known in England, and is very intelligent. Some years ago there was one in the Zoological Gardens who had been taught to crack nuts with a stone, if he found them too hard for his teeth. He taught a companion the same art, and it was most absurd to see the two sitting side by side, and cracking nuts alternately. They never seemed to quarrel about the pos_session of the stone, but as soon as one had cracked a nut, he put down the stone and the other took it up. They had worn the stone quite smooth by continual use.

Another possessed the rather dangerous faculty of lighting lucifer-matches, and knocking them about with his hands while blazing. Nothing pleased him so much as a flaming "fusee," as it blazed more fiercely than an ordinary match, and remained alight much longer. The sides and back of his cage were covered with the marks of the matches which he had lighted.

Other monkeys employ artificial methods of nut-cracking, as is shown by Mr. C. B. Brown.

He had found a number of Brazil nuts on the ground, enclosed in their hard, shelly cases. "My men used to open

BROWN MONKEY.

them by chopping off their ends with a cutlass, which, owing to their hardness, was no easy operation. The quatas, or large black spider-monkeys, spent a good deal of their time in trying to open them by beating them against the branches of trees, or on hard logs upon the ground ; and as we passed a grove of Brazil-nut-trees it was amusing to hear the hammering sounds produced by these fellows at their self-imposed tasks. Where a single monkey was thus employed the blows were most laughably 'few and far between,' the creature showing its true indolent character by the slow way in which it performed its work, resting for a few minutes between every blow. It also showed an amount of perseverance, however, that one would not look for in a monkey, and a knowledge that it would eventually reap a reward for its hard labour.

" Goodness knows how long it takes one of these monkeys to break a nut-case ; but the time must be great, for on one occasion, we got quietly amongst a lot of the nut breakers, and secured a nut-case which one in its hurry had left upon a log, and which was worn smooth by the friction of the monkey's hands. This had evidently been pounded for a length of time, but showed no signs of cracking. Its natural aperture was large enough to allow the monkey's finger to touch the ends of the nuts inside, which were picked and worn by its nails. Near the same place we saw a nut-case split in two, on the flat surface of a large granite rock, that had evidently been broken by a monkey, for there were no Brazil-nut trees from which it could have fallen, overhanging the spot."

There are several species belonging to the genus *Cebus*, and they are called by the general name of Capucins.

MONKEYS AND MISSILES.—Waterton, as will here be seen, entirely denies that any monkey can use a missile, and recurs to the subject in one of his essays. In this article he offers to accompany any one to any collection of monkeys, and to supply the animals with stones, tiles, lead, pewter-pots and sawdust, all of which articles he has been told had been used as missiles against human beings by monkeys. He offers, in his own amusingly trenchant style, to give the monkeys every opportunity of hurling these objects at him, and that if one of them does so, he will admit that the knowledge which he had acquired " during a long sojourn in the forests of Guiana (the native haunts of monkeys) is rotten, and not worth one single farthing."

There can be no doubt that Waterton is perfectly right in denying that any monkey which he had seen threw stones or any missiles by way of defence. Most monkeys can catch a missile, and many are adroit enough to catch flies on the wing. But, although they can catch, they seldom throw. Still, they are able to drop branches, &c., from the tops of trees, not because the branches are dead and brittle, and have been accidentally broken by the passage of the monkeys among them, but with the deliberate intention of driving away a supposed foe.

Waterton never saw such a feat performed, and he is right to say so. But there are other travellers quite as worthy of credence as Waterton, who definitely state that they have been eye-witnesses to such a proceeding. No one, I would presume, would impugn a direct assertion of Mr. Alfred R. Wallace. Yet in his well-known work on the Malay Archipelago, among the islands of which he was continually travelling for more than seven years, he has the following observations :—

" I afterwards shot two adult females and two young ones of different ages, all of which I preserved.

" One of the females, with several young ones, was feeding on a Durian tree with unripe fruit ; and as soon as she saw us she began breaking off branches, and the great spiny branches with every appearance of rage, causing such a shower of missiles as effectually kept us from approaching too near the tree.

" This habit of throwing down branches when irritated has been doubted, but I have, as here narrated, observed it myself on at least three separate occasions. It was, however, always the female Mias who behaved in this way, and it may be that the male, trusting more to his great strength and his powerful canine teeth, is not afraid of any other animal, and does not want to drive them away, while the parental instinct of the female leads her to adopt this mode of defending herself and her young ones."

Perhaps it may be said that Wallace travelled in the Malay Archipelago, and wrote of the orang-outan, while Waterton travelled in Guiana, and wrote of the Coaita which inhabits that country. Still, his sweeping assertion included all members of the monkey race, and moreover, a traveller and naturalist, who spent much time in Guiana, writes as follows of the Coaiti, or Quata :—

" When engaged in the forest, cutting our portage, we were frequently visited by bands of large Coiata monkeys, which were very numerous on the banks of the upper part of this river (the Essequibo). They were the black-bodied, red-faced kind of large spider monkey, and uttered a sort of barking grunt. Their cry, when calling to each other, has a wailing sound, and is very loud.

"On seeing us, they used frequently to hurl down large dead branches, some of which came rather too close to our heads at times to be comfortable. The manner in which they performed this was singular : they held on by tail and hind-feet to a live bough in a tree top, alongside of a dead one, and pushing with their hands with all their force against the latter, generally succeeding in breaking it off, when down it came." (C. B. Brown, *Canoe and Camp Life in Guiana.*)

I have lately received ocular proof that a monkey can fling missiles with a good aim. At the Crystal Palace there is a baboon which is fastened by a chain. If a visitor should give nuts, &c., to any other monkey, the baboon flings the straw of its cage both at the donor and recipient.

MORA (*Mora excelsa*).—One of the many giants of the vegetable kingdom which are found in Guiana, sometimes attaining a height of two hundred feet.

Mr. C. B. Brown gives the following description of this fine tree :—

"The band of Mora-trees lining both banks of the Essequibo continued along it as far up as we went, but did not grow on the banks of the Rupununi up to Pirara landing. The Mora grows only on a moist soil along the borders of the river, forming a band on both sides of varying width, according to the breadth of the band of flooded country during the rainy season. In places it is often not more than 100 yards in width. Up many small side streams the Mora has marched to their sources, while along others it has not attempted to spread.

By their solid-looking tops, composed of massive dark green leaves, and their great height, they attract attention and excite admiration; and when portions of their tops are sprouting new leaves, which are of a light liver-colour at first, turning red, and then green, a forest of them presents many varied tints. Each branch throws out shoots and gets new leaves at all times of the year, independent of other portions of the same tree."

The seeds of the Mora are rather pink inside, and used by the natives as food, being boiled, grated, and then mixed with cassava meal, giving it a brown colour, but a pleasant and sweetish taste. Three varieties of this tree are recognised, namely, the Red Mora, White Mora, and Mora Bucquia. The timber is excellent for ship-building, and is one of the eight first class woods at Lloyd's.

MOSQUITO (*Culex pipiens*).—Several species of Gnats are called by the name of Mosquito, which signifies a little fly. They are found all over the world, and infest hot and cold countries equally, though their bite seems to be fiercer in the former than in the latter.

Even in England the Mosquito can be more than unpleasant. I have had my right hand laid up for a long time by the bite of a single Mosquito just at the base of the thumb. The insect settled on my hand in broad daylight, and I killed it as soon as I felt the prick of its beak; but the mischief was done, and I had to carry my arm in a sling and have the hand covered with ice for several days. As to the hand, it looked more like a discoloured boxing-glove than a hand.

It is only the female Mosquito which bites, the male being perfectly harmless.

There is a larger and longer legged species of Mosquito in Guiana. Its scientific name is *Culex pulicularis*, and it is popularly known as Gally-nipper.

MUSK DUCK (*Cairina moschata*).—Popularly, but wrongly called the Muscovy Duck.

N

NANDAPOA.—Sometimes called Negrocope, *i.e.* Black-head (*Tantalus loculator*), a species of Ibis. The Jabiru, *q. v.*, is also called Negrocope.

Mr. C. B. Brown's observations on this bird agree exactly with Waterton's passing description. He mentions that "they are white, with black wings, and are frequently seen soaring high in the heavens in circles, mounting higher and higher till they appear like mere specks." The head and neck have no feathers, and are covered with a black, wrinkled skin.

NONDESCRIPT.—This wonderful specimen of Waterton's skill in taxidermy is formed from the head and shoulders of the Red Howler monkey, *q. v.* In manipulating it, Waterton has so modelled the skin that he has discharged from the face every vestige of the original features, and has substituted those of a man, grotesque enough, but still human. As bare skin always becomes black when dry, the contrast of the black face with the fiery red hair has a very striking effect and adds to the resemblance.

In his witty review of the Wanderings, to which reference has already been made, Sydney Smith says of the frontispiece, which represents the Nondescript, "Upon stuffing animals we have a word to say. Mr. Waterton has placed at the head of his book the picture of what he is pleased to consider a nondescript species of monkey. In this exhibition our author is surely abusing his stuffing talents, and laughing at the public. It is clearly the head of a Master in Chancery—whom we have often seen backing in the House of Commons after he has delivered his message. It is foolish thus to trifle with science and natural history."

The principal difficulty in preparing this grotesque head lay in the change of the facial angle from that of the monkey to that of the man. This could not have been done if the skull, or any part of it, had been allowed to remain, and the really wonderful feat could only be performed by Waterton's system of removing the whole of the bones, and paring down all the bare skin until it was not thicker than ordinary writing-paper.

The drawing of the head, however, scarcely does justice to the original, for Waterton made the nose much more aquiline and thinner than is shown in the engraving, which also makes the face look as if it were hairy, whereas it is absolutely bare. If any visitor to Ushaw College can manage to obtain a profile view of the Nondescript, he will be greatly struck with the ingenuity which has changed the flattened nose of the monkey into the aquiline nose of a human being.

Many persons indeed, on seeing the Nondescript, really thought that it was human, and said that Waterton ought not to have been allowed to kill natives in order to show his skill in preserving their skins.

NUTMEG (*Myristica moschata.*)—Mace is the scarlet envelope which surrounds the seed. It becomes reddish-yellow when dry.

O

OLOU, sometimes written Oolu.—The tree is a large one, running to eighty or ninety feet in height, and found in loose sandy soil on the Essequibo. It produces scented gum much like that of the hayawah, and seems to be also a species of *Icica*. The wood is recommended for wardrobes, entomological cabinets, and the like.

OPOSSUM (*Cheironectes Yapock*).—Sometimes, on account of its predatory habits and its semi aquatic life, it is called the Demerara Otter. Buffon also terms it an otter.

It is really a curious being, and has greatly puzzled systematic naturalists. Most of the opossum tribe inhabit trees, but the Yapock passes the greater part of its time in the water, and is never found far from rivers. The feet are webbed, the cheeks are furnished with large pouches, and the fore-feet look exactly as if they had six toes instead of five.

It is rather prettily marked, the ground colour being grey, on which are bold black marks. In the young, the grey is lighter and the black darker than in the adult animal.

OPOSSUM.

ORANGE (*Citrus aurantium*).—Those who have travelled in the West Indies say that the Orange cannot be appreciated unless eaten off the tree, and that the best "China" Orange of our shops is but bad brown sugar and water to the Orange when fresh. The only drawback is, that the aromatic oil of the peel is so powerful that the lips are blistered, unless every particle of peel be removed.

OTTER (*Pteronura Sanbachii*).—The following account of this animal is given by Mr. C. B. Brown :—

"We frequently came up with parties of Otters, composed of from five to eight individuals, which tried to dispute the passage of the river with us. They used to approach the canoes, and all popping their heads out of water together, would snort and snarl as if trying to intimidate us. Seeing that our advance was not to be checked, they took long dives away, and quickly disappeared beyond a bend in the river, to be seen no more. They were of a brownish colour, with a patch of white under the throat. I could not resist the temptation of having a shot at one occasionally, but never could tell whether it took effect, for, as they always disappeared beneath the surface at the instant of the report, it was difficult to say whether they had dived at the flash or were killed and sunk to the bottom.''

The length of one which was shot by Mr. Brown was five feet four inches, nearly two feet more than the average length of our English otter. The burrows seem to have two entrances, one opening into the river and the other leading to the bank.

OURAH (*Arundinaria Schomburgkii*). — Waterton did not know the reed called Ourah, neither did the Macoushies, who were in the habit of purchasing it. It is a very local plant, and according to Schomburgk, is only to be found on a sandstone ridge of the Upper Orinoco River. In some respects it resembles the bamboo, and, like that plant, grows in thick clusters, with long slender branches that wave in the wind like magnified tufts of grass.

Nowhere is the stem more than half an inch in diameter, and the first joint, which is used for the blow-gun, is fifteen or sixteen feet in length, without a single knot, hollow, and polished within. Though its walls are very thin, they are of great strength, owing to the tubular form of the reed, and are thus able to uphold the slender branches, which sometimes reach forty feet in length.

P

PACOU (*Myletes pacu*).—How this fish is taken by means of poisoning the water is described under "WOURALI." Poison, however, is not absolutely necessary, for the Pacous have a fashion of coming to the surface of the water, showing their heads and parts of their backs, and then disappearing. Waterton used to shoot pike in the same manner as they came to bask on the surface of the water, after the custom of their kind. The flesh of the Pacou affords excellent food.

PADDLE.—The Paddles are really curious objects. They are made from the wood of the Paddle-tree (*Aspidospermum excelsum*), a most strange-looking tree. It runs to a considerable height, and the outline of the trunk is most remarkable.

The reader will remember that the Ceiba (see p. 395) has the lower part of the trunk modified into buttresses, but the Paddle-tree seems to be all buttress, and bears a curious resemblance to the clustered pillars found in some of our old cathedrals. Indeed, the section of the tree looks very much like a piece of one of those intricate puzzle-maps and pictures which used to be found in the toyshops.

As the wood is soft while fresh, an Indian, when he has to make a new paddle, splits off one of the "flutes," as these buttresses are called, trims it carefully into shape, and then hands it over to the women, who paint it in divers patterns of black and red.

The Paddle-wood tree is called by the natives Yarari or Massara. When dry, the wood is very light, very elastic, very hard, and very strong. This oddly-shaped tree averages sixty or seventy feet in height, and five feet in diameter. A good section of it is in the Technological Museum of the Crystal Palace.

PAPPAW or PAPAW-TREE (*Carica papaya*). — This tree is planted by the natives near all their permanent settlements, and is seen in company with the cotton and red pepper. It not only furnishes an edible fruit, but possesses the singular property of making tough meat tender when rubbed with the acrid juice of the unripe fruit, or even with the leaf. In fact, as Tom Cringle says, it can convert a piece of bull's hide into a tender beef-steak.

PAINT, RED, used by Natives.—The natives are fond of decorating their bodies with paints during feasting times. Red and black are the two chief colours. Red is obtained from the seeds of the Arnotto plant (*Bixa orellana*), and the black from the juice of the fruit of the Lana tree (*Genipa Americana*). The Bixa is the plant that furnishes the annato dye, with which we colour our cheeses. The natives call the paint by the name of Rucu.

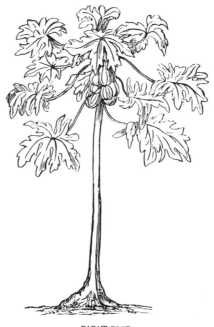

PAPAW-TREE.

PARIMA, LAKE.—Ever since the time of the great adventurer, Raleigh, there has been great discussion as to the Lake Parima and El Dorado, or the Golden City. Some geographers have denied the existence of either lake or city, while others have been so certain as to the former, that a map in my possession places it about forty miles north-east of Fort St. Joachim, in the loop of the Tacatu River, between Lat. 4 and 5 N.

Waterton could find no traces of it, and the inhabitants of Fort St. Joachim had not been more successful. Schomburgk, who went much by the tracks of Waterton, reached the very spot, and found that Waterton's cautious suggestion was more than correct. He has given a beautiful drawing of the spot, which would have been the centre of the lake, had it existed, but on which was a small settlement of native huts. Of the lake he writes as follows :—

"The vast savannahs upon which St. Pirara is situated, are encompassed by the Pacaraima mountains to the north, the Canoku and Carawaimi mountains to the south, the thick forests of the Essequibo and isolated mountains, to the east, and the mountains of the Mocajahi, and branches of the Sierra Parima to the west; and, according to a superficial computation, cover a space of fourteen thousand four hundred square miles. The geological structure of this region leaves but little doubt that it was once the bed of an inland lake, which, by one of those catastrophes of which even later times give us examples, broke its barriers and forced a path for its waters to the Atlantic. May we not connect with this inland sea that fable of El Dorado and Lake Parima ? "

Thus Schomburgk has proved that Waterton's conjecture was correct, and that we may erase El Dorado and Lake Parima from our maps and memories.

PARROT, SUN, or HIA-HIA (*Deroptyus accipitrinus*).—It derives its popular and appropriate name from the way in which the feathers of its neck can be spread into a sort of flaming glory round its head. There is a splendid specimen in Waterton's museum. It is sometimes called Anacá.

PATACA.—There seems to be no possibility of identifying this bird. No description is given, and its name is only once casually mentioned. As it is named in connection with the maroudi, it may belong to the same group of birds. See " Maroudi."

PECCARY, sometimes called Wild Hog (*Dicoteles tajacu*). —This is not a large animal, weighing only some fifty or sixty pounds, but it is greatly dreaded, not only by the natives, but by Europeans. The tusks of the boars are so small that they can scarcely be seen beyond the lips, but they are terribly sharp, cut like lancets, and can be wielded with singular swiftness and force.

Moreover, the Peccaries, until they have learned respect for man from long experience, seem to be entirely without the sense of fear, and to be in the habit of taking offence at the least sound, and charging at the spot. There is scarcely a hunter who has not been forced to climb into the branches of

PARROT. SUN.

trees in order to escape a herd of Peccaries, and even when they have driven him into the tree, they will sit round it, gnashing their tusks in anger. The sound of the clashing tusks is well known to hunters, and warns them to prepare for a charge.

The jaguar preys upon them, but is afraid of them. They always go in herds, and if one be attacked, the rest are sure to come to the rescue. So, the jaguar silently follows the herd, strikes down a straggling Peccary and makes for the nearest tree. There it remains until the Peccaries are tired of waiting for it, and it then descends the tree, finishes the Peccary, and then follows the herd in search of another. Instances have been however known where the jaguar has not had time to escape, and has been cut to pieces by the lancet-like tusks of the Peccaries.

Two species are known in Guiana, one the Collared Peccary, having a white band over the neck, and the other the White-lipped Peccary, which has a white streak upon the jaws. Both

PECCARY.

species have on the back a fetid open gland, which must be cut out as soon as the animal is killed, as if it were allowed to remain, the flesh would be uneatable. The White-lipped Peccary is larger than its relative, fiercer, and more dreaded. The natives use the white tusks for necklaces and other ornaments.

PEE-AY-MAN.—The word is spelt variously by different travellers, some using the word Piaiman. The pronunciation however is the same in both cases.

The Pee-ay-man, or sorcerer, is a very great man indeed, like the medicine man of North America or the prophet of South Africa, and has to endure a curiously similar ordeal of bodily torture and exhaustion before he can be admitted to the coveted rank. The mode in which he exercises his art is narrated by Mr. C. B. Brown. He had procured a guide who was full of wild legends relating to the locality, and would insist on telling them.

"He turned out to be a famed sorcerer, or Piaiman; and at a village called Itabay, where we stopped one night in returning, he left the house in which we had put up our hammocks, telling the interpreter to inform me that his absence for the night was unavoidable, owing to his having to go up amongst the mountains to roam about for the night, whilst his good

PEE-AY-MAN.

spirit remained in one of the houses to cure a sick man, who had demanded his good offices.

"In two minutes after he had left us his powerful voice was heard making the most discordant sounds imaginable, chanting, howling, coughing, and many other diabolical noises, to these were added the *shishing* sound of an instrument called a shak-shak, made of a small round calabash filled with seeds, and placed on a handle, by which it is shaken.

"All the fires in the house had been put out in anticipation of his arrival, and the place was pitch dark, so that the illusion that he was not there in the flesh might be kept up. Owing to the noise I did not get a wink of sleep until about two o'clock in the morning, and often thought, during the night, what a good thing it would have been if his spirit had only accompanied his body to the mountains.

" The house being close to the one I was in, the interpreter could hear all he said, and at my request, but with evident reluctance, told me what it was. It seems that he entered the house silently, and then commenced the sort of din above mentioned, beating with a palm-branch on the floor. He then asked in a deep, sepulchral voice what it was that ailed the patient, to which the sick man's wife responded that some evil spirits or kanaimas had ' done him bad.' The sorcerer then said, ' Well, I don't know whether I can cure him, but I will do my best.'

" He then called to his aid the good spirit of a bird, called the maroudi, the descent of which from the roof was made known by the shaking of the palm-leaf raised up and gradually lowered to the floor.

" On the arrival of this good spirit, it at first complained of having had a long journey, and that it was much heated by the haste it had been obliged to make when so suddenly summoned. It made the usual amount of noise, interlarded with whistlings (in imitation of the maroudie's call), and promised to do its best. When its best, which consisted of discordant sounds, had been done, its egress through the roof was made known by the shakings of the palm-leaf, and a dead silence of a minute's duration succeeded, when the fluttering of the leaf announced the arrival of the spirit of an alligator, which in its turn was replaced by a duraquara, and so on."

PEGALL.—A native basket, very light, elastic, and strong.

PELICAN (*Pelecanus fuscus*).—Several Pelicans are known, such, for example, as the frigate bird, and all of them have the under part of the skin of the neck and throat modified into a pouch, which can be greatly distended. It is chiefly used for carrying fish to its young, and being large enough, when fully distended, to hold two gallons of water, it can carry a plentiful supply.

Keepers of travelling menageries are in the habit of exhibiting the capacity of the pouch by thrusting their bent arms into it. Yet when it is not needed for use, it can hardly be seen, so elastic are the membranes of which it is composed, and the pelican only looks like a bird with a long, straight beak.

As far as can be judged from its behaviour in captivity, it is a playful bird, but rather quick-tempered. While watching the pelicans at the Zoological Gardens, I was able to secure a few of their characteristic attitudes.

Fig. 1 represents a bird that had just been fed, and was resting after its dinner.

1 2

Fig. 2 is the same bird as it appeared at feeding time, when it was scolding another for eating a fish which it wanted for itself.

Fig. 3 shows the attitude of a pelican while sunning itself, with the pouch slightly expanded.

Fig. 4 gives the attitude when the bird is startled by an unexpected noise.

Fig. 5 represents the bird in the act of preening the feathers of the breast. This attitude gave rise to the fable of the pelican feeding its young with its own blood drawn from its breast, the red tip of the beak having a blood-like look against the white feathers.

3

Fig. 6 shows the bird with the mouth half open, and Figs. 7, 8, 9 are ordinary attitudes.

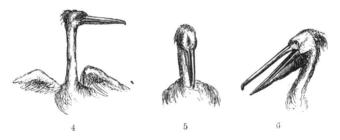

4   5   6

The reader will see that the pouch is scarcely shown at all in these figures, the whole of which were sketched from the

7   8   9

living birds. The colour of the pelican is white with a delicate rosy tinge.

PEPPER-BLACK. (*Piper nigrum.*)

PEPPER-RED (*Capsicum annuum*).—Few plants are more valued both abroad and in England than the Capsicum. In its small state it is known as "chili," and is sometimes gathered before it has obtained the red stage of existence. When ground, it is sold as Cayenne pepper, the species usually employed for this purpose being *Capsicum frutescens.*

It grows well in England, if care be taken of it, and is a very pretty and ornamental plant, especially when the pods attain their brilliant red hue.

PERAI (*Serrasalmus piraya*).—This fish is quite as much dreaded as the alligator or cayman in the rivers, or the shark in the sea. Indeed, its teeth, sharply pointed and razor-edged, very much resemble those of the shark. Its voracity seems to know no bounds. It will attack other fish, such as the gilbacker, lowlow, paraima, &c., bite large pieces out of their fins and tails. Even when scarcely larger than an English gudgeon, the Perai, which is sometimes called the Blood-fish of the Orinoco, can make fatal attacks on human beings, its numbers compensating for its small size.

The following account of it is taken from Mr. C. B. Brown's work to which reference has already been made :—

" The Corentyne and its branches were literally teeming with fish of various kinds, the greater number being haimara and Perai. The latter were so abundant and ferocious that at times it was dangerous, when bathing, to go into the water to a greater depth than up to one's knees. Even then small bodies of these hungry creatures would swim in and make a dash close up to our legs, and then retreat to a short distance. They actually bit the steering paddles as they were drawn through the water astern of the boats. A tapir which I shot swimming across the water had its nose eaten off by them whilst we were towing it to the shore.

" Of an evening the men used to catch some of them for sport, and in taking the hook from their mouths produce a wound from which the blood ran freely. On throwing them back into the water in this injured condition, they were immediately set upon and devoured by their companions. Even as one was being hauled in on the line, its comrades, seeing that it was in difficulties, attacked it at once. One day, when the boat was hauled in to some rocks, a few of the men were engaged shooting fish near by, and in so doing wounded a large haimara.

"Having escaped from its human tormentors, it made for the open river, but was instantly attacked by Perai attracted by the blood escaping from its wound, and was driven back to the shelter of the rocks close to the boat, from which I had a

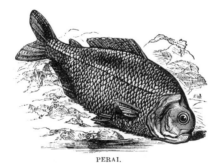

PERAI.

good view of the chase. The large fish followed by its savage enemies reminded me of a parallel case on land—a stricken deer pursued by wolves.

"The Perai, fortunately, lie only off sand-beaches and in quiet pools, not frequenting the cataracts, where their presence would be anything but acceptable to the men while working in the water. I was fortunate enough to find the spawning place of some Perai on the matted clusters of fibrous roots of some lianes, which hung from the branches of a tree into the water, amongst which much earthy sediment had collected, and many small aquatic plants had grown. The sediment gave weight to the roots which kept the clusters under water, and the force of the current made them buoyant, giving the lianes a slope when the river was high, which kept them not far from its surface.

"My attention was attracted to them by two Perai lying close to them, with their heads up stream, as the men said, engaged in watching their eggs. Procuring one of the roots, I examined it, and found amongst it numbers of single eggs and clusters of small, jelly-like young, which had been already hatched. The eggs were white, and of about one-eighth of an inch in diameter, with a hard exterior. The young were very little larger, and had a glutinous surface, which caused them to adhere together on being taken from the water. They had not acquired any powers of locomotion, but could just wriggle their tails like tadpoles.

"Under a lens they resembled the egg devoid of its covering, with a gelatinous ridge around three-quarters of its circumference, one end of which expanded into a knob (probably the head), while the other termination was flattened and tail-like. I could not detect any eyes or mouth in them, but their bodies were speckled with grey markings of colouring matter."

Stedman mentions the fish under the title of Peery.

The Waraw palm-dwellers (see Æta) dispose of their dead simply by dropping the bodies into the lake, where the flesh is rapidly stripped from the bones by the Perai, just as our ants can do with frogs, mice, and small birds. If the deceased should happen to be a man of importance, the body is lowered in a net, and the skeleton, when quite cleaned, is drawn up, dried, painted red, and hung in the hut.

PETREL, STORMY (*Thalassidroma pelagica*).—This bird is too well known to need description.

PHAETON. *See* "Tropic Bird."

PI-PI-YO. Nothing is known of the bird, except that its cry is shrill, and is thought to resemble the syllables forming its name.

PINE APPLE (*Ananassa sativa*).

PIWARRI.—It is singular that a drink prepared as is Piwarri should not only have been invented and drunk at all, but that it should have been employed by nations who could have had no connection with each other. Piwarri (which is also spelled Piari or Paiworie) is prepared as follows.

Cassava bread is chewed, and then placed in a large pot, in which is some of the expressed cassava juice already mentioned. It is boiled for twelve hours, and then put into jars, where fermentation takes place, and it is ready for use. It has an intoxicating quality of a very feeble character, but the natives compensate for lack of quality by quantity, and, by dint of drinking successive bowls of the liquid, they do succeed in intoxicating themselves.

When the natives can get brandy, they prefer it to any other liquid, because it makes them drunk so soon, but next to brandy they like piwarri.

Not only is it a favourite beverage, but it has a kind of sanctity attached to it, and is drunk at their solemn feasts. Here we have a most singular resemblance to the kava drinking of Polynesia. The Mexicans prepare a drink called "mudai" in a similar manner, except that they employ apples instead of cassava or kava. Those who have been obliged to drink Piwarri for reasons of policy, say that it rather resembles very weak table beer. In some of the larger settlements, they have enormous Piwarri bowls, shaped like canoes, of about the same size, and called by the same name.

PLANTAIN (*Musa paradisaica*).

PLOVERS. There are many species of Plover in Guiana. The most common are the Black-breasted (*Charadrius Virginianus*), the Ring-neck (*C. semipalmatus*), and the Sandy Plover (*Strepsilus interpres*).

PORCUPINE.—The species mentioned by Waterton is the Tree-Porcupine, or Coendoo (*Cercolabes prehensilis*), which, like the sloths, finds its nutriment in the trees and not on the ground. In Northern America there is an allied species, also living in trees and called the urson, cawquaw, or Canadian porcupine, from which the "Indians," as they are called, procure the quills with which they decorate their dresses and other articles, previously staining them with dyes extracted from various herbs.

The Coendoo, however, may be distinguished by its long prehensile tail, which can be coiled round the branches like that of the spider-monkey and the little ant-eater, which has been already described.

Its food consists of leaves, flowers, young twigs, and similar substances, and its flesh is said to be delicate and tender. If so, it very much belies the odour which proceeds from its body, and which is thus described by Charles Kingsley :—

PORCUPINE.

" More than once we became aware of a keen and dreadful scent, as of a concentrated essence of unwashed tropic humanity, which proceeded from that strange animal, the Porcupine with a prehensile tail, who prowls in the tree tops all night, and sleeps in them all day, spending his idle hours in making this hideous smell. Probably he or his ancestors have found it pay as a protection ; for no jaguar or tiger-cat, it is to be presumed, would care to meddle with any thing so exquisitely nasty, especially when it is all over sharp prickles."

As to the theory that any animal, even the skunk itself, is

protected by an evil odour, Waterton always treats it with
contempt. In an essay on the weasel, he has the following
remarks :—

"Many of the weasel tribe have the power of emitting a
very disagreeable odour from the posterior part of the body.
We are gravely informed in the *American Biography of Birds*,
that the pole-cat has this faculty 'given him by nature as a
defence.' And, pray, at what old granny's fireside in the
United States has the writer of this picked up such an important piece of information? How comes the polecat to be
aware that the emitted contents of a gland (I use gland in
the singular number, for the sake of brevity, but the animal
has two glands), inoffensive to itself, should be offensive to all
its pursuers? I say, *inoffensive* to itself, because I cannot
believe that our Creator would condemn an unoffending animal
to produce its own punishment by means of a smell which
never leaves it—whether it roam up and down as a solitary
animal, or whether it have a partner and a family of young
ones to provide for.

"Although this odour from individuals of the weasel tribe
is very distressing to our own nasal sensibilities, it by no
means follows that the scent should have a similar effect upon
those of all other animals. For example, the smell from
purulent carrion is certainly very disagreeable to us bipeds;
still it cannot prove so to the dog—for, in lieu of avoiding it,
this quadruped never loses an opportunity of rolling in it.
If the polecat has had the fetid gland 'given him by nature
as a defence,' then must nature have given a sweet one to the
civet for its destruction; seeing that, whilst we shun the first
on account of its insupportable stench, we pursue and kill the
last in order to obtain its perfume. Now, as both these
animals are of the same family, I cannot help remarking, with
Sterne, in the case of the 'poor negro girl,' that nature has
put one of this tribe sadly over the head of the others, if the
North American theory be sound.

"Again, if nature has given this abominable stench to

many of the polecat tribe 'as a defence,' she has cruelly neglected our former invader, the Hanoverian rat. The polecat is not much exposed to destruction, as its movements are chiefly nocturnal, and, in general, it is apt to shun the haunts of men. But our Hanoverian, having a most inordinate appetite for the good things of this world, is ever on the stir, in the very midst of its enemies, to satisfy the cravings of its capacious stomach; and it will cater for itself the four-and-twenty hours throughout. Hence your housekeeper complains that it will try its tooth on primest Stilton in broad daylight, and that it will have its whiskers in the creambowl, even whilst the dairymaid is gone up stairs with butter for the breakfast table. Still my darling Hanoverian has nothing but an ordinary set of teeth wherewith to protect itself, although exposed to ten times more danger than the foumart, which last has a fetid gland given it by nature 'as a defence,' —in addition, I may add, to vast muscular strength, and to two full rows of sharp and well-assorted teeth.

"This being the case, let us reject the Transatlantic theory as a thing of emptiness; and if we are called upon for an opinion as to the real uses of the fetid gland in polecats, let us frankly own that we have it not in our power to give anything satisfactory on the subject."

POLECAT (*Galera barbara*).—Called Tayra by natives. It is an active, lively little creature, black, with a white patch on the throat. Colonists are apt to call the opossum by the name of polecat. *See* "Opossum."

POTATO, SWEET (*Convolvulus batatas*).

POWISE (*Crax alector*).—This fine bird is one of the Curassows, of which there are several species. It seems to bear our climate very well, and as it is easily tamed, and will take its place in the poultry yard, attempts have been made to acclimatize it like the turkey, the guinea-fowl, and the peacock. As yet, however, the enterprise has met with small success, which is the more to be regretted as the great size of the bird, nearly equalling that of the turkey, and the delicacy of its flesh, would make it a welcome addition to our poultry.

Within the tropics, however, it is a very common inhabitant of the poultry yard, where its only drawback is, that it assumes authority over the turkeys and guinea fowls, and pecks them to death if they do not obey. In many parts of

POWISE.

Guiana there is a belief that if a dog licks up the blood of a wounded Powise, or mumbles its bleeding feathers as dogs love to do, it will go mad.

PURPLE-HEART (*Copaifera publiflora*).—This most useful tree derives its name from the purple colour of its wood, which is very hard, close-grained, durable, and tough.

It is, however, chiefly valued for its bark, which is used in making canoes. Mr. C. B. Brown gives the following account of the manufacture :—

" The bark canoes used by Indians are called ' Woodskins ' by the Creoles, and are made of one piece of bark, stripped from a tree called the Purple-heart (*Copaifera publiflora*).

The bark of the locust-tree or simiri (*Hymenœa courbaril*) is also sometimes used. This bark is from one-eighth to one-fourth of an inch in thickness and very heavy, being of greater specific gravity than water; so that in the event of the canoe shipping water to any extent, it sinks immediately, leaving its occupants to find their way ashore.

"They are ticklish things to travel in at first, and to stand up in one, until acquainted with its freaks, is a dangerous experiment, ending in an undignified exit over one side, the canoe shooting away in the opposite direction.

"To make one of these woodskins, a large Purple-heart tree is cut down, and the bark of the requisite length taken off. A wedge-shaped piece is then cut out of the trough-shaped bark, from the top downwards, at a distance of three feet or so from both ends on each side. The ends are then raised till the edges of the cuts meet, when holes are pierced on either hand, at a distance of six inches from the cut, and numbers of turns of a strong withe or liana, called Mamurie, passed through them and made fast in a neat manner to a small round stick placed along the inside. Two strong pieces of wood fastened across at the splits prevent the sides from closing in. The ends are then trimmed down level with the sides, and a ticklish but serviceable little craft is turned out. The seats are made of curved pieces of the same bark, and are very low.

"The whole process of making one of these woodskins, including the drying of the bark, occupies a space of three weeks. In this period, must, I think, be included some loss of time from laziness on the part of the Indian canoe-builder. Woodskins vary in size, but usually are from fifteen to twenty-five feet in length, and an ordinary sized one will carry three or four people with their hammocks and provisions."

The tree when full grown, rather exceeds one hundred and fifty feet in height, and the useful bark is smooth, and of a dark brown colour.

Two varieties are known by the natives as Koorooboorelli and Marawinaroo.

Q.

QUAIL (*Ortyx virginana*).—Partly migratory.

QUAKE.—A basket of open work and very elastic and expansive. The drawing is from my own specimen.

QUAKE.

QUIVERS.—These are of two kinds, the one for holding the arrows for the blow-gun, and the other for containing the poisoned heads of the hog-arrows. A very fine specimen of one of the former was given to me by Waterton, and is here represented.

The cover is not of peccary but of capybara skin, and has the hair inside, so that by giving it a kind of screw when put on, it remains firmly in its place.

The layer of kurumanni wax, with which the quiver is wholly covered, is of considerable thickness, so that if the hunter were to allow the quiver to fall into the water, it might float for hours without any moisture penetrating to the interior, and so weakening the wourali on the arrows.

The coil of silk-grass, and the scraper of perai-teeth are seen hanging to the quiver. When the scraper is used, the arrow-point is placed between two of the teeth, which are flat, pointed, and edged like razors. The arrow is then drawn between two of the teeth, and is thus shaved down to the needle-like point which is required.

A small basket shaped like a flask, but slightly flattened, is mostly carried with the quiver. This basket is used to hold the wild cotton with which the arrows are fitted to the bore of the blow-gun. Thus, with an equipment weighing altogether little more than three pounds, the native hunter can

QUIVER, BLOW-GUN.

QUIVER, HOG-ARROW.

carry with him a powerful gun and about three or four hundred deadly missiles.

The Quiver for the heads of hog-arrows is very much smaller, and is only a piece of bamboo about seven or eight inches in length, and having a cover to guard it from damp. The Indian generally ornaments it by wrapping cotton-strings round it in patterns, as is seen in the illustration, which is taken from one of my specimens.

R.

RATTLESNAKE (*Uropsophus durissus*).—This is so familiar a reptile, that I shall not occupy valuable space by describing it.

I have already mentioned that when the sloth arrived in England, Waterton was able to point to it as a proof that he had been right in his description of that animal. Similarly, when a box of live Rattlesnakes, twenty-seven in number, were exhibited at Leeds, he had an opportunity of proving that he was not romancing when he described his encounters with deadly snakes.

He invited a large party of friends and scientific men to meet him at Leeds, whither he had sent a large glass case, so that the snakes might be properly seen. After cautioning the visitors to refrain from moving or speaking, he, with his bare hands, transferred the snakes from the box to the glass case and back again.

He explained his mode of handling a venomous serpent by the following illustration. He assumed my hand, wrist, and arm to be part of a Rattlesnake, the hand being the head, the wrist the neck, and the arm part of the body. He then approached his hand silently, slowly, and quietly to my wrist, which he by degrees clasped, but did not press. He next lifted the arm gently from the table on which it was resting, and put it down again in the same slow and cautious manner. He trusted for his immunity to the sluggish nature of the serpents generally, which if disturbed, will glide gently away, but if they are trodden upon or hurt, will, in self-defence, strike at their assailant.

He said that after that lesson, I should be as able to carry living Rattlesnakes as he was. Perhaps so, but I should feel rather nervous about trying it.

RED HOWLER. *See* " Howler, Red."

REDSTART (*Setophaga* or *Muscicapa ruticilla*). — It has nothing to do with the English Redstart.

RHINOCEROS BEETLE (*Megasoma Titan*), popularly called the Great Brown Sawyer.

ROUCOU.—*See* "Paint."

S.

SACAWINKI.—One of the Squirrel Monkeys.

This tiny monkey, several times mentioned by Waterton, is plentiful in Guiana, and is noticed by Schomburgk.

"A troop of little Sacowinkis, or squirrel monkeys, some of the most beautiful and active of their kind, leaped with the agility of a tame squirrel from branch to branch, and,

SACAWINKI.

alarmed by our appearance, uttered their painful call, resembling much more the cry of a bird than that of an animal, and then, hastening away, were soon hidden among the thick foliage of the large forest trees."

Several species of squirrel-monkey appear to be included in the general name of Sakawinki. Stedman figures the Marmoset (*Jacchus vulgaris*) under the name of Sakawinki, while Waterton, who mentions it as being black, and scarcely six inches in length, evidently refers to the White-whiskered Tamarin (*Jacchus leucogenys*), which exactly accords with his description and has accordingly been figured.

SALEMPENTA (*Teius Teguexin*).—This fine lizard is some-times called the Safeguard, because it is supposed to give notice of the approach of the alligator, just as the African monitors are believed to warn travellers against the crocodile.

It is a large animal, stoutly made, and reaching five feet or more in length. It is handsomely coloured with black,

SALEMPENTA.

yellow, green, and white, arranged so variously that hardly any two specimens are alike. For this reason it is called the Variegated Lizard.

Like the iguana, the Salempenta affords very delicate food, which is thought to resemble the flesh of a very delicate young chicken. New comers are at first averse to eating a lizard of any description, but they very soon find out their mistake, and would even prefer an iguana or Salempenta cutlet to a chicken.

SAMOURAH.—The palm which is known by this name is called *Ireartia setigera*, and like the ourah, is of very small diameter in proportion to its length.

SAND FLY (*Simulia Pertinax*), called by the natives Mapire, and mostly haunting the sea shore. What the mosquito is by night, the Sand Fly is by day, and is a still greater pest. It flies very rapidly, settles, bites, and fills itself with blood almost instantaneously, having nothing of the deliberate action of the mosquito. The bites afterwards become exceedingly painful.

SANGRE DO BUEY (*Pyranga rubra*).—Sometimes called the Scarlet Tanager. As is the case with many brilliant birds, the splendid hues of the plumage belong only to the adult male, the female having the body dull green and yellow instead of scarlet, and the wings and tail brown instead of black. It is about six inches in length.

SAWARI or SOUARI (*Caryocar tomentosum*).—This is the tree which furnishes the well-known butter-nuts. The nuts grow in the interior of large fruits, filled with a whitish meal. The roots are used for making floors, and in the futtocks of ships. It thrives best on the hills. The natives are so fond of the nuts, that the possession of the finest trees is said to be an acknowledged cause of war. When the nut is cracked, the kernel is found to be filled with a white almond-like jelly.

SCARLET GROSBEAK.—*See* "Grosbeak, Scarlet."

SCARLET GROSBEAK.

SCIROU (*Rhamphastos toco*).—*See* "Toucans."

SCREAMER, HORNED (*Palamedea cornuta*).—This fine bird is about as large as a turkey, and derives its popular name from a small horn-like appendage situate upon the upper part of the head. The object of this appendage is absolutely unknown. Some zoologists believed it to be employed as a weapon, but such an opinion is simply absurd, as no bird strikes with any part of its head except the beak, and even if the Screamer did so, the horn would be quite inadequate as a weapon of offence.

HORNED SCREAMER.

When it wishes to attack any foe, it uses the sharp spurs, which are attached to the wings, are very strong, and about an inch in length.

The natives call it by the name of Kamichi.

SILK-GRASS.—This peculiarly useful fibre is obtained from the leaf of one of the Aloe tribe (*Agave vivipara*).

The fibres run nearly parallel to each other throughout the whole length of the leaf, and are extracted by steeping the leaves in water until they are quite soft, and then drawing them through a loop of cord, so as to clear off the decayed pulp and preserve the fibres. These are then dried in the sun and tied in bundles.

The Silk-grass is of incalculable value to the natives, who always have a supply on hand. The strength of the fibre is really wonderful, and though so fine that it seems as if it would snap at a touch, it seems more like steel wire than a vegetable fabric. A coil of it is always attached to the quiver. Why it is not largely used in this country I cannot imagine. It grows in the greatest abundance, can be easily extracted from the leaf, and is not only strong, but light.

SILK-GRASS.

SILOABALI.—This name is sometimes spelt as Ciroubali, or Siruabali. There are several trees going by this name, all belonging to the genus *Eperna*, and therefore allied to the wallaba tree, *q.v.* The wood is excellent for ship-building, and Mr. McTurk, who collected specimens of Guianan woods for the Paris Exhibition of 1878, says that it is even better than greenheart, *q.v.*, and ought to be classed at Lloyds among the A 1 woods. As the wood is light, and floats well, it is much used for boat-building.

When freshly cut, it has a strong aromatic scent, and the juice is bitter. The ship-worm (*Teredo*) will not touch it, and it is therefore useful for planking boats.

SLOTH, THREE-TOED, or AI (*Bradypus tridactylus*). — Waterton's account of this animal is so full and accurate that little needs to be added. The mark on the back of the male is most singular, and looks exactly as if it had been stamped with an oval-shaped iron, very hot along the centre, so as to burn away the hair nearly to the skin, and blacken it. Then, if the iron be not quite so hot on either part of the centre, it would press down the fur and turn it brown. Lastly, supposing the iron to be only hot enough towards the edges to scorch the fur slightly, we shall produce a fair imitation of the mark impressed by nature upon the otherwise long, and hay-like fur.

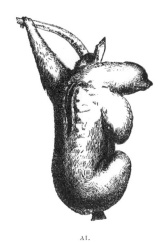

AI.

The central line then is black, and very decidedly marked. On either side, the fur is still short, but of a creamy colour, and it fades by short bands of brown into the grey hue of the fur.

Stedman says that the animal is popularly called the Loggurree or Sheep-Sloth, and that the names Ai, or Heeay, are given to it on account of its plaintive cry. The natives seemed to be very much afraid of its claws, and the first specimen which was brought to him had been deprived of all its feet, so as to render it harmless.

The illustrations are taken from a specimen in Waterton's

museum, and are given in order to show one of the characteristic attitudes assumed by the animal, as well as the
position and shape of the mark on the back of the male.

AI.

SLOTH, TWO-TOED (*Bradypus didactylus*).—It is well-known
that Waterton was the original discoverer of the real habits
of the Sloth, and showed how entirely false were the accounts
of Buffon and others. So full is his description that no
traveller has been able to add any important particulars which
Waterton has not mentioned.

In Surinam, the popular name for this animal is Dog-Sloth.
When motionless, it clings to the branches in such a manner,
that even if seen, it would be mistaken by most persons
for a mere excrescence on the bark. The specimen which I
saw in the Zoological Gardens was remarkable for the extremely wet state of the muzzle.

SPOONBILL (*Platalea ajaja*).

SPUR-WING.—*See* "Water Hen, Spur-winged."

STABROEK.—The reader will bear in mind that the
country now known as British Guiana, was originally
Dutch Guiana. The capital of Demerara then was called
Stabroek, but since Guiana has passed into the possession of

England, the name of the capital was changed, and it is now called Georgetown.

STING RAY (*Trygon vastinaca*).—Many species of Sting Ray are known, and they all belong to the Skate family. They are well known by their long whip-like tails, and the sharp, doubly barbed bone which proceeds from the base of the tail, and becomes a weapon which can be wielded with terrible effect.

As a rule, the Guianan natives are not a warlike race, but when war is forced upon them, their weapons are very formidable. War arrows, for example, are sometimes headed with the bone of the Sting Ray, and are nearly sure to cause death, as, when the arrow strikes the enemy, the force of the blow causes its very brittle head to snap asunder, and to leave several barbs imbedded in the body. The Polynesian warriors probably took the bone of the Sting Ray as a model for their many-barbed spears.

SUGAR-CANE.—The principal plant which is used for the production of sugar is the gigantic grass known as Sugar-cane (*Saccharinum officinarum*). It was originally brought from the E. Indies to Southern Europe by the Crusaders, and so made its way into the colonies. There are many species of saccharinum, or sugar-grasses. Some of our own grasses have a perceptible saccharine flavour.

SUN-BIRD.—Sometimes called the Sun-Heron (*Eurypyga helias*).—In Barbadoes it is called Tigri-Fowlo.

The following account of the bird is from C. Kingsley's *At Last* :

"These are strange birds too. One, whom you may see in the Zoological Gardens, like a plover with a straight beak and bittern's plumage, whose business it is to walk about the table at meals uttering sad metallic noises and catching flies.

" Its name is Sun-Bird, ' sun-fowlo,' of the Surinam negroes, according to dear old Stedman, ' because, when it extends its wings, which it often does, there appears on the interior part of each wing a most beautiful representation of a sun. This bird,' he continues very truly, 'might be styled the perpetual motion, its body making a continual movement, and its tail keeping time like the pendulum of a clock.'"

Stedman also calls it by the name of Flycatcher, one of the many instances of misleading nomenclature which are to be found in books of travel. The colour of the sun-bird is reddish, spotted with black, and there is a round black spot on the small head. The beak and legs are green.

T.

TANGARA. — Mis-spelling for Tanager.—*See* "Sangre do Buey."

TAPIR (*Tapirus terrestris*).—The Tapirs form one of the links connecting the elephants with the swine, and the only species which survive, *i.e.* in Tropical America, Malacca and Sumatra, really look as if they were extinct pachyderms that had been restored to the world.

The Tapir is never found far from the water, in which it disports itself as if it belonged naturally to that element. If alarmed on land, it always makes for the river, into which it plunges, and then can escape from any foe except man. It is a vegetable eater, feeding mostly on wild gourds, melons, and similar fruits. It is easily tamed, and soon becomes as familiar as a dog.

TAURONIRA (*Humirium floribundum*).—Found plentifully in sandy ground near swamps, but not in them.

The natives perfume their hair with a minute fungus which always grows in the newly-cut wood of the Tauronira. The timber is chiefly used for house-frames and wheel-spokes. The tree is about ninety feet in height.

TIGER.—*See* "Jaguar."

TIGER-BIRD.—There are several species of these birds, which evidently derive their popular name from the mottled brown and yellow under-surface in some of the species. That which is mentioned by Waterton is *Capito Cayanus*. They are all little birds, being on an average, about as large as the bullfinch. Most of the species are South American, but some are from Africa. Some totally distinct birds belonging to the genus *Tigrisoma* are also called Tiger-birds.

TIGER-CAT.—One of the small Leopards known as Margays (*Leopardus tigrinus*). Several species of leopard are called by this name. Waterton tamed one of them, brought it home, and actually trained it to run with the fox-hounds. It was very useful as a rat-catcher.

TINAMOU.—These birds all belong to the genus *Tinamotis*, and are all natives of South America. They are on an average about the size of a grouse. They have very short tails, which gives them rather a lumpish appearance. They seem to be rather stupid birds, and can be caught by a noose fixed to the end of a long stick. The species which is mentioned by Waterton under the name of Maam is probably *Tinamotis elegans*.

TIRANA.—*See* "Sun bird."

TORTOISE.—This is the Box-Tortoise (*Cistuda Carolina*), so called because it can not only draw its limbs and head

TORTOISE.

within the shell, but can fold the shell together, so that it is quite invulnerable.—*See* Sydney Smith's simile on page 19. The negroes call it by the name of Cooter.

It is always to be found in dry situations, preferring the pine forests, because they also love a dry soil. It is of small size, and as it is very prettily coloured, it is sometimes manufactured into a snuff-box, being mounted in silver, and having the movable plates fitted with hinges, and spring-clasps. The colour is most variable, but black and yellow are the most conspicuous hues.

TOUCAN.—Tropical America produces an inexhaustible variety of living creatures, and there is perhaps none more remarkable than that extraordinary group of birds known as Toucans, from the native name Toco.

TOUCAN.

Kingsley seems to have been greatly impressed with the appearance of the toucan, and agrees with Waterton that it is essentially a fruit-eating bird :—

" A Toucan out of the primæval forest, as gorgeous in colour as he is ridiculous in shape. His general plumage is black, set off by a snow-white gorget fringed with crimson ; crimson and green tail coverts, and a crimson and green beak, with blue cere about his face and throat.

" His enormous and weak bill seems made for the purpose
of swallowing bananas whole ; how he feeds himself with it
in the forest is difficult to guess (*see* " Banana ") ; and when he
hops up and down on his great clattering feet—two toes turned
forward and two back—twisting head and beak right and left
(for he cannot well see straight before him) to see whence the
bananas are coming ; or when again, after gorging a couple, he
sits gulping and winking, digesting them in serene satisfaction,
he is as good a specimen as can be seen of the ludicrous—
dare I say the intentionally ludicrous ?—element in nature."

It is true that in confinement the Toucan will eat little
birds, just as a monkey will eat a mouse, but I very much
doubt whether either toucan or monkey touches animal food
in its native woods. Toucans make great inroads on the
plantations of oranges, guavas, and other fruit, but, as they
are shot in considerable numbers, the delicacy of their flesh
makes amends for their depredations. Waterton seems to
have eaten his Toucans boiled.

There are many species of Toucan. The Bouradi of Waterton is *Rhamphastos erythrorhynchus*, and the Scirou is
Rhamphastos Ariel, as shown in the illustration. The
Toucanet is *Rhamphastos vitellinus*. It is an active little
bird, uttering its yelping cry either by day or in the evening,
and jerking its head about in a most ludicrous fashion.

TRIBES, NATIVE.—The five great tribes are given on p. 237.
Taking them in their order, the Waraws, or Guaraons, as
Humboldt calls them, are more exclusively aquatic than the
others, one great division of them living wholly in lake
dwellings built in the stems of the ita or moriche palm. *See*
" Æta." They are also the best canoe makers, and can carve
canoes out of tree trunks, some of which are able to carry
very large numbers of men. They sell these canoes to other
tribes.

The Arowacks are taller and fairer than the other tribes,
averaging from 5 ft. 4 in. to 5 ft. 6 in. in height, and the mixed
progeny of Arowack and European is said to be remarkable

for its beauty and intellect. The Acoways wear scarcely
any clothing, and indeed, when no white men are near, do
not trouble themselves about clothes at all. They wear their
coarse black hair very long, and are accustomed to carry a
piece of wood in the cartilage of the nose

REAL AND IDEAL.

The Caribs are also nude, and wear ornaments in their
under lips. Lastly, come the Macoushies, who are the best
wourali makers, and sell it to other tribes.

In the accompanying illustration I have brought together
three figures, in order to show the difference between the
European and Guianan types of the human frame. The
"Painter's Ideal" is copied from an imaginative drawing
of a young Indian girl, as depicted by a well-known artist.
The model is clearly of an English type, with the abundant

wavy hair, sloping shoulders, ample brow, full eyes, and straight delicate nose. Substitute an English archery dress for the skin robe, and a bow for the spear, and there is a handsome English girl at an archery meeting.

The Sculptor's Ideal of the same subject is wholly Greek. Substitute a crescent diadem for the plumed circlet, a light classical chiton for the feather apron, and there is Diana.

How different is the real figure of the Guianan type of female beauty, copied exactly from a photograph in my possession ! Note the difference of size, the coarse, straight hair, the little eyes, the high cheek-bones, the short neck, the square shoulders, the in-turned feet, and the spreading toes. Dress her as you will, or even change her complexion, she can never look English or Greek.

TROELY.—This is a palm with very long and wide leaves, which are much used in the construction of houses. Stedman mentions the palm under the name of Trooly, and states that the leaves diverge directly from the ground, like those of the young coucourite. The leaves sometimes reach a length of thirty feet, and are proportionately wide. They will last for ten or twelve years when made into thatch, so that a native will make a week's voyage in order to obtain a boat-load. Another name is Bussú. The scientific name is *Manicaria saccifera*.

TROPIC BIRD (*Phaeton æthereus*).—This beautiful bird is one of the Pelican family, and derives its popular name from the fact that it is never seen outside the tropics unless blown by gales too violent to be resisted, even by its powerful wings. Like its relative, the frigate bird, it can remain on the wing during the whole day, and has been met at sea at least a thousand miles from the nearest land. It can, however, rest its wings by sitting on the water.

There are several species of these birds, one named the Roseate Tropic Bird, being in great request among the natives of the South Seas, who use their long tail-plumes as ornaments in their head-dresses of ceremony. In this species, the tail feathers are scarlet, and are fastened into a plaited fillet which surrounds the head, very much as the Guianan natives make their feather-crowns with the tail-feathers of macaws.

On account of the aerial habits of the bird, it is not easy to procure these feathers, and these islanders manage to supply themselves by watching their nesting-places, crawling up to them, and jerking out the feathers as they sit on their eggs.

Waterton had great difficulty in obtaining one of these birds, but at last shot one, in a voyage across the Atlantic.

TROPIC BIRD.

He offered a guinea for the recovery of the bird, when a Danish sailor plunged into the sea after it. He nearly lost not only the reward, but his life, for no boat could be launched, and the ship was going so fast through the water, that in trying to back, she missed stays, and they had to wear her. However, the man kept himself afloat, and delivered the bird to

Waterton, who had a special affection for it ever afterwards. The illustration is taken from a sketch of this very specimen, as it stood in his museum.

TROUPIALS.—There are many of these birds, the best known of which is the Rice Troupial (*Dolichonyx orizivorus*).

It obtains its name from its extreme fondness for rice, and is sometimes called the rice-bunting. As it has a very wide range, is extremely plentiful, and possesses a beautiful voice, it has received a variety of popular names, such as butter-bird, because it becomes so fat in harvest time; reed-bird, because it is fond of settling in vast numbers among seeds; bob-o-link, bob-linkum, &c.

TRUMPETER, sometimes called Waracaba (*Psophia crepitans*).

TRUMPET.

—This bird is allied to the crane. Waterton mentions that it can be domesticated, and in such cases, it usually considers the house as its own, and is madly jealous of any other pet which it fancies may deprive it of its master's affections. As for cats, it cannot bear them, and always turns them out of the room if possible.   Even dogs yield to it unless they are very courageous, for the Trumpeter attacks them after a very peculiar fashion, jumping on its foe's back, and kicking and pecking him until he is quite bewildered.

It is usually a beautiful bird, especially in the breast, where the black feathers are richly glossed with gold and purple upon their edges.

TURTLE, FRESH-WATER.—Several reptiles are known by this name.   That to which Waterton here refers is probably the larger of the two (*Podocnemis expansa*), called Sachapana by the natives.   Its eggs are large, spherical, and with white shells.   The smaller species (*Emys tracaxa*), called by the natives Taracai, lays soft oval eggs.   The eggs of both species are valued as food, and only the yolk is eaten.   It is allied to the well-known chicken tortoise of North America.

V.

VAMPIRE (*Vampirus spectrum*).—As to the Vampire bats which would not bite Waterton, who did his best to allure them, and would insist on biting everybody else, who did not wish to be bitten, C. Kingsley has the following remarks :—

"Then we inspected a coolie's great toe, which had been severely bitten by a Vampire in the night.

"And here let me say that the popular disbelief of Vampire stories is only owing to English ignorance, and disinclination to believe any of the many quaint doings which John Bull has not seen, because he does not care to see them.   If he comes to these parts, he must be careful not to leave his feet or hands out of bed without mosquito curtains ; if he has good horses, he ought not to leave them exposed at night without wire-gauze round the stable shed—a plan which, to my surprise, I never saw used in the West Indies.

"Otherwise, he will be but too likely to find in the morning a triangular bit cut out of his own flesh, or even worse, out of his horse's withers or throat, whose twisting and lashing cannot shake the tormentor off; and must be content to have himself lamed, or his horses weakened to staggering and thrown out of collar-work for a week, as I have seen happen more than once or twice. The only method of keeping off the Vampire yet employed in stables is light; and a lamp is usually kept burning there. But the negro—not the most careful of men —is apt not to fill and trim it; and if it goes out in the small hours, the horses are pretty sure to be sucked, if there is a forest near.

"So numerous and troublesome, indeed, are the Vampires, that there are pastures in Trinidad in which, at least till the adjoining woods were cleared, the cattle would not fatten, or even thrive; being found, morning after morning, weak and sick from the bleeding which they had endured at night."

The coolie in question—a Hindoo—made very light of the injury, although the toe bled considerably, and the wound could scarcely be healed. Why the Vampire should always select the withers of the horse and the toes of the human being is a problem as yet unsolved. Neither do we know how the Vampires lived when they had neither horses, cattle, nor human beings to suck, any more than we know how countless millions of mosquitos, fleas, land-leeches, and other noxious creatures contrive to exist without the blood of man or beast.

VANILLA (*Vanilla planifolia*).—The plant which furnishes the well known Vanilla, so much used by pastry-cooks, is a curious parasitic orchid.

It originally starts from the ground, and then ascends the trunk of a tree. The stem is square, and throws out a number of little rootlets, which make their way into the bark and drain the tree of its sap.

Indeed, so entirely does it depend upon the juices of the tree for its life, that if it be cut away below, so as to sever its connection with the ground, it will continue to grow as well as ever. Our ivy, if cut, always dies, because it derives its whole subsistence from the ground, and none from the tree, and, as is shown by the sketches of the Ivy Tower on pages 43 and 66, flourishes as well on stone walls as on trees.

The flowers grow in spikes, and are richly perfumed, and the pods are very flat, and open along the side. Very little genuine vanilla finds its way into England, not more than a few hundred-weight being imported. Its place is supplied by the common and much cheaper balsam of Peru.

VULTURE, AURA (*Cathartes aura*).—The name of this bird will always call to mind the memorable controversy between

VULTURE, AURA.

Waterton and Audubon, in which the former came off the victor. The whole controversy is printed in the volumes of *Essays*, and it is too long to be inserted in this book, and too valuable to be judged by means of extracts. I strongly recommend the reader to procure these essays, and admire the masterly manner in which Waterton handled the subject, and the completeness with which he cut away the ground from under the feet of his antagonist.

The Aura Vulture, popularly known as the Turkey Buzzard, is very common in its own country, and in civilized places is protected by law, on account of its value as a scavenger. Waterton states, in corroboration of his own view of the case, that during the dreadful plague in Malaga, which has already been mentioned on p. 11, the Vulture did inestimable service.

"So great was the daily havoc of death, that no private burials could be allowed, and many a corpse lay exposed in the open air until the dead carts made their rounds at night-fall to take them away to their last resting-place, which was a large pit, prepared by the convicts in the day time.

"During this long-continued scene of woe and sorrow, which I saw and felt, I never could learn that the Vultures preyed upon the dead bodies which had not had time enough to putrefy. But, when the wind blew in from the Mediterranean, and washed ashore the corrupted bodies of those who died of the pestilence, and had been thrown overboard from the shipping, then it was that the vultures came from the neighbouring hills to satisfy their hunger."

The popular name of turkey buzzard is given to the bird on account of its resemblance to the common turkey, and many a new comer has found himself an object of derision because he has shot an Aura Vulture, taking it for a turkey.

VULTURE SUNNING ITSELF.

The smaller illustration is taken from a sketch at the Zoological Gardens, representing the Vulture in a favourite attitude, sitting on its ankles, with its wings half spread, rejoicing in the sun.

VULTURE, KING (*Sarcorhamphus papa*).—Being one of the

longest and most powerful of the Vulture tribe, this bird has
derived its name from the tyranny which it exercises over the
aura and black vultures, not allowing them to eat until its
own hunger is satisfied. The beautiful colours which adorn
the beak are well and accurately described by Waterton, and
it is on account of these fleshy excrescences that the bird is
called by the scientific name of Sarcorhamphus, or "flesh-
beaked." These colours, however, are not to be found in the
young bird, and do not make their appearance until the fourth
year. The name of *papa* is equivalent to that of pope, and
signifies that the bird is a sort of pope among the other vultures. Its curious facility for discovering dead carrion and
snakes has already been mentioned on p. 380.

W.

WALLABA TREE (*Eperna falcata*).—So called from the shape
of the pods, which resemble a sickle, Lat. *falx*. " I passed
. . . the Wallaba Tree, with its thin curved pods dangling
from innumerable bootlaces six feet long."—C. Kingsley.
The wood of the wallaba splits freely, and is used for staves
and shingles. The oily resin exudes from the tree when
wounded. Also, *see* " Siloabali."

WALLABABA.—*See* " Cotinga, Pompadour."

WARACABA.—*See* " Trumpeter."

WATER-HEN, SPUR-WINGED (*Parra Jacana*).—Several species
of Jacana are known, and are at once recognizable by the
enormous proportionate length and slenderness of the toes.

This provision of nature enables them to walk with safety
upon the floating leaves of water-plants, and so to procure its
food, which consists of aquatic insects, &c. It is a good
swimmer and diver, but its powers of wing are trifling. The
magnificent leaf of the Victoria regia is a great favourite with
the Jacana, which finds a firm footing on a leaf which is able to
sustain the weight of a little girl some six or seven years old.

On each wing is a sharp and rather strong spur, which has earned for the bird the popular name of Spur-wing. It is also remarkable for a curious leathery excrescence, which rises from the base of the beak, both above and below.

SPUR-WINGED WATER-HEN.

WATERMAMMA.—Throughout the whole of Guiana there is a superstitious dread of some strange being which, like the nippen of Norway, the gnomes, goblins, and other malignant semi-spiritual beings of Europe, the jinns of Asia, and the jumbies of Africa, take a demoniacal delight in waylaying and murdering travellers.

The Watermamma seems to be able to assume various forms, though it generally prefers that of a human being. Mr. Brown mentions it under the name of water-child.

"On our way we passed a deep pool, where there was an eddy, in which the guide informed us there lived a "water-child" covered with long hair. A woodskin (*i.e.* canoe) with Indians was passing the spot one day, when the water-child came to the surface, caught hold of, and upset the canoe. One of its occupants sank with it, and, being seized by the child, never came up to the surface again."

This account, it will be seen, tallies exactly with that of Waterton.

The same writer mentions this semi-supernatural being under another name, *i.e.* "didi."

"The first night after leaving Peaimah we heard a long, loud, and most melancholy whistle, proceeding from the direction of the depths of the forest, at which some of the men exclaimed, in an awed tone of voice, 'The didi!' Two or three times the whistle was repeated, sounding like that made by a human being, beginning in a high key, and dying slowly and gradually away in a low one. There were conflicting opinions amongst the men regarding the origin of these sounds. Some said they proceeded from the wild hairy man, or 'didi,' of the Indians; others that they were produced by a large and poisonous snake which lives in one tree from its youth up, when it attains a great size, living upon birds which are so unfortunate as to alight near it, and thus become victims to its power of fascination. The 'didi' is said by the Indians to be a short, thick-set, and powerful wild man, whose body is covered with hair, and who lives in the forest. A belief in the existence of this fabulous creature is universal over the whole of British, Venezuelan, and Brazilian Guiana. On the Demerara river, some years after this, I met a half-bred woodcutter, who related an encounter that he had with two didis—a male and female—in which he successfully resisted their attacks with his axe. In the fray, he stated that he was a good deal scratched. His story requires to be taken with a very large grain of salt."

WAX.—*See* "Kurumanni."

WHIP-POOR-WILL.—*See* "Goatsuckers."

WHIP-SNAKE (*Philodryas viridissimus*).—Several Snakes are called by this name, because their long, slender bodies look very much like the plaited thong of a hunting whip. Indeed, more than once a Whipsnake has been grasped under the impression that it was a whip-thong, which had been dropped in the path.

Some of them are venomous, but that which is mentioned by Waterton is perfectly harmless. It is about two feet in length, of a lovely green colour, and very active, darting among the leaves and branches with such rapid agility, that the slightest twig scarcely bends under its weight.

WHO ARE-YOU.—A Goatsucker; species uncertain.

WILLY-COME-GO.—Ditto.

WOODPECKER, RED-HEADED (*Melanerpes erythrocephalus*).

WOODSKIN. — Popular name for a Bark Canoe. *See* " Purple-Heart."

WORK-AWAY.—A Goatsucker; species uncertain.

WOURALI.—The information acquired by Waterton is most interesting, and it is to his energy and perseverance that we owe our knowledge of the most wonderful poison ever invented by savage races. As may be seen from Waterton's account, its manufacture is evidently the result of experience. More than one substance is used in it, and as the Wourali made by the Macoushis, one of the five great tribes, is so superior in quality that the other tribes are glad to buy it, there is no doubt that very great skill is required for its preparation. Even among the Macoushis there are some families which are celebrated for the strength of the Wourali made by them, and the secret of its manufacture is said to be handed down from father to son, the pi-ay-men, or conjurors, being the chief manufacturers.

Several instances are known of experiments made in Europe with Wourali, and which have failed. I have little doubt that the poison with which they were made was not genuine, or that it had been neglected. The savages of Guiana are quite as expert at adulteration as the civilized milkman, publican, or grocer, and are perfectly capable of making Wourali for the market, but not for use.

Waterton never failed with the experiments which he made with the poison which he himself obtained from the Macoushis while dwelling among them. Nor, as far as I know, has any one failed with Waterton's poison. I made a few experiments with some of it, and found that his account of it was literally true.

Death was not instantaneous, but the creature which was wounded seemed to be immediately deprived of all wish to move. On the spot it was wounded, there it remained, its eyes giving no indication of sensitiveness when touched, and its limbs gradually relaxing as if in sleep. Yet the poison which I used had been preserved nearly forty years at Walton Hall, but it had been carefully kept from damp, which injures, even if it does not destroy its powers.

In his essay on the Monkey family, Waterton makes a passing, but valuable remark on the Wourali :—

" If you are in want of a tender monkey, a month old or so, to boil for broth or to educate as a pet, your only chance of success is to shoot the poor mother, but not with a fowling-piece. Nine times out of ten the wounded mother would stay in the clefts of the trees, where she would ultimately perish with her progeny. An arrow, poisoned with Wourali, is your surest weapon.

"Take a good aim, and in a few minutes the monkey will be lying dead at your feet. The Wourali poison totally destroys all tension in the muscles. Now, a gun-shot wound, even though it be mortal, has not such an immediate effect.

"Knowing this to be the case, whenever a monkey was wanted, recourse was had to poisoned arrows. By this precaution, the ill-fated animal's existence was not prolonged under the painful anguish of a deadly wound. The Wourali poison would act as a balmy soporific, and the victim would be dead at your feet in a very short space of time."

The necessity for some such poison is evident from the fact that on account of the exuberant luxuriance of tropical vegetation, a mortally wounded monkey, if only able to traverse a couple of hundred yards, would be hopelessly lost, and whether the body remained wedged among the boughs or fell to the ground would be a secret only known to the vultures and carrion-feeding insects.

The peculiar " Quake " or basket into which the Wourali-maker puts his materials, is shown on page 463.

Chief among the materials is the Wourali Vine (*Strychnos toxifera*). This, as its name imports, is allied to the plant which furnishes the well-known strychnine poison.

When full grown, its vine-like stem is about three inches in diameter, covered with a rough greyish bark, like that of the vine. The dark-green leaves are oval in shape, and are set opposite to each other. It is a tolerably common plant in certain places, but it is very local, and among the abundance of herbage is not readily distinguishable. It bears a round fruit, shaped like an apple, and containing seeds imbedded in a very bitter pulp.

The "root of a very bitter taste " is evidently the hyarri, or haiarri, a plant belonging to the genus *Lonchocarpus*, chiefly used in poisoning fish. Of this plant the following description is given by the Rev. J. H. Bernau, in his *Mission-ary Labours in British Guiana* :—

" The haiarri is a papilionaceous vine, bearing a small bluish cluster of blossoms, producing a pod about two inches in length, containing some small grey seeds. The root itself is stronger in its effects than the vine, and is always preferred by the Indians. A solid cubic foot of this root will poison an acre of water, even in the rapids. In creeks and standing water, its effects are still more extensive."

When used, the soft yellow roots are pounded with a stone or mallet and steeped in water, which is then thrown into the river. Heaps of the pounded roots are often found on the stones on the river bank, showing that the fish have been lately poisoned. They appear to be stupefied by the poison, and float on the surface, when they are either shot with arrows or simply lifted out by hand.

No injurious effect on the flesh is produced by the poison, which has been conjectured to paralyse the gills, and so to

kill the fish, or at least to render it senseless, by asphyxiation.
Perhaps the paralysing effect of the Wourali may be due to
the haiarri juice.

In Mr. C. B. Brown's work on Guiana, there is an interesting account of this mode of fish killing :—

"I set out at an early hour one morning, with Ben, Eruma,
and Yackarawa, in a wood-skin, for a place where the Cowen-
amon Indians were going to poison a pool so as to obtain its
fish. After about two hours hard paddling we arrived at a
large cataract, called Cartoweire, and, taking our canoe into
smooth water above, found the Indians, eleven in number,
busily engaged in beating bundles of a soft yellow root
with sticks. These haiarie roots were each about two inches
in diameter, and of a light yellow colour, containing a yellow
creamy juice, having a disagreeable raw smell. Each bundle
was about a foot in diameter and two feet in length. When
thoroughly pounded into pulp, they were thrown into canoes,
in which a little water had been previously placed, and then
the juice was wrung from them. The enclosure to be acted
upon was of an irregular shape, occupying about two acres of
river, and formed by dams of rock, built into the spaces between rocky areas and small islands. In building this the
Indians had left two large gaps open, one being where the
greatest body of water ran in, and the other where it flowed
out. When we arrived they had closed these gaps with a
wattle arrangement, so that all chances of escape for the fish
were cut off. Three canoes, containing the juice of six bundles
of haiarie, were then taken to the upper end of the enclosure,
and the subtle poison discharged from them. It was borne
down by the slight current, and mingled rapidly with the
pure dark water. Most of the Indians then got into the
canoes and pushed out, bows and arrows in hand, into the
middle of the enclosure, whilst the remainder, with my men
also furnished with the same weapons, stood upon the rocks
at the edge. In ten minutes time numbers of small fish came
to the surface, and swam uneasily about, trying to rise above

water ; then soon were floating about quite dead.   After an interval of five minutes more, a single pacu showed its back fin, and also tried to raise its head above water.   An instant more, and the whole place swarmed alive with large fish, pacu and cartabac, all struggling and flapping at the surface or whirling round and round.   Many tried to force themselves out of the water up the sloping surface of the rocks, and two were successful in this, dying on the strand.   From the excited manner in which they struggled, it seemed to me as if the poison had an intoxicating effect upon them.   It might have been that the contact of the poison with their gills had produced a feeling of suffocation—hence their endeavours to escape from their native element.

" It was a most exciting scene for a time, as the Indians shot arrow after arrow into the bewildered dying fish and hunted them ashore or into the canoe.   In about an hour the murderous work was over, and 150 fine pacu and cartabac were lying dead upon the rocks around the pool, the victims of Indian prowess and poison.   During the whole proceedings I stood on the rocks at the upper end of the pool, and had a fine view of the scene, the finest part of which was to see the naked savage, in all his glory, drawing his bow with strength and ease and letting fly his arrows with unerring aim."

Another plant, called Konamie, is used for the same purpose.   It belongs to the *Compositæ*.

The " two bulbous plants " which supply the glutinous matter I cannot identify.

As to the red-pepper, ants, and snake-fangs, I do not believe that they have any effect in strengthening the poison.   When rightly prepared, it has about the consistence of treacle, and possesses a fragrant and penetrating odour peculiarly its own. Although so deadly when it directly enters the blood, it is, like the poison of snakes, harmless when swallowed.   I have tasted some with which Waterton furnished me, and found it to be intensely bitter, with somewhat of a quassia-like aroma, and that its taste was as unique as its smell.

Waterton not only succeeded in procuring the manufactured poison, but also the whole of the materials of which it is made. Unfortunately, the canoe was capsized in the falls of the Essequibo river, the precious parcel was lost, and there was no second opportunity of replacing it. As to the abandonment of the temporary hut after the Wourali has been made, subsequent travellers have said that the hut is not only abandoned, but burned to the ground, so as not to leave a trace of the mode by which the poison was prepared.

WREN (*Troglodytes eudon*).

Y.

YAM (*Dioscorea alata*).—The plant is closely allied to our common Bryony. Several species are cultivated.

YAWARACIRIS. — These pretty little birds are popularly called Blue Creepers, on account of the prevailing hue of the plumage. They belong to the genus *Cœreba*. Waterton's descriptions of the two commonest species are admirable. The first of his Yawaraciris is *Cœreba cyanea*, and the second, " still lovelier than the first " is *Cœreba cærulea*. I regret to say that vast numbers of both birds are killed in order to furnish decorations for ladies' hats.

TAXIDERMY.

TAXIDERMY.

THE late Arthur Strickland, of whom Waterton speaks in such high praise as to say that " he had more orthodox ornithology in his little finger than most of our mighty closet naturalists have in their entire carcass," and that his collection of British birds was without a rival ; never would have his birds stuffed, keeping the skins in drawers.

Many years ago, when he was showing me his collection, I rather wondered to find that the skins had only just enough cotton wool in them to keep them slightly open, but soon found that he was right. Could he have put them all under Waterton's magic fingers he would have been glad enough that they should be " set up," but he was too good a naturalist to entrust them to ordinary bird-stuffers.

In the chapter added to the *Wanderings*, and to be found on page 335, Waterton gives the first account of the art which he created, and even with the aid of those few pages, any one with ordinary intellect, a thorough knowledge of the animal, and a fair acquaintance with anatomy, especially that of the skeleton, would be able to produce specimens of taxidermy far superior to those which are ordinarily to be found in museums. But art must be progressive, and as he gained experience Waterton was perpetually discovering improvements in taxidermy. Most of these improvements are given in one or two portions of his *Essays*, the principal part of which will presently be extracted.

First, we come to his mode of preparing birds' eggs. When I was a boy, I used to be terribly annoyed to find that valuable eggs, which had been obtained almost at the risk of my life, were putrid, and swarming with maggots, owing to the decay of the lining membrane. Waterton's gradual improvement in egg preservation was very interesting, as showing the growth of the art.

Of course, he introduced the solution of corrosive sublimate, but he did so by sucking it into the egg by a hole at one end, while the lips were applied to the other. Now, he soon found that making a hole at the end of the egg spoiled its contour, and he then made the two holes at one side. Afterwards, he only employed one rather large hole, and emptied the egg by shaking it in water.

I have found, however, that a single small hole on the side will suffice. Get a piece of ordinary glass tubing, about eighteen inches long, and not more than a quarter of an inch in diameter, heat it red-hot in a spirit lamp or a gas flame, and then draw it out in the shape of an elongated hour-glass. Break it asunder, and you have a tube with a point about as large as a darning needle.

Now break up the yolk of the egg with your needle, introduce the glass point, and you can suck out the contents of the egg in the tube. Inject water once or twice so as to clean it completely, and then, by the same means, introduce the poison.

For soft-shell eggs like those of the snake or turtle, the best plan is to empty them, poison them, fill them with sand, and let them dry, hanging them separately in pieces of net or muslin to keep them from flattening. When quite dry, the sand can be shaken out and the egg will ever afterwards re-tain its shape. If the egg be "hard-set," the best plan is to cut out a small piece of the shell, dry it on a curved surface, lest it should lose its shape, and extract the contents through the opening. When it is dry, the piece of shell can be replaced with a little thin paper and diamond cement, and if neatly done, the junction will scarcely be visible.

There are some eggs, notably those of the kingfisher, which alter their colour when empty. The kingfisher's egg, when fresh, is almost translucent, and a beautiful rosy white, but when blown, it becomes as opaque and as dead white as the egg of a fowl. I hit upon a plan of restoring the colour which answered admirably, and is very easy. Mix carmine powder with melted white wax, and make it much darker than the required hue, as the shell absorbs much of the colour.

Empty and poison the eggs as before, and get the wax to boiling point. Heat the egg and glass tube as much as they will bear, draw a few drops of the wax into the tube, blow it into the egg, and keep turning the egg over and over in front of a fire until every part of it is equally coloured. Remove it from the fire and continue to turn it until it is cold, and the colour will then be so perfectly restored that if it be placed among a number of fresh eggs, the keenest eye will not be able to distinguish it. If the egg be laid down before it is cold, the wax will run downwards and make the colour streaky instead of regular.

Here is Waterton's account of the improvements which he made in taxidermy after he published the *Wanderings*.

" Those who preserve quadrupeds for cabinets of natural history seem not to be aware that, after the skin of the animal has been taken off, there is a necessity for some parts of it to be pared down from within. These parts are chiefly the nose, the lips, and the soles of the feet. Unless they be rendered thin by the operation of the knife, there will be no possibility of restoring to them that natural appearance which they were seen to possess in life. The inner skin of the ears, too, must be separated from the outer one, until you come close to the extreme edge. Nothing short of this operation can save the ear from becoming a deformity.

" Every bone in the skin, to the last joint of the toe, next the claw, must be taken out, in order to allow the operator an opportunity of restoring the skin to its former just proportion.

"The mouth must be sewed up from the inside (the skin being inside out when you sew it), beginning exactly in the front, and continuing the operation each way to the end of the gape. When the skin is taken out of the solution, it must be filled quite full of chaff or saw-dust (but I prefer chaff), not minding whether the fur be wet or dry. When this has been done, the skin has almost the appearance of an inflated bag, quite deficient in feature and in muscular appearance.

"There are now no obstacles either from without or from within, to impede the artist's progress. The skin is perfectly free from all chance of putrefaction, is quite supple, and will remain so as long as required. There is no hard body inside to obstruct the transit of a working iron; there is not anything in the shape of wires to prevent him from lengthening or shortening the neck, body, thigh, and legs, according to his own judgments.

"Now we proceed to support the skin in any attitude the artist may wish to place it in.

"Join two pieces of wood in the shape of a carpenter's gimlet, and of size corresponding to the size of the animal. When you have nearly filled the abdomen with chaff, introduce this machine, and let the shank hang down outside of the skin, just as though it were a fifth leg in the centre of the body, equi-distant from the fore and hind legs. This fifth leg, or what may be called the shank of the gimlet, is of any sufficient length, and is passed through a hole in the table before you, and then fastened with a couple of wedges. By this contrivance you can raise the animal as high as you wish, or you can lower it at your pleasure, and the feet will just touch the table, without requiring any wire inside to support them.

"Everything is now ready for the artist to exercise his abilities.

"With a piece of iron, from the size of a large darning needle to that of a ramrod (or larger and thicker still, if the bulk of the animal require it), and shaped at one end like a carpenter's pricker, he will push out every part of the skin

which ought to be pushed out, and then reduce with the end of
his finger any part that may be too prominent; having already made divers small holes in the skin with his penknife,
in order to afford entrance to the working iron. Thus, a small
hole on the top of the head will enable him to reach the nose,
upper lip, and cheeks; another behind the root of each ear;
another under the jaws; others, again, on the back, that he
may reach the legs, and the remaining parts of the body.
Under each foot there will also be a hole, to give him the opportunity of getting at the toes. The lips are by far the most
difficult part to manage. The operator must have a working
iron in both hands. One of these will do the work within the
head, and the other that without, for the lips require to be
reformed with a beautiful rotundity, and this can only be
effected by means of the inner and the outer irons working in
opposite directions. During the actual operation, the animal
need not be kept in its original position. A smaller animal
may be placed on the operator's lap, the larger may be thrown
on the ground, or on the table. Every day the nose, and lips,
and orbits, ought to be touched with the oil and turpentine, in
order to keep them moist. At first, after you have used the
working iron in every quarter where it is required, there will
be no appearance of a re-formation of the features. Nevertheless, in the due course of time, as the skin stiffens, the
artist will see the features gradually appear; and every day he
will be more and more content with his work. At last, the
skin will retain the slightest impression communicated to
it by the touch of the working iron. Then the artist will
have it fully in his power to reproduce wrinkles, or warts, or
hollows, or a smooth surface, just as occasion may require.

"The fur will be equally under his command. He will
raise it, or depress it, according to circumstances, and it will
retain the position ever after. Thus a stuffed cat in anger
will exhibit a tail of the same extraordinary bulk which it
does when a dog threatens its existence.

"As there are parts of a quadruped's skin which are bound

down, as it were, to the bone (at the eyes for example), it will be necessary to pass a thread, with a sufficient knot at one end, through these parts, and to let the end without a knot hang loose after it has been drawn out at the opposite quarter. Thus, there must be a thread in the extremities at the gape of the mouth, and one at the corners of the eyes ; and others in different parts of the body, according to the operator's judgment. By pulling these at the end which hangs out, he will be enabled to depress the parts into their natural shape.

" The artificial eyes must be put in on the first day of the operation, and taken out and put back again every time the head of the specimen is modelled.

" When all is completed, and the skin has become perfectly dry, the artist takes out the chaff or saw-dust, and he finds that the specimen is quite firm enough to stand without any support from wires. He cuts three sides of a square hole under the feet, to let out the chaff, and when this is done, he returns the skin to its place.

" A slit must be made in the crown of the head, or under the jaws, to allow him to fit the artificial eyes with a little putty or wax. The slit, if properly done, will leave no mark on the fur.

" If the quadruped be stuffed in distant countries, with an intention to be sent home, it may be cut up, when finished, into three or four different pieces, and this will facilitate the carriage. When dividing it, the operator must take care to hold his knife so as to humour the angle which the fur forms with the skin. Thus, were I to cut a preserved skin in two parts, the blade of my knife would point to the head, and the haft to the tail of the animal. By attention to this, not a hair of the fur will be cut during the operation.

" I will just add here (although it be a digression), that there is no difficulty in making the legs and feet of eagles, turkeys, and other large birds, retain their natural size. You may go through every known museum, and you will find that the legs of these, and of all large birds, are dried and shrivelled, as though they belonged to the mummies of ancient days. In order to give the legs of birds a natural appearance, and a natural size, the skin from the very claws to the top of the leg must be separated from the bone by running a working-iron betwixt it and the bone, and then modelling the skin with the working iron.

"The wattles of fowl, the caruncles of turkeys, and the combs of cocks, by the simple process of internal modelling, may be made to retain their natural size."

PEGGY.

All improvements are gained by experience, and, when I first knew Waterton, he had abandoned the box of cotton wool, and employed a far superior mode of fixing his subject.

Instead of a box, he had made a simple framework, as here shown, both ends being open and the upper part projecting considerably. This was bored full of holes at irregular intervals, so that an upright rod might be inserted into any of them. An ordinary wine cork was bored and passed over the rod, so as to slide rather stiffly up and down. A stout pin was stuck into the cork, a piece of twine tied to it, and the simple apparatus was complete.

The sketch was taken while Waterton was preparing a pheasant. A large lump of wax is pressed on the beak and from it projects a sharp needle point, which can be thrust into the cork. It will be seen that the bird can be thus supported in any position, and the wings raised or depressed at pleasure. For convenience sake, Waterton usually placed his bird-stand on a little oak table, which he called "Peggy," and which could be turned about so as to enable him to reach every part of the bird. The piece of twine attached to the pin was used for giving the proper position of the head, the twine being hitched into notches cut in the side of the stand.

On such a stand I have prepared birds in the act of standing, flying, swimming or feeding, and found it to be invaluable. It also answers well for the smaller animals, but the larger kinds must necessarily have stands of corresponding size.

I found it better to wash all birds and animals in soft, warm water and soap, then rinse them thoroughly, and then, if birds, soak them in the poison. I used generally to dry them by tying a piece of strong tape to their legs and swinging them backwards and forwards, so that not even the most delicate down was matted. It was wonderful to see how beautifully their colours came out after the washing.

It is better to make absolutely sure of the various parts of the skin to be noted, such as the position of the joints, &c. A very simple way of doing so is by fixing the animal in the required attitude before skinning it, and passing a fine white thread through the skin at the different points, letting the ends hang down. They will come out easily when the operation is completed. Measurements, and if possible, a sketch to scale should be taken, so as to guard against the usual error of making the body too long, legs unequal, and, if a bird, the wings too wide apart or too close together.

Now for the poison.

Corrosive sublimate is not easy to procure, and the shortest way is to get an order from a medical man to purchase a pound or two at Apothecaries' Hall. Chemists may not sell it without such an order. Being very difficult to dissolve, it must be reduced to an almost impalpable powder. It is better to have this done by a chemist, as the powder is apt to fly about and is very dangerous.

Alcohol, even when methylated, is rather costly. Waterton suggested to me to try water instead of spirit. I did so, and found it answer for all kinds of fur and most kinds of feathers. But, owing to the closeness of the plumage of water-birds, spirit is absolutely necessary for them, and they must not only be thoroughly steeped, but continually turned and the feathers repeatedly raised and pressed. As long as a single bubble of air is left among the feathers, there will be a spot which the poison has not reached, and which the moth or mite is sure to find out.

Take great care not to dip the hands in the solution. Should there be a scratch on them, they will suffer intense pain for a long while, and the nails will always be stained a deep brown which cannot be removed but by the gradual growth of a new nail. Good India-rubber gloves are very useful.

The right strength of the poison is of very great importance, and can be secured by Waterton's plan of making it too strong at first, and then adding spirit until it leaves no white deposit on a black feather which has been dipped in it and dried.

For moths and butterflies, spirit is also necessary, as water glides off their scale-covered wings, leaving no poison behind it. They should, when "set," be dipped in the solution, and placed to dry just inside the window, with their heads inwards, so that a draught of air shall blow up the hairy down with which so many are adorned, and which will be matted together if this precaution be not taken. A pair of small bellows will be found very useful, especially if the nozzle be kept heated with a spirit lamp. A drop of the solution is sure to form at the end of the wing, and should be removed with blotting paper, as it is apt to bend the tip downwards and spoil the shape.

Large-bodied moths should have the abdomen removed, the contents extracted through the wound, the inside painted with poison, and stuffed with cotton-wool. When body and abdomen are both dry, they can be joined by diamond cement. Not a trace of the junction will be visible. The insect will not only be impervious to mites, but it will always preserve its shape, and it will never be subject to "grease," that terror of all entomologists.

Eyes will be found exceedingly troublesome, and the very greatest care is needed, especially in the management of the skin at the corners. Always let it be remembered that eyes in life never start spherically out of circular sockets. Care must be taken to have the eyes of the right colour. Most eyes can be procured from the shops, but there are some, notably those of the toads and snakes, which must be made by the operator. The best plan is to have a number of little hollow glass globes, like those used for doll's eyes. Paint them *on the inside*, fill them with melted wax, push a piece of iron wire into the wax, and they will answer admirably, giving a life-like aspect which can never be obtained by the glass eyes of the shops.

Two golden maxims for the followers of Waterton, are, first, never be discouraged; second, never be in a hurry.

There is need for them both, especially the former. Nothing can be more discouraging to a beginner than the look of a bird newly skinned, and partly filled with cotton-wool. It is more like a bundle of miscellaneous feathers than a bird. The upper and lower beaks are quite independent of each other, the neck looks like a sausage, the wings are turned in different directions, and the legs and tail dangle about helplessly. No vestige of an attitude can be seen, and the operator feels very much inclined to give it up in despair.

Day after day he works at it according to instructions, and seems to make no progress whatever. Presently, however, he is encouraged by finding that the skin begins to respond to his touch, and before very long, it becomes as plastic as clay in the hands of the sculptor.

Now comes the time for the second maxim. The skin, as Dickens's butcher said of his meat, " must be humoured, not drove," and if any attempt is made at hurrying, it will be totally spoiled.

Waterton's deliberation while preparing a bird or animal was almost exasperating. He would give it a touch here and a touch there, smooth down a starting feather with the instrument which he mostly used, a blow-gun arrow from which the poison had been removed ; or, he would slightly alter the pose of the head, or mould afresh a piece of skin which was beginning to shrivel. He thus kept every feather and hair under command, and put in touch after touch to the skin just as a painter does to his canvas. The result was absolute perfection, but the means appeared strangely inadequate.

No one could prepare a humming-bird like Waterton. Except in his collection, it is next to impossible to find a stuffed humming-bird in which the glittering gorget is not disfigured by little dark spots. Each such spot shows that a feather is missing.

Now Waterton found that such missing feathers had rarely been pulled out of their sockets and lost, but had been dragged under the other feathers by the contraction of the skin. He always searched for them, found them, drew them from their concealment and laid them in their places. So, the breasts of his humming-birds simply blazed with gold, ruby, azure, or emerald, according to their species, as they did in life.

The same patient care enabled him to give to all feathers and furs the "flow" which they possessed in life, and which no method except his own has been able to restore.

Waterton also found that two pieces of skin if properly moulded together while wet, would adhere to each other firmly, and that a little fine glue would cause them to unite as one piece. It was through the knowledge of this fact that he was able to produce the ludicrous combinations of different creatures which he placed in his museum and ticketed with all kinds of quaint names.

There was for example, "Noctifer," or the Spirit of Night, made of portions of a bittern and an eagle owl, both nocturnal birds.

Then he had an absurd group of John Bull surrounded by difficulties. John Bull was a tortoise with the head of an

NOCTIFER.

exceedingly stout but exceedingly worried man. He was supporting the eight hundred millions of national debt, to which such frequent reference is made both in the *Wanderings* and *Essays*. Clinging to his back, and driving its claws into him, is perched "Diabolus bellicosus," a sort of grinning lizard all over abnormal spikes and horns. Before him goes "Diabolus ambitiosus," with outspread wings. "Diabolus illudens" is guiding him on his path, and "Diabolus cæruleus," with its open mouth and sharp teeth, is bringing up the rear.

The museum was full of these taxidermal jokes, and not long before his death I procured for him a quantity of the exuviæ of the serpents in the Zoological Gardens, so that he might work them into new combinations. Whether he did so I do not know.

Not least of the excellences of his system was the portability of the objects prepared by it. We know how heavy is

POLECAT

even a stuffed dog of ordinary size, with all its internal paraphernalia of iron bars, wood, tow, &c. But Waterton's specimens are absolutely empty, the skin depending wholly on itself for support, and being as light and elastic as thin horn.

Moreover, his plan of cutting the prepared skins to pieces which could be packed within a small compass, reduced their volume as well as weight. They could be taken to pieces and put together again in a few minutes, without showing the least sign of a junction. Such, for example, is the specimen here given. No one would ever suspect that it was not an unbroken skin, so admirably has it been prepared, and so perfectly are the junctions concealed by the fur.

Marvellous, however, as were Waterton's achievements in taxidermy, there was one problem which he never succeeded in solving, namely, how to prevent bare skin from turning black.   He could model the form of a hand, a lip, or an ear, to the minutest wrinkle, but, do what he would, the skin always turned black.   It is much the same with insects, such as dragon-flies, the colour of which depends on living tissues under the skin.   He suggested that the body might be taken to pieces, cleaned, painted on the inside, and put together again.   I tried this plan, and it answered very well as far as the abdomen went, but utterly failed in the thorax and head, which persisted in turning black.   For the solution of this and other problems in taxidermy, we want another Waterton. Where shall we find him ?

INDEX.